# Montana's Wildlife Legacy
## Decimation to Restoration

by
**Harold D. Picton**
and
**Terry N. Lonner**

*"The State and each person shall maintain and improve a clean and healthful environment in Montana for present and future generations. The legislature shall provide for the administration and enforcement of this duty. The legislature shall provide adequate remedies for the protection of the environmental life support system from degradation and provide adequate remedies to prevent unreasonable depletion and degradation of natural resources."*

—From the Montana Constitution as adopted and ratified by the People, 1972

*"Montana is one of the few areas where wild game abounds. It is regarded as one of the greatest of the state's natural resources, as well as the chief attraction for visitors. Wild game existed here long before the coming of man. One who acquires property in Montana does so with notice and knowledge of the presence of wild game and presumably is cognizant of its natural habits."*

—Montana Supreme Court, 1939

*"...and which shall include a prohibition against the diversion of license fees paid by hunters for any other purpose than the administration of said State fish and game department...."*

—U.S. Congress, Pittman-Robertson Act, 1937

*"The central thesis of game management is this: game can be restored by the creative use of the same tools which have heretofore destroyed it— the axe, plow, cow, fire, and gun..."*

—From Game Management by Aldo Leopold, 1933

Published by Media Works Publishing, Bozeman, Montana

Library of Congress Control Number: 2008926645



First Printing

ISBN 978-0-615-18849-2

10 9 8 7 6 5 4 3 2 1

For Information:
Media Works Publishing
3602 Good Medicine Way
Bozeman, Montana 59715
Phone: 406-587-3583
E-mail: mail@mediaworksmt.com
Websites: www.montanaswildlifelegacy.com
www.mediaworksmt.com
www.mediaworkspublish.com

Cover:
Montage based on paintings and illustrations by:
Ron Jenkins, Robert Neaves and Joe Thornbrugh
Photos:
Robert Cooney, Jim McLucas, Gary Olson and
Montana Fish and Game Department Collections
Design:
Kathy Lange and Martha Lonner
Media Works, Bozeman, MT
Interior design and production:
Martha Lonner, Kathy Lange and Becky Sheehan
Media Works, Bozeman, MT
Individual animal paintings & illustrations:
Ron Jenkins, Robert Neaves and Joe Thornbrugh
Photos, paintings, maps, tables and illustrations:
Copyright 2008 (or before) is held by individuals
or organizations
Website design and development:
Martha Lonner, Kathy Lange and Kory Sutherland
Media Works, Bozeman, MT
Printing:
Advanced Litho Printing, Great Falls, MT

*This book is dedicated to generations of people who made Montana's current wildlife resources possible...*

*and to Irene who adopted and supported this project, making it a part of her life.*

*Early Montana Mule Deer Hunters. c. 1908* *(Courtesy Ken Hamlin Photo Collection)*

# Table of Contents

*End of an aerial trip on January 3, 1947 at the Basin Creek landing strip in the South Fork of the Flathead drainage to drop off Joe Gaab and Merle Rognrud for a 3 week inspection trip of the area. The Travel Air airplane was flown by Bob Johnson of Johnson Flying service in Missoula. Night time temperatures sometimes dropped to 50° below zero. Left to right - Joe Gaab, Faye Couey, Merle Rognrud and Bob Johnson* *(Courtesy Merle Rognrud field notes and Photo Collection)*

# Acknowledgements

We would like to thank Jim Williams, Glenn Erickson and Don Childress who contributed leadership and access to important resources essential for the completion of the project. Also to Spence Hegstad and the board of the Montana Fish, Wildlife and Parks Foundation for their support and endorsement.

We are indebted to Martha Lonner for her expertise in editing, artistic design and technical layout and to Kathy Lange and Becky Sheehan of Media Works for their technical skills and artistic expertise with graphics, design and layout. We especially thank all of them for their patience and dedication in the execution of this long running project.

Special thanks to Gary Dusek, Al Harmata, John Weigand and Jim Williams for critical review of the book. Thanks also to Jean Granger for her proof reading skills and Josephine Odonnell for critique of layout.

Thank you to people, families and organizations that provided photos, illustrations, paintings, figures, tables and maps. Photos, illustrations, paintings and figures are appropriately credited throughout this book, except for the individual animal illustrations and paintings. We especially thank the following artists who gave permission to use their illustrations or paintings in this Montana Wildlife Legacy Project: Ron Jenkins for upland game birds; Robert Neaves for big game and furbearing mammals, predators and nongame; Joe Thornbrugh for birds of prey.

Trapping and transplanting tables and maps were compiled and designed from Montana Fish, Wildlife and Parks' (aka The Montana Fish and Game Department) records or other sources footnoted in each table. Species distribution maps were primarily designed based on information from Montana Fish, Wildlife and Parks' documents or records.

Special thanks to Montana Public Broadcasting, KUSM-TV, Montana State University - Bozeman and staff for providing support and promotion of the entire project.

Thank you to the following individuals who provided valuable assistance with transcripts and other summaries: Kirstan Boyle, Tammy Doll, Terrance Enk, Tom Manning, Dee Topp and Margaret Morrelli.

We would like to express our appreciation to the following people for interviews or help with this Wildlife Legacy Project. While not all could be cited in the text, all did contribute information and assistance essential to understanding and telling the story.

Kurt Alt
Neil Anderson
Roy Anderson
Keith Aune
Lydia Bailey
Charles Baraby
Joann Bergeson Anderson
Don L. Brown
Jerry Brown
Arlie T. Burk
John D. Cada
David Cameron
Tom Carlsen
Nick Carvey
Robert F. Cooney and Family
Faye Couey and Family
John Craighead
James H. Cross
Jim Curtis
Bob Daniels
Rich DeSimone
Tom Dickson
Arnold Dood
Kristi DuBois
Susan Duncan
Joe Egan
Leroy Ellig
Robert L. Eng
Charles Eustace
Hayden Ferguson
Doris Fisher
Dennis Flath
Kevin Frey
Michael Frisina
Joe E. Gaab
James Garry
Brian Giddings
John Gilpatrick
Stephen Gilpatrick
Winston Greely
Kay Greene
Robert Greene
Kenneth Greer
Pat Gunderson
Mike Gurnett
Mike Korn
Ken Hamlin
Gary Hammond
Al Harmata
Jeff Herbert
Robert Henderson
Paul Holcomb
Reuel Janson
Charles Jonkel
Craig Jourdonnais
John Karlock
Wayne Kasworm
Sam Kirkaldie
John Kirsch
Steve Knapp
Richard Knight
Quentin Kujala
Genie A. Ladd
Robert Lane
Tom Lemke
Land Lindbergh
Brent Lonner
Alan Lovaas
Rick Mace
Richard Mackie
Tim Manley
Tom Manning
Neil Martin
John J. McCarthy
James McLucas and family
Dale S. Miller
Richard Munro
Thomas W. Mussehl
Isabella Mustard
Rick Northrup
Barney Old Coyote
Gary Olson
Dave Pac
Jim Phelps
Deric Picton
Irene Picton
James Posewitz
Bill Potter
Duane Pyrah
Don C. Quimby
Ryan Rauscher
Derek Reich
Merle Rognrud
Howard Rostad
Mike Ross
Tony Schoonen
Eldon Smith
Paul Sneed
Bruce Sterling
Ron Stoneberg
Jack Stonnell
Jim Stradley and Family
Marilyn McDowell–Stonehocker
Jon Swenson
Richard Taber
Tim Thier
Lorry Thomas
Mike Thompson
Nels Thoreson
Dan Tyers
Ken Walcheck
Nancy Weckworth
John P. Weigand
Dan Wesen
Bill West
Harry T. Workman
Cliff Youmans
Heidi Youmans

Major Funding for the Book Phase of the Project

***Tim Crawford - Pheasant Farms, LLC***

with support from

***Montana Chapter of the Wildlife Society***

***Montana Fish, Wildlife and Parks***

***Federal Aid in Wildlife Restoration***

---

Major Funding for the Video Phase of the Project

***Montana Fish, Wildlife and Parks***

***Federal Aid in Wildlife Restoration***

***Montana Fish, Wildlife and Parks Foundation***

***Media Works***

***The Plum Creek Foundation***

---

Other funding sources for the Video Phase of the Project

***John Cada and Bill Oyler Families***

***Montana Wildlife Federation***

***Montana Chapter of the Wildlife Society***

***The Montana Wilderness Society***

*Eating table in the Jenny Creek Cabin, south fork of the Flathead River drainage. A bear had broken into the cabin before Montana Fish and Game fieldmen arrived on October 13, 1947. They cleaned up a mess the bear left and put a manti over the window (a manti is a square of canvas used to package goods to be carried on a pack horse). Before arriving at the cabin, fieldman Merle Rognrud collected two mountain goats for a mountain goat study in the area - note the skulls on the table and hide on the chair.*
*(Courtesy Merle Rognrud field notes and Photo Collection)*

# List of Tables

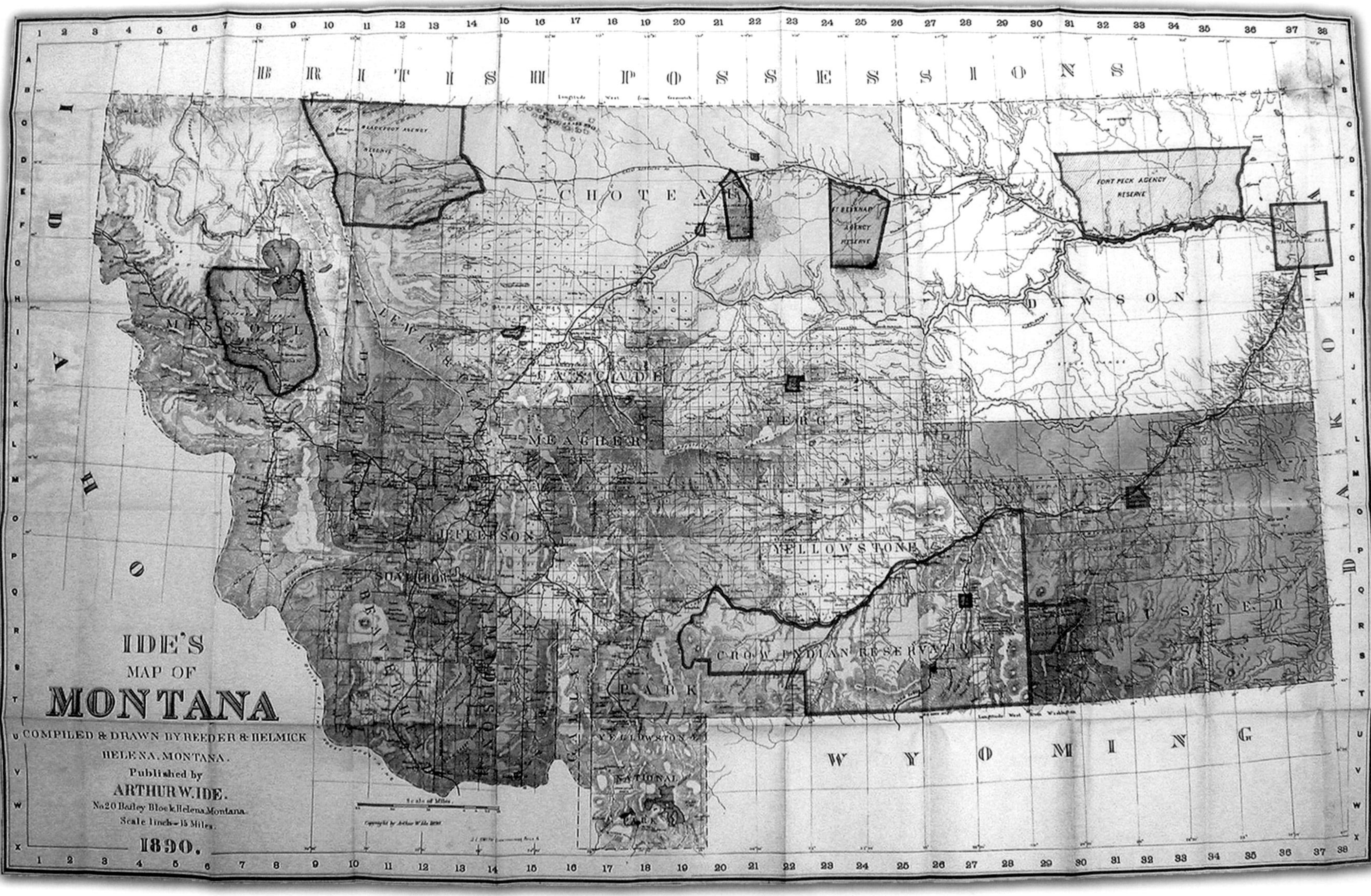


*Map of Montana in 1890. The Montana Territory was formed out of the existing Idaho Territory by an Act of Congress and signed into law by President Abraham Lincoln on May 28, 1864. It was an organized territory of the United States that existed between 1864 and 1889, when Montana officially became a state on November 8, 1889.* *(Courtesy Montana State Library special collections)*

# List of Figures, Illustrations and Maps

# Foreword

Montana is a land of stunning natural beauty, majestic mountains, vast open spaces and abundant wildlife. Although most of eastern Montana is prairie grassland, its name was derived from Spanish and means mountainous. It is a place where the sky appears bigger than the land. A place called Big Sky Country. It is also known as The Treasure State because of its rich abundance and diversity of natural resources, especially wildlife. In area it's the fourth largest state, but 47th in human population density with 6.5 people per square mile. Before the new world or the Americas and long before the United States of America, Montana was a far different place.

About twelve thousand years ago, small bands of hunters and gatherers or Paleo-Indians lived in the area now called Montana. Then the landscape was far different than today with receding glaciers, glacial lakes and a diversity of wildlife species many of which are now extinct. For thousands of years their culture was somewhat stable with simply survival in mind. About 200 years ago significant cultural changes occurred that were stimulated by four major factors: introduction of horses in the 18th century, guns (brought or traded west and south by tribes who acquired them from British and French fur traders), exploration by the Lewis and Clark Expedition and establishment of global enterprises that marketed many of Montana's natural resources including its wildlife.

Present day Montana was part of the Louisiana Purchase when Lewis and Clark and the "Corps of Discovery" crossed it in 1805-06. Following the Missouri River to its headwaters and later exploring the Marias and Yellowstone Rivers, the expedition spent one quarter of its entire journey within the current boundary of Montana. They recorded an abundance and diversity of wildlife on a landscape that could have been called the American Serengeti. After their historic journey, "New Americans" discovered Montana. The fur trade, hide hunting, mining, homesteading, logging and livestock industries in the 1800s had a significant impact on its wildlife. Montana had more homesteaders than any other state or territory. Exploitation of wildlife resources during the settlement of Montana produced a catastrophe by the end of the 19th century. At the beginning of the 20th century elk were known to occur only in the Sun and South Fork of the Flathead River drainages and Yellowstone National Park. Only 3,000 pronghorn antelope remained and American Bison were almost extinct, reduced from millions at the beginning of the 19th century to only a few hundred by the end of that century. Furbearers, especially beaver, were severely depleted. Wolves, grizzly bears and mountain lions were nearly erased from Montana's landscape. Pheasants, turkeys and Hungarian partridge had not yet been introduced.

This book tells the story of a catastrophe caused by exploitation and depletion, need and greed. Ultimately, a story of restoration and rebirth spawned by a people's dedication to restore Montana's wildlife. Passage of protective laws during the latter years of the 19th century and early 20th century, coupled with gradually increasing efforts to enforce those laws, accounts for a portion of Montana's wildlife restoration. However, most of the restoration success came from hunters, ranchers, farmers, government agencies and universities all cooperating in a wide-ranging wildlife restoration effort to trap and transplant wildlife. This effort spread across the state with a single goal in mind - replenishing what had been lost during the 1800s and early 1900s.

Restoration of Montana's wildlife resource was an epic effort extending through 6 generations, 5 wars, an economic collapse and the greatest North American climate disaster of the 20th century. By the end of this century, wildlife was more abundant in Montana than any time during the previous 130 years. Most of this story is largely untold and is the subject of this book.

Over a decade ago a small group of wildlife biologists formed an ad hoc committee which began serious discussions about the need to document and pay tribute to the many people who sacrificed and were passionate about restoring Montana's wildlife. Harold D. Picton, a Montana Fish and Game wildlife biologist in the late 1950s-early 1960s and professor emeritus of Fish and Wildlife management at Montana State University in Bozeman, was contacted and agreed to help lead the way with this ambitious wildlife legacy project by writing a book. His research started in 1999 and involved videotaping discussions with dozens of people who had made a career of wildlife restoration and conservation in Montana. Most of the people interviewed were wildlife pioneers in the 1940s and 1950s and are responsible for many of the abundant wildlife species and populations we have today. This oral history of Montana's wildlife legacy would probably have been lost if these discussions were not videotaped, transcribed and archived. Several people videotaped have since gone to the "Happy Hunting Ground". Additionally, thousands of hours were spent reading, researching and discovering documents and historic photos filed away in obscure or hard to find places and private collections.

After reviewing videotaped interviews and materials collected, the ad hoc committee realized the value of what had been initiated and decided that a historical video documentary be produced before a book. I was contacted to help with this project because of my background as a Montana Fish, Wildlife and Parks wildlife research biologist and experience with video productions. More videotaped interviews were conducted and included long-time citizen wildlife enthusiasts. Finally in December 2005, a two-part (one hour each) historical documentary entitled "Back from the Brink – Montana's Wildlife Legacy" was completed. Since then, Montana PBS has aired it several times and numerous public showings occurred throughout the state. The DVD is sold in bookstores, gift shops and sporting goods stores and can be purchased online through the Montana Fish, Wildlife and Parks Foundation at www.backfromthebrinkmt.org or Montana PBS at www.montanapbs.org/Shop/AllPrograms/. Educators in Montana's Schools and Universities are also using it to teach students about Montana's Wildlife Legacy.

While developing the script and conducting more videotaped interviews for the video documentary, a wealth of additional historical photos, old home movies, documents and personal field notes became available. Only a small portion of this "mother lode" of wildlife memorabilia could be used in the video. This gave motivation to complete the initial goal of the project and write a book.

Dr. Picton and I were again recruited to help continue this phase of the project. Information gathered during production of the video laid the foundation for the book, but thousands of additional hours were spent researching background material along with acquiring or developing more illustrations, photos and maps. All the effort put forth and materials gathered have made the book detailed and information rich, including the only complete compilation of Montana's wildlife trapping and transplanting records specific to capture and release sites and number of animals. These records in the form of tables and augmented with maps, illustrations and many historical photos would have been lost if not collected during this overall project.

Critical support from state wildlife administrators Jim Williams, Glenn Erickson and Don Childress; Spence Hegstad of the Montana Fish, Wildlife and Parks Foundation; Tim Crawford – Pheasant Farms LLC and Media Works were instrumental in the completion of this project. Other contributors are credited in the acknowledgements of the book and in the video documentary.

The book contains over 600 photos, illustrations, tables and maps. Many of the photos are historic and have seldom been seen. This book along with the video documentary will be valuable to educators, junior high, high school and university students, historians and anybody else interested in Montana's wildlife and its history. We hope it will serve as "The Written Reference" for Montana's Wildlife Legacy for years to come.

Terry N. Lonner

Terry N. Lonner

*The Hide Hunters, 1872, ink on paper by Martin S. Garretson. Bison roamed most of the West by the millions until they were decimated during its settlement in the 19th century. By the end of that century their numbers were down to only a few hundred. (Image loaned for educational purposes by JKM Collection, National Museum of Wildlife Art, Jackson, WY)*

*Bison in Lamar Valley, Yellowstone National Park. c. 1940s. Yellowstone National Park and Montana served an important role in keeping bison from extinction after their decimation during the 1800s. (Montana Fish and Game photo)*

# Introduction

After the ecosystem collapsed at the end of the last ice age a new system arose in which man the hunter helped shape its creation. Mankind is dangerous to do business with. Changes brought by human exploitation and technology caused many wildlife populations in Montana to be decimated by the end of the 19th century. Some of our current wild companions were near the point of vanishing into the mists of time along with the dodo bird and passenger pigeon. However, as we enter the 21st century, Montana is blessed with exceptional wildlife resources. Such abundance is not due to chance or accident. Therein lies a story that is the subject of this book. For wildlife populations to occur, appropriate ecological conditions must exist and humans must be willing to share the landscape. The history presented here is of thoughts and adventures of the people of Montana as they sought to restore and maintain their wildlife legacy and weave it into their social and economic system. It tells of the beginning of the conservation movement in Montana. This epic effort is also summarized in a DVD entitled "**Back from the Brink - Montana's Wildlife Legacy**."[1]

Virtually all Montanans participated in this restoration effort. Everyone who ever bought a Montana hunting or fishing license contributed. This alone includes the majority of the state's population. Montana's wildlife restoration is truly a product of its culture.

Here we focus upon trapping and transplanting carried out to restore healthy wildlife populations in a healthy environment. However, restoration involved far more than trapping and transplanting. New management methods and approaches had to be created and developed. Hundreds of research projects had to be carried out and fit into the jigsaw puzzle of knowledge furnished by other disciplines. Adventures involved in these other efforts remain to be told.

Presented in this book is the only complete compilation of Montana's wildlife trapping and transplanting records. Erosion of information over time and problems of maintaining complete records under adverse field

[1] Lonner, T. N. (Producer) 2005. Back from the brink - Montana's Wildlife Legacy. 2005. DVD and Montana PBS television documentary, Montana Fish, Wildlife and Parks Foundation, Helena. www.mfwpfoundation.org

*"Wildlife must be so managed that when the boys who are fighting for us return, they will be able to again enjoy the pleasures and the solace of the outdoors and the wild things that are so much a part of it. We certainly can do no less."*

– Biennial Report, Montana Fish and Game Commission 1941-1942

conditions led to occasional inconsistencies in tabulations. Not all inconsistencies could be resolved.

We have attempted to present restoration efforts in context of the time in which they occurred because social, financial and working conditions differed so much from that which we experience today. Raising five dollars to buy a train ticket for an elk would not be much of a problem today, but raising it when the amount represented two or more days pay gives a different picture. Statements made by the Montana Fish and Game Commission during World War II have a very special meaning when put in historical context. "Wildlife must be so managed that when the boys who are fighting for us return, they will be able to again enjoy the pleasures and the solace of the outdoors and the wild things that are so much a part of it. We certainly can do no less."[2] Throughout the 20th century Montana sent a higher proportion of its population to the military than other states.

BIENNIAL REPORT

MONTANA FISH AND GAME COMMISSION

1941 1942

*Cover photo of Roy E. Daniels on snowshoes near Lolo Pass. During the winter of 1935-36 he and his crew snowshoed 850 miles to survey elk, moose and deer. They documented over 2,500 dead elk and spent the entire winter in over a million acres of wilderness on the Montana/Idaho border in west central Montana.*[3]

The "new" ecosystem that developed after the ice age was balanced on the knife edge of extinction in the late 19th century. Main-street citizens began restoration efforts providing energy, manpower and resources to start the program. Government agencies participated as needed. Knowledge from newly developing sciences of ecology and wildlife management was rapidly put to use as it became available. Passage of the Pittman-Robertson Act (P-R Act) by the U.S. Congress in 1937 was a critical element in providing money to populate habitat with animals. Chronic low pay and long periods away from home often wore upon professional field workers. These were balanced by a high level of interest and enthusiasm for the work; summarized in a common saying about pay from the 1950s, "a hundred dollars a month and a million laughs." Join with us in visiting some of the trials and laughs from this Montana epic.

[2] Biennial report, 1941-1942. Montana Fish and Game Commission, Helena. p9.

[3] Personal communication with Bob Daniels. 2008. Information from his father's field notes while working for the U.S. Forest Service.

PART I

# From Legend to Living Memories

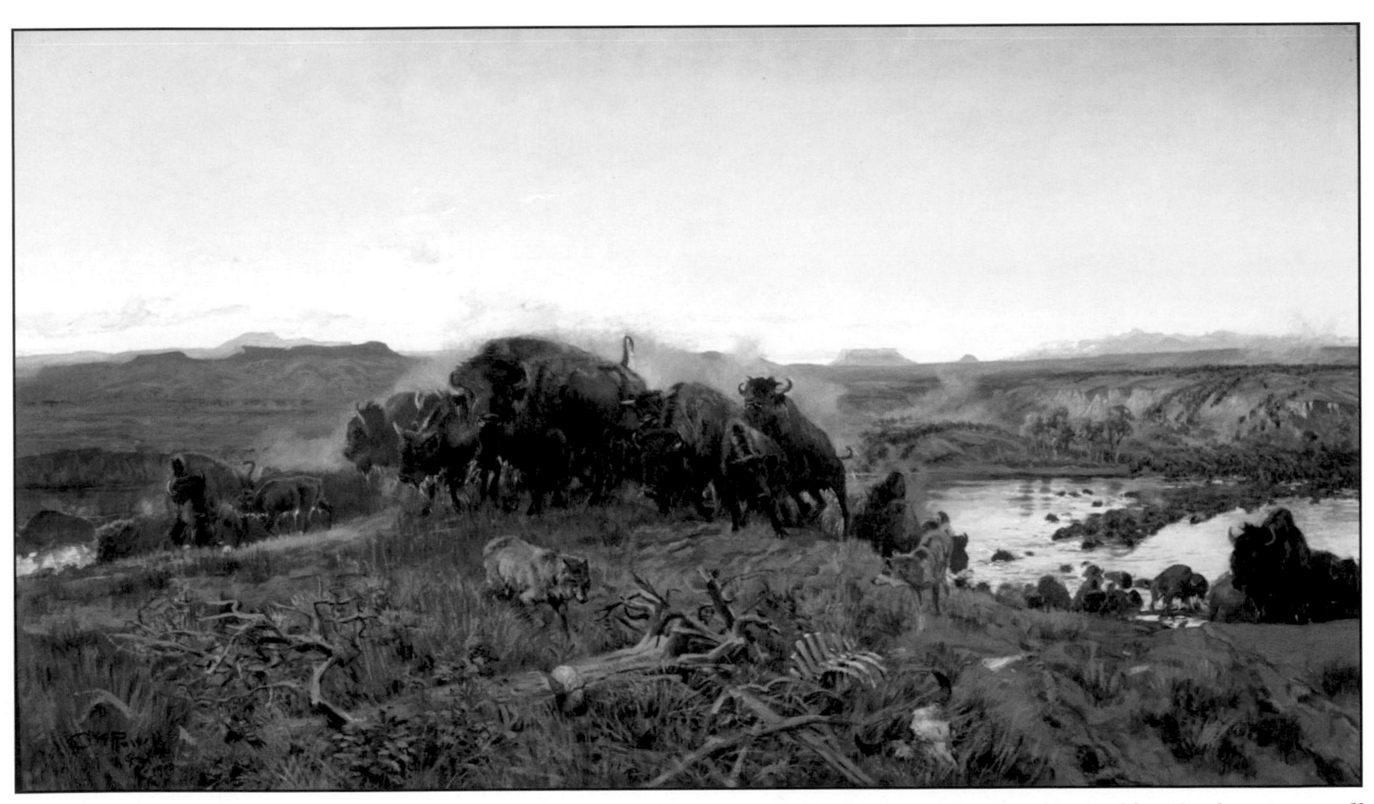

*When The Land Belonged to God by Charles M. Russell*
*(Courtesy Montana Historical Society, Helena)*

EDGAR

## Chapter 1

# The Beginning of a Legend

A small party of hunters was making their way along the Shields River north of the present town site of Livingston. Hunting had been poor for some time. Mammoths and other large mammals had declined and the party's food had run out. Very cold winters and hot, dry summers were becoming more and more common. Some of the younger and weaker members of the small human band would not survive. The band would bury them on a knoll overlooking the river valley. Red ochre, perhaps from the nearby Bridger range, was used to honor their passing. Beautiful points and blades of chert, crafted in Clovis fashion, complemented tools left for them to use in the afterlife.[1] The chert was from sites 35 to 120 miles distant from the burial site. Melting of the enormous Beartooth-Yellowstone ice cap several thousand years before left obsidian exposed for human use.

These Clovis hunters, 11,000 years ago[2], were witnessing the death of an ecosystem that had been in existence for hundreds of thousands of years. Short faced bears, mastodons and many other kinds of animals had already vanished. Horses, camels, woodland musk ox, mountain deer and antique bison would soon disappear. Jefferson ground sloths, Jefferson (imperial) mammoths, American lions, saber toothed cats and dire wolves would be among those to add their remains to the bone beds of Montana.[3]

This time of species disappearance also brought the birth of a new

*These Clovis hunters, 11,000 years ago[2], were witnessing the death of an ecosystem that had been in existence for hundreds of thousands of years.*

*Homeland, mural depiction of a Clovis burial now known as the Anzick site in Park County, Montana.* (Courtesy Larry Lahren, Ph.D.[1])

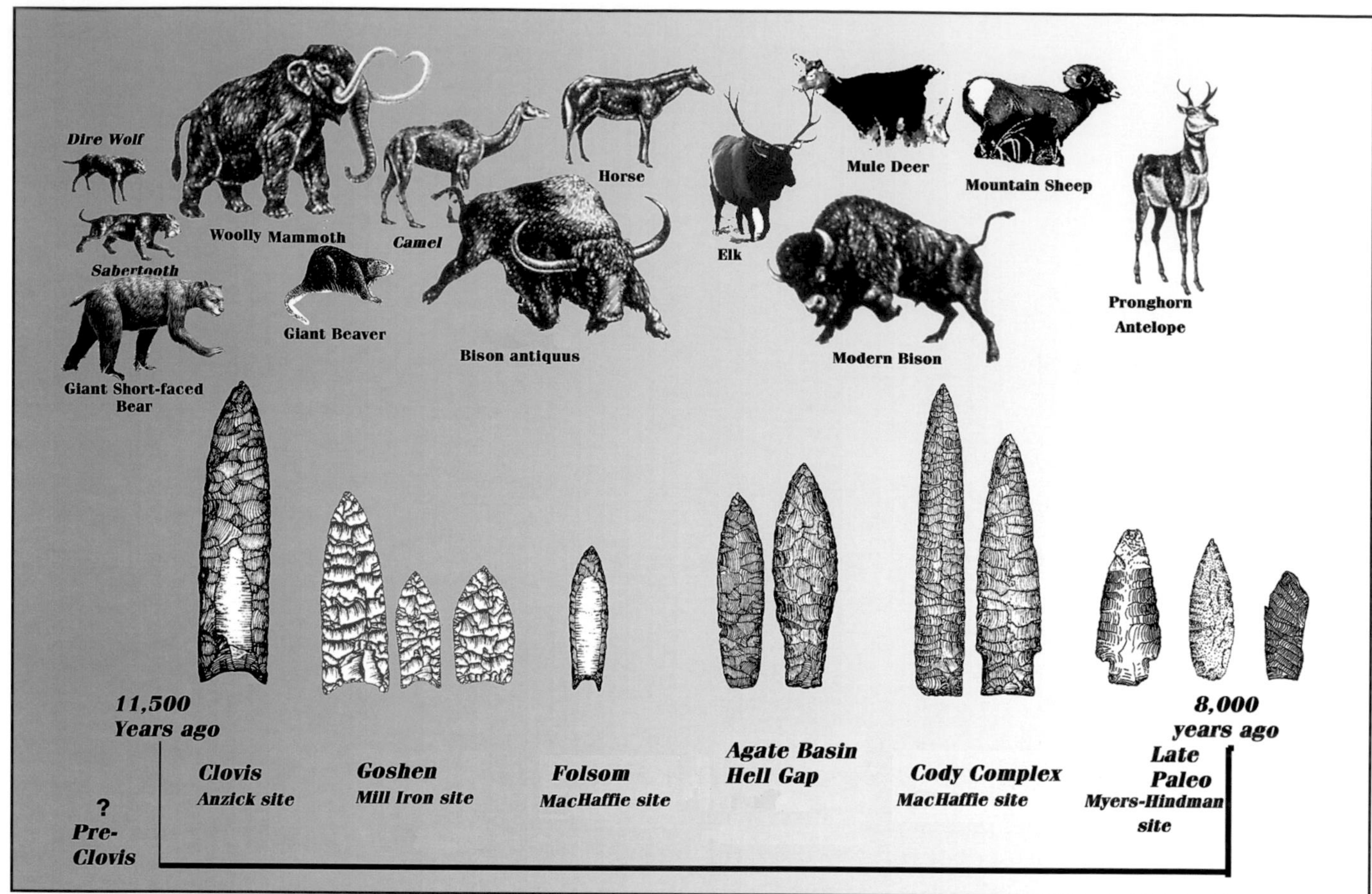


*Montana's Paleoindian Cultures timeline, representing fauna and projectile point styles between 11,500 and 8,000 years BP. (Courtesy Larry Lahren, Ph.D.[1])*

ecosystem that would develop over the next 50 centuries. This new ecosystem would include hunting by man as one of the selective forces operating upon animal populations. The end of the last ice age involved many things beyond the simple vanishing of the ice. The axis of earth was tilted to a more extreme position and it would be almost 11,000 years before Polaris would become the pole star in the northern sky.[4] The North American continent, with its broad arctic expanse and mountain ranges along both coasts, would continue in its role as a modifier of climatic change.[5]

*Huge glacial lakes including Lake Missoula, Lake Great Falls, Lake Jordan, Lake Circle, Lake Glendive[6] and smaller ones covered a large portion of what is now Montana during the last ice age.*

Huge glacial lakes including Lake Missoula, Lake Great Falls, Lake Jordan, Lake Circle, Lake Glendive[6] and smaller ones covered a large portion of what is now Montana during the last ice age. As these lakes drained, their dry lake beds provided exposed soil for massive dust storms in the hot dry winds of summer. The well watered landscape became drier and semi-arid. The axis of the earth continued to make its slow and stately shift making Thuban the pole star fifty centuries ago. The new relationship of earth to sun moderated climate to that like today. Major animal components of this new ecosystem were modern bison, elk, deer, pronghorn antelope, black and grizzly bears, wolves, mountain lions and MAN THE HUNTER.

Clovis hunters originally hunted mammoths, but they and those that followed adapted to faunal changes. The varied topography of Montana provided a home to a variety of animals. Over 320 bison kill sites have

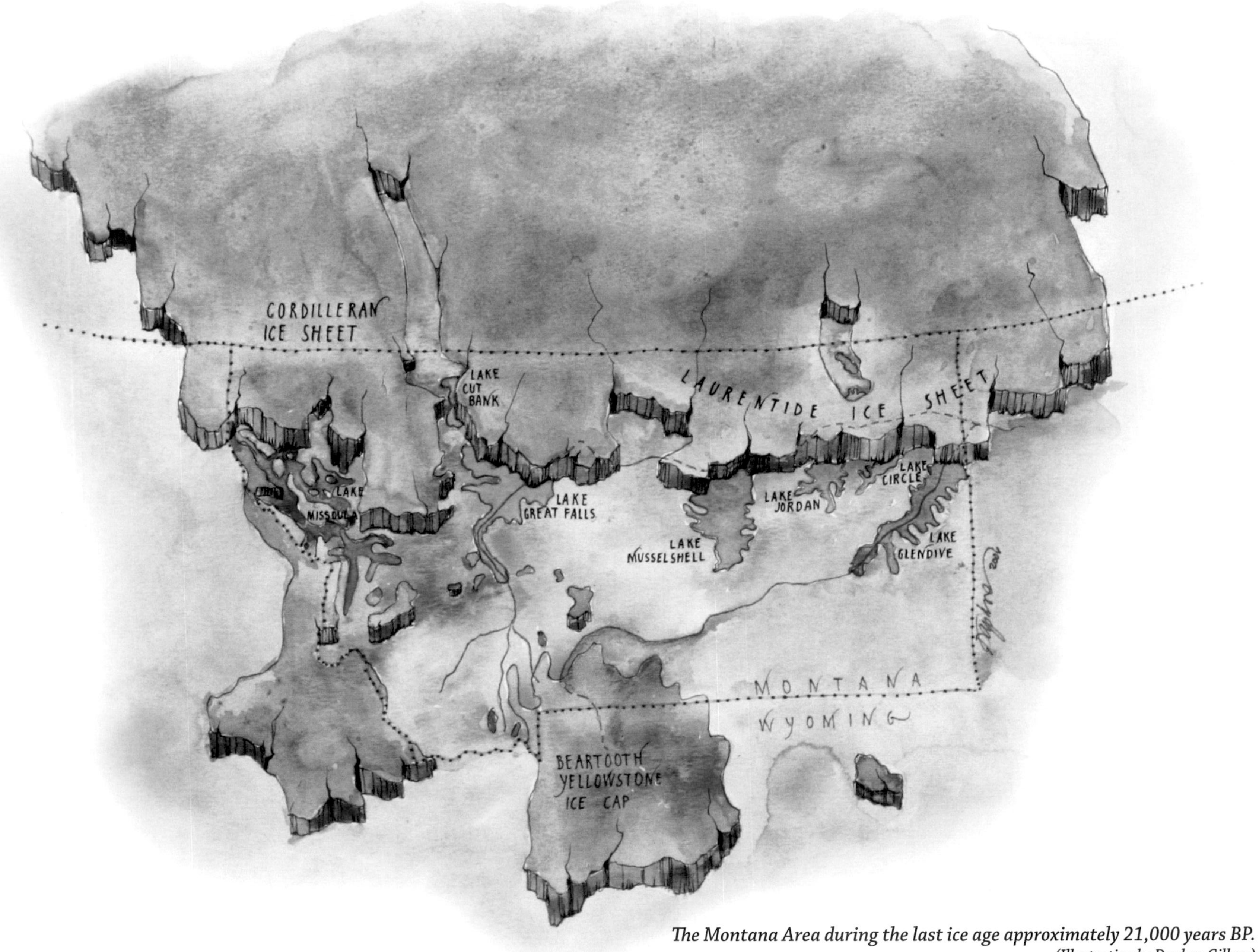


*The Montana Area during the last ice age approximately 21,000 years BP.*
*(Illustration by Daphne Gillam)*

*Clovis hunters originally hunted mammoths, but they and those that followed adapted to faunal changes. The varied topography of Montana provided a home to a variety of animals.*

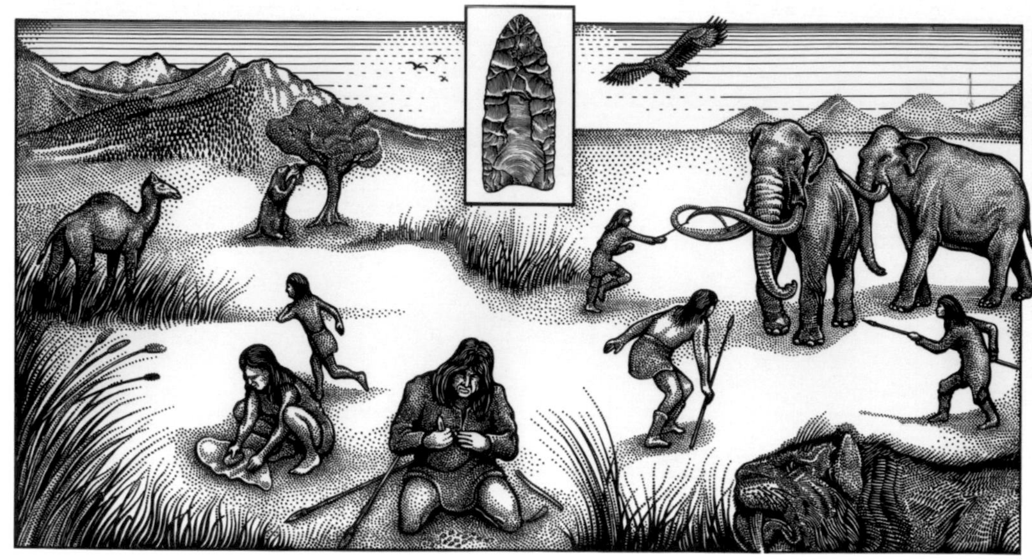

*Pen and ink illustration of Paleoindians and their artifacts by Brad Wolverton.*
*(Courtesy Utah Division of State History, Salt Lake City)*

been documented in the state.[7] Earliest of these involved antique or ancient bison[8], a variety somewhat larger than our modern form. Later sites contain modern bison. Kills at these sites range from a few in a corral type of trap set in a coulee to an estimated 200,000+ at the Highwood site where bison were driven over a cliff during its centuries of use.[9] Other groups of humans used traps, ambushes and nets to take bighorn sheep as their major food. Pronghorn antelope were sometimes driven into traps as well as hunted individually on the open prairie. Hunters and their dogs developed a successful hunting and gathering culture that persisted for thousands of years. Travel was by foot and dogs served as beasts of burden, hunting companions and occasionally food. These hunters applied selective pressure on their ecological companions; bison, elk, deer, pronghorn antelope and bighorn sheep.

*The Antelope Hunt by Charles. M. Russell*
*(Courtesy Montana Historical Society, Helena)*

The axis of earth continued its swing across the heavens and finally pointed at Polaris as its pole star. Horses again appeared on the northern plains in the 1700s. Offspring of horses, brought to North America by the Spanish in the 1500s proved to be a revolutionary force for tribes of the plains. With the arrival of the horse loosely connected and scattered bands of hunter gatherers organized into large tribes in the course of a human generation. Thus, the great horse-buffalo cultures of plains people began. The full impact of this dramatic social and ecological revolution is still

*Fresh Meat by Charles M. Russell (Courtesy Larry Len Peterson)*

***Offspring of horses, brought to North America by the Spanish in the 1500s proved to be a revolutionary force for tribes of the plains. . . Thus, the great horse-buffalo cultures of plains people began.***

not fully understood. Certainly hunting patterns changed and thousands of horses competed for food with the wildlife assemblage. Wildlife populations of Montana survived these changes and continued to provide 30,000 to 50,000 humans residing in the area with food, shelter, clothing and tools. Other tribes as distant as those from the east slope of the Cascade Mountains made 1,000 mile round trips to hunt on the Montana plains.[10] Increased mobility provided by the horse helped spread new diseases introduced by European explorers and settlers. A smallpox epidemic occurred among native tribes in the 1780s followed by others in 1802, 1833 and 1837. This was the Plains Indian Culture that Lewis and Clark and their Corps of Discovery came into contact with during their epic 1804-1806 trip to the Pacific Ocean and return.

David Thompson led another early expedition to Montana, but from Canada. In his classic explorations for the Northwest Company, he made his way down the Kootenai River in 1808. In 1809 he established a fur trading post near the present town site of Thompson Falls.

Lewis and Clark and the Corps of Discovery found an unprecedented abundance of large grazing animals ranging wild over the plains. But during their mountain travels in the western third of Montana they experienced food shortages when timbered habitat, annual movements and cycles of local animals made them difficult to find. News of the wildlife abundance seen by their expedition and others found ears of those willing to exploit resources. It was this wildlife abundance that provided economic incentive for initial settlement of western territories and for maintaining them as part of the United States - not the British fiefdom of the Hudson's Bay Company.

***Lewis and Clark and the Corps of Discovery found an unprecedented abundance of large grazing animals ranging wild over the plains.***

Beaver and buffalo were the first species to be treated as a commodity in markets of the world. Cold environments of the Gannett Peak neo-glacial age in the Rocky Mountains 1300 to late 1800s (Little Ice Age in Europe) created a strong demand for warm

*"We can send out at any time and obtain whatever species of meat the country affords in as large quantity as we wish."*

—Captain Meriwether Lewis, referring to buffalo, antelope, deer, elk and bear near the Milk River on May 8, 1804.

*Herds of Bisons and Elks on the Upper Missouri by Karl Bodmer*
*(Courtesy Rare Books Division, Special Collections, J. Willard Marriott Library, University of Utah, Salt Lake City)*

clothing.[11] This demand could be fulfilled by buffalo robes and beaver pelts. Beaver pelts were often made into beaver hats or other items of high fashion. Indian tanned buffalo robes were in much demand for use in coaches and sleighs as well as for manufacture of buffalo coats. Trading posts to collect furs and buffalo robes harvested by

*Buffalo Coat and Beaver Hat*
*(Photo courtesy Martha A. Lonner)*

*Beaver Pelts (Photo courtesy Martha A. Lonner)*

***Free Trapper* by Charles M. Russell**
*(Courtesy Montana Historical Society, Helena)*

tribes were established along the Yellowstone River in eastern Montana by Manual Lisa in 1807. The Missouri Fur Co. (1806-1824) operated trading posts along the Missouri and Yellowstone Rivers. The American Fur Co. (1826-1840) replaced the Missouri Fur Co. in operating trading post and native trapper/hunter systems. The Rocky Mountain fur trapping system had a different approach to fur trading in the Rocky Mountains from 1825 to 1838.[12] This approach relied upon large parties of mainly non-native "mountain men" or fur trappers to take beaver. Trappers held an annual rendezvous with company representatives to trade furs for manufactured goods.

Everyone involved relied upon wildlife for food and much of their clothing. Residents of fur trading forts as well as military forts used wildlife to supplement their diet. Travel was very difficult during winter and natives stayed in winter encampments. Trappers, traders and military forts in Montana were largely isolated from the "outside world" for eight months of the year.

***Residents of fur trading forts as well as military forts used wildlife to supplement their diet.***

Thousands of horses added to grazing pressure on rangelands. Streams of Montana were widely recognized as the richest source of prime beaver pelts. Buffalo robes and beaver pelts began to bring the focus of economic forces upon the area. Exploitation of Montana's wildlife was now in full swing.

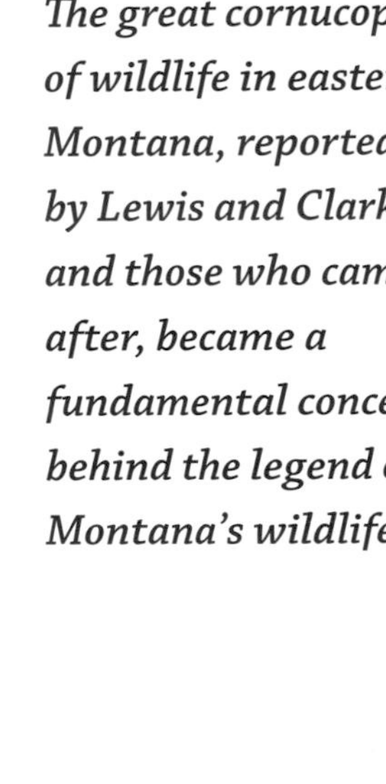

***The great cornucopia of wildlife in eastern Montana, reported by Lewis and Clark and those who came after, became a fundamental concept behind the legend of Montana's wildlife.***

***Nature's Cattle* by Charles M. Russell** *(Courtesy Larry Len Peterson)*

# Footnotes

[1] Lahren, L. and R. Bonnichsen. 1974. Bone foreshafts from a Clovis burial in southwestern Montana. Science 186:147-150.

Lahren, L. 1999. The Anzick site: The Clovis culture. Anthro Research, Inc., Livingston, MT. 3 pp.

Lahren, L. 2006. Homeland: An archaeologist's view of Yellowstone Country's past. Cayuse Press, Livingston, MT. 239 pp.

[2] Waters, M. R. and T. W. Stafford Jr. 2007. Redefining the age of Clovis: Implications for the peopling of the Americas. Science 315:1122-1126. The Clovis site in the Shields River valley (Anzick site) has been dated at 11,040 years before present, ±35 years. Another site, Indian Cr. (south of Helena) has been dated at 10,980 years before present + or - 110 years. These are among the oldest Clovis sites so far found.

[3] Lange, I. M. 2002. Ice Age Mammals of North America. Mountain Press, Missoula, MT. 225 pp.

[4] Pielou, E. C. 1991. After the ice age: The return of life to glaciated North America. University of Chicago Press, Chicago. 366 pp.

See <http://www.nasa.gov/goddard> for information concerning the pole stars of earth.

[5] Flannery, T. 2001. The Eternal Frontier. Grove Press, New York. 404 pp.

[6] Taylor, R. L. and J. M. Ashley. Geological map of Montana and Yellowstone National Park: Late Quaternary glaciation. Dept. of Earth Sciences, Montana State University, Bozeman.

Fullerton, D. S., R. B. Colton, C. A. Bush and A. W. Straub. 2004. Map showing spatial and temporal relations of mountain and continental glaciations on the northern plains, primarily in northern Montana and northwestern North Dakota. United States Geological Survey Scientific investigations map 2843. 36 pp.

[7] Fisher, J. W. and T. E. Roll. 1995. Ecological relationships between bison and native Americans during the late prehistory and early historic period. International Symposium on bison ecology and management in North America. Montana State University, Bozeman. 283-302.

[8] Waters, M. R. and T. W. Stafford. 2007. Redefining the age of Clovis: Implications for the peopling of the Americas. Science 315:1122-1126. The Mill Iron site in Carter Co. of eastern Montana has been dated at 10,840 years before present + or - 60 years.

[9] Ibid.

[10] Farr, W. E. 2003. Going to buffalo: Indian hunting migrations across the Rocky Mountains, Part 1. Montana the magazine of western history. 53(4):1-21. Farr, W. E. 2004. Part 2. 54(1):26-43.

[11] Fagan, B. M. 2000. The Little Ice Age: how climate made history 1300 - 1850. Basic books, New York, NY. 246 pp.

[12] Wishart, D. J. 1979. The fur trade of the American west 1807-1840. University of Nebraska Press, Lincoln. 237 pp.

# Chapter 2

# Demise of a Legendary Resource

Geopolitical conflict in the 1820s, between the United States and Great Britain, increased pressure upon wildlife resources. These countries were locked into competition for the Oregon Territory (Oregon and Washington). The Northwest Company, of David Thompson, and its Flathead trading posts had been acquired by the Hudson's Bay Company. Sir George Simpson, governor of the company, issued instructions to his large parties of trappers to create a "fur desert" in western Montana and Idaho. The object was to keep American trappers out. The strategy succeeded in creating a fur desert but didn't keep Americans from settling Oregon. By 1845 food requirements of the fur trading industry, added

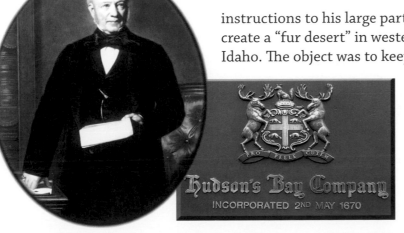

*The U.S. and Canadian northwest boundary proposed by David Thompson. c. 1810. (Illustration by Media Works, Bozeman, MT)*

***Sir George Simpson, Governor of the Hudson's Bay Company, 1821 - 1860.*** *(Courtesy Hudson's Bay Company Archives, Archives of Manitoba, Canada - Winnepeg. by Stephen Pierce, 1857.)*

to those of local Indian residents, depleted small bison herds of the Snake River basin and other western mountain basins to a few scattered animals.[1] By the late 1850s an Indian agent in Montana expressed the view that buffalo populations on the eastern plains of Montana had begun to decline. He blamed much of this upon introduction of the "iron arrowhead."[2] (After the white people came to North America, arrowheads could be made from iron. Many ironclad wooden wagon wheels were discarded by traveling settlers. Indians would salvage the iron for use in making stronger arrowheads.)

The fur trade brought rapid adaptation of steamboat technology to the difficult navigation on the Missouri River. Boats were designed that could carry up to 500 tons of cargo in only 50 inches of water. Equipped with booms and winches, these boats worked their way among and over myriads of sandbars in the "Big Muddy." Steamboats also offered a means for transporting hides to market in St. Louis and thus stimulated the hide hunting industry. Steamboats had a difficult time, particularly above Fort Union which was located at the junction of the Yellowstone and Missouri Rivers. In years of high water such as 1878, between 46 and 60 boats reached Fort Benton with their loads of freight from St. Louis.[3] "Wood hawks" worked riverside forests along the banks to provide 30 cords of firewood needed per day to fuel each boat. Much of the food for passengers and crews came from wildlife killed along the way.

*". . . we saw another big band of buffalo—thousands of them—crossing the river going south and the boat headed for them and struck about the middle of the herd. . . ."*

—John Napton, 1867

". . . we saw another big band of buffalo—thousands of them—crossing the river, going south and the boat headed for them

*Disputed Passage* *(Courtesy J. E. Trott - Artist)*

and struck about the middle of the herd. Then the wheel reversed, in order to hold the boat amongst them, and everybody commenced shooting with pistol, shotgun or rifle . . . three or four cows were hauled aboard and this ended the slaughter."

—John Napton, 1867

High quality Indian-tanned hides of young buffalo were always in demand for robes, coats and overboots needed to handle the winter cold as well as to protect firemen fighting fires. New industrial methods of tanning hides, which were developed in the 1860s, opened the door for industrial use of even the heaviest of bull buffalo hides. This new tanning process made bison hides prime material for tough and elastic industrial belts. These hides were preferred material for thousands of miles of leather belts that connected machines of the industrial revolution to their power sources. Buffalo were not the only object of the hide trade. Elk, deer, antelope and wolf hides were also in strong demand.

Steamboats also brought unwelcome passengers. Smallpox epidemics spread both from Fort Edmonton in Canada and from sick steamboat passengers in 1833 and 1837, further decimating native peoples. Fur trading posts attempted to warn their native customers to leave the vicinity before the disease arrived, but warnings were often unheeded.

Gold was discovered in Montana in 1854. This and subsequent discoveries brought a surge of people into the area. Prospectors arrived by steamboat, by land over a branch of the Oregon Trail called the Bozeman Trail and another branch that connected the Deer Lodge Valley to the main Oregon trail in Idaho and Utah. Wildlife was the major food source for new arrivals.

Judge Callaway of the Montana Supreme Court provides us with a description of the valley of Alder Creek as miners began to arrive to found Virginia City and exploit its great gold strike.

*Virginia City, Montana Territory late 1870s. Photograph by E. H. Train, Helena, MT (Courtesy Montana Historical Society, Helena)*

"Upon that day antelope ranged the hills which sloped to Alder Creek; elk were upon the lower ridges of the surrounding mountains; on the high ridges mountain

*Pioneer Prospectors by Charles M. Russell (Courtesy - Big Sky Collection, Larry & LeAnne Peterson)*

sheep were plentiful; while mule deer were all about in the timbered mountains near the head of Alder Gulch; bear were entirely too numerous for man's comfort. Grouse were everywhere along the creek of Alder and its tributary steams. . . . But a year later where was all this game? Gone, most of it. . . ."[4]

*The arrival of cattle also brought livestock diseases such as anthrax and hoof and mouth disease. Brucellosis was added to the sickening mix late in the 19th century.*

Local agriculture and cattle ranching were getting started but could not yet meet the demands for food. As gold and silver fields at Gold Creek, Bannack, Virginia City, Helena, Butte, Diamond City and many other locations expanded, supplies of wildlife food began to run short. Market hunters were forced to range farther and farther afield. Cattle and domestic sheep began to be brought into Montana in 1850. In 1862, the American Fur Company brought cattle into eastern Montana and the major period of the expansion of cattle herds began.[5] Arrival of cattle also brought livestock diseases such as anthrax and hoof-and-mouth disease. Brucellosis was added to the sickening mix late in the 19th century.

*Cattle on the Range from the Edna Tracy Collection*
*(Courtesy Montana State University Library Special Collections, Bozeman)*

Hide hunting for bison and other species continued in full force into the 1880s in the eastern portion of the state. Both white-tailed and mule deer hides were always valued items in the fur and hide trade. Hide hunters took 1,700 deer during a winter from a hunting area near Lewistown in the 1860s.[6] As a result of restoration similar numbers of deer are now harvested annually from the same area. A fresh buffalo hide was worth several days' pay during the 1860s and 1870s. This made it financially attractive to engage in buffalo hunting in spite of many risks and difficulties of the endeavor. The great buffalo hunt ended abruptly in 1883 with the species teetering on the brink of extinction, however, the

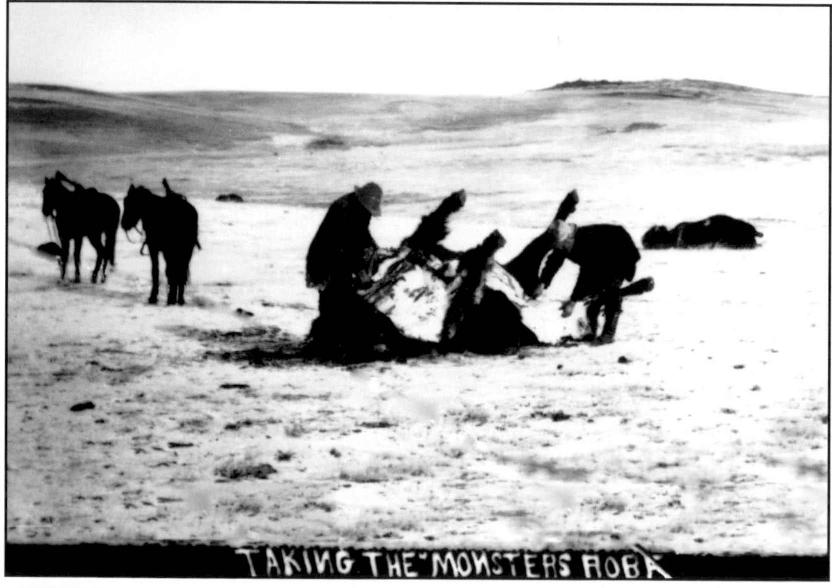


*Taking the Monster's Robe -January, 1882. Photograph by L. A. Huffman*
*(Courtesy Montana Historical Society, Helena)*

hide market remained strong for other species. In 1874, 12,000 antelope hides were shipped from Bozeman alone. This nearly exterminated pronghorns from the Yellowstone valley.[7]

Some isolated areas still had prestine vistas absent of man. A visit to the Centennial Valley of southwestern Montana in August of 1886 produced the following observation: " Shortly, as we came in sight of the (Red Rock) river where it broadened and hardly appeared to move, I said to him, " that certainly is curious looking water," and he said, "that isn't water, it's ducks." Believe it or not, for space that covered half an acre, the water could not be seen for the waterfowl. I believe the ducks and geese along that river and upon the lakes at that time would run into the hundreds of thousands.... At least 5,000 antelope were then ranging in the Centennial Valley."[8]

Commercial hunters usually hunted animals when they were most vulnerable on their winter ranges. Furthermore, many of these hunters clearly had little knowledge of the migratory habits of wildlife in Montana. They did not understand that when they eliminated animals from foothill winter ranges, they also eliminated them from the mountains. This misconception, that mountains were unoccupied by wildlife, is an error in understanding that still haunts us over a century later.

The U.S. census of 1870 reported 20,595 people in Montana, Native Americans were not counted. In 1867, the Montana Territorial Legislature passed some laws intended to protect the dwindling wildlife resources. These laws accomplished little because of their confusing nature, virtual lack of wildlife law enforcement, and actions of the U.S. Congress that declared all of the laws passed by the Territorial Legislature null and void. However, laws passed by the 1867 Territorial Legislature did indicate concerns about wildlife and that the "hearts" of legislators were in the "right place." Agriculture was just beginning, particularly in such locations as the Gallatin and Helena valleys. Devastating outbreaks of Rocky Mountain Locusts occurred every year from 1861 to 1877 despite their more usual cycle of once every three years. Eight of these years had truly major outbreaks with billions of insects stripping most of the vegetation from areas as large as 190,000 square miles of the Great Plains, portions of which were in Montana.[9] The 150,000 acres of farms in the state were heavily impacted. Even in best of times these farms could not produce enough food for miners and military forts in the territory. In the 1860s grain production was just starting out and there was not enough grain for the human population let alone as feed for domestic animals. The shortage led one Gallatin Valley homesteader to shoot antelope to feed his chickens during winter. As Charles Blakely noted, there were plenty of wild competitors seeking to feed on crops in the Gallatin Valley, including grizzly bears.[10]

Meat markets routinely sold wild game in growing communities, which added variety and enhanced the meat supply available from new farms. In 1873, many people preferred elk over beef and at 7 cents per pound elk was cheaper in Bozeman markets. Both fish and wildlife, taken along the route, supplemented rations of the "Montana Column" of the U.S. Army infantry in their 400 mile march from Fort Shaw to the Little Bighorn, where they discovered the bodies of Custer's command in June of 1876.[11]

***. . . However, laws passed by the 1867 Territorial Legislature did emphasize concerns about wildlife by the people of Montana and that the "hearts" of their representative legislators were in the "right place." This occurred before the end of the bison slaughter and over 3 decades before the national conservation movement began.***

***In 1873, many people preferred elk over beef and at 7 cents per pound elk was cheaper in Bozeman markets.***

Although efforts to extend railroads to Montana began in 1864, it was not until December 26, 1881 that the Utah and Northern line reached Butte. About the same time, construction crews of the Northern Pacific Railway crossed over the North Dakota line into eastern Montana. The Northern Pacific completed their line on September 8, 1883.[12] To encourage construction of a rail line to the Pacific coast, Congress gave the Northern Pacific Railroad Company a land grant of 40 sections (square miles) of land for each mile of track constructed. This land grant affected wildlife habitat for the next 135 years. These land grants later triggered a complex series of land trades in the West Gallatin River drainage, which converted a large block of it into public ownership in the early 21st century.

*. . . To encourage construction of a rail line to the Pacific coast, Congress gave the Northern Pacific Railroad Company a land grant of 40 sections (square miles) of land for each mile of track constructed. This land grant has influenced wildlife habitat for the next 135 years.*

Great bison herds provided much of the food for local people. Indian tribes from western Montana as well as Idaho and Washington made trips to hunt bison in eastern Montana. These hunts continued until the last of the herds was killed off in 1883. Less than 600 U.S. Army troopers were stationed in Montana during most of this period. A few of these troopers were charged with providing safe escort for tribal hunts past new towns and ranches until the great hunt ended.[13]

Wild game provided much of the food for railroad construction workers. As the Northern Pacific Railroad pressed westward, it provided buffalo hide hunters with a new transportation system to get their hides to the industrial market. The great bison herd of the northern plains was subsequently propelled into its final collapse. During the winter of 1881-1882, 250,000 bison hides were shipped on the Northern Pacific route from the lower Yellowstone River and western North Dakota. In 1883 the last bison of the northern herd were taken by Sitting Bull and his people and a few buffalo hide hunters along the Cannonball River in southwestern North Dakota. Grazing competition by thousands of horses and cattle, inroads of diseases brought

*Cheyennes Watching Union Pacific Track Layers by Charles M. Russell*
*(Courtesy - Big Sky Collection, Larry & LeAnne Peterson)*

by livestock and over-hunting had almost eliminated this great wildlife resource. These events also signaled the near extermination of wildlife resources that had provided food and economic resources for the settlement of Montana. Interestingly, the great

***Hide Yard. c. 1870s.***
*(Courtesy Kansas State Historical Society, Topeka)*

amount of meat left on the plains, when hides were stripped, also appears to have produced a boom in the populations of wolves, eagles and other scavengers. This bumper crop of predators often depredated free-ranging livestock to the dismay of many stockmen.

In 1886, William Hornaday came to eastern Montana to collect some remaining buffalo for the Smithsonian Museum. He believed that less than 300 bison still remained in the United States. Others estimated up to a few thousand. His first hunting party traveled northwest from Miles City in May. They saw only prairie dogs and rabbits during their first two days of travel. On the third day a few antelope were seen. Eventually the party found a live buffalo calf and two fresh skeletons, as well as other wildlife specimens. Another hunting expedition in September and October was more successful. A total of 25 bison specimens were collected. The collection area included what is now the southwestern portion of Garfield County and adjacent portion of northern Rosebud County.[14] A family group of six buffalo was prepared for display at the Smithsonian. This historic family group taxidermy mount has now been refurbished and returned to Fort Benton for display.

"I was delighted with our remarkably good fortune in securing such a prize, for, owing to the rapidity with which the large buffalo are being found and killed off these days, I had not hoped to capture a really old individual.

***In 1886, William Hornaday came to eastern Montana to collect some remaining buffalo for the Smithsonian Museum. He believed that less than 300 bison still remained in the United States. Others estimated up to a few thousand.***

***The Hornaday family group of bison was initially prepared for display at the Smithsonian Institution in Washington, D. C. between 1887 and 1888. This historic taxidermy exhibit has now been refurbished and is on display at the Agricultural Museum in Fort Benton, MT.***
*(Photo courtesy Terry N. Lonner)*

"... Nearly every adult we took carried old bullets in his body, and from this one we took four of various sizes that had been fired into him on various occasions. One was found sticking fast in one of the lumbar vertebrae."

—William Hornaday, 1889. This specimen is the big bull in the family group mount now in Fort Benton, Montana.[15]

Nearly every adult we took carried old bullets in his body, and from this one we took four of various sizes that had been fired into him on various occasions. One was found sticking fast in one of the lumbar vertebrae." William Hornaday, 1889. This specimen is the big bull in the family group mount now in Fort Benton, Montana.[15]

Cattle herds expanded as buffalo declined. The 1880s was the era of "bonanza" grazing, when open range was viewed as having few limits and stocked with no limitations in mind. In Montana, cattle and sheepmen did not have conflicts and often cattle herds and flocks of sheep ran side by side. Many local ranches grazed both cattle and sheep. The severe winter of 1886-1887 brought the era of "bonanza" grazing to an end. An early snow had been converted to an ice cover on the drought depleted range. This was followed by several feet of snow on the prairie and temperatures that reached 60 degrees Fahrenheit below zero.[16] In this winter, 60 percent or more of the cattle in Montana were lost. Once again scavengers were well fed. Following this winter, open ranges were broken up into smaller ranches and domestic sheep herds increased.

As herds declined, some people including a few hide hunters began to become concerned about bison. One of the champion buffalo hunters was "Yellowstone Vic" Smith. In 1879 he captured live buffalo calves for ranchers who wanted to cross them with cattle and also for shipment to private zoos.[17] However, as Teddy Roosevelt found out in his buffalo hunt in the fall of 1883, the concept of conservation was foreign to commercial hunters. They followed the economic rule of "use a resource to extinction then move on to something else." This contrasts with the conservation concept of "use wisely and keep for future use" held by Roosevelt and other conservationists.

*The commercial hunters followed the economic rule of "use a resource to extinction then move on to something else." This contrasts with the conservation concept of "use wisely and keep for future use" held by T. Roosevelt and other conservationists.*

At about this same time, more successful buffalo conservation was occurring in western Montana. Walking Coyote (also known as Samuel Wells), a member of the native Salish peoples, had taken a second wife, thus breaking a major law of this Christian tribe. He was lashed and expelled. Later he was tired of being an outcast and wished to return to his tribe. A knowledgeable trader on the Marias River, Charles Aubrey, suggested to Walking Coyote that if he brought a penitence gift of buffalo to his people, Father Ravalli, a missionary, would help reinstate him into the tribe. In 1873 Walking Coyote captured seven buffalo calves in the Milk River area of north central Montana and held them in a corral at

*Waiting for a Chinook. 1886 Watercolor by Charles M. Russell*
*(Used with permission from the Montana Stockgrowers Association, courtesy Montana Historical Society, Helena)*

a trading post on the Marias River. In spring, when they were almost a year old, a determined Walking Coyote began a successful 200-250 mile journey with his bison south and west across the Rocky Mountains to the south end of Flathead Valley. One of the bull calves died during the journey. His herd had expanded to 12 or 13 animals by 1882-1883 when he sold them to Michael Pablo and Charles Allard, both of whom were highly successful Indian ranchers on the Flathead Reservation. Additional bison were added to the Pablo-Allard herd from Montanan Jacob Smith and the Nebraska herd of "Buffalo Jones." By 1896, the herd had grown to over 700 buffalo.[18] The death of Charles Allard in 1897 led to his half of the herd being subdivided among his heirs. Pablo retained his half of the herd intact.

In 1905 Congress passed the Reallocation Act that opened portions of the Flathead Indian Reservation to homesteading. This congressional action forced Pablo to sell his herd and nudged buffalo closer to extinction. At the time, the wild bison herd in Yellowstone National Park (NP) was estimated at 25 to 50.[19] President Theodore Roosevelt wanted to purchase Pablo's entire herd but Congress refused to approve his proposal. Congress did approve, however, the purchase of 18 bison for Yellowstone NP. The Canadian government expressed eagerness to buy as many of the bison as Pablo could catch and ship. After a three year long roundup effort, about 709 buffalo were sold to Canada for their national parks. Some of the Pablo herd remained behind, being too wild to capture. A portion of the Allard herd had been acquired by a Kalispell banker, Charles Conrad. Upon his death, his widow provided 37 of these bison to become the initial stock of the National Bison Range at Moiese, Montana. Some buffalo also had been sold to private ranchers over the years. In 1900, an estimated 80 percent of the buffalo in existence owed their lineage to the herd begun by Walking Coyote and developed by Pablo and Allard.[20]

As Montana wildlife grew scarcer, animals were often captured and

***Congress did approve purchase of 18 bison for shipment to Yellowstone National Park to supplement the 25 to 50 wild bison surviving in the Park.***

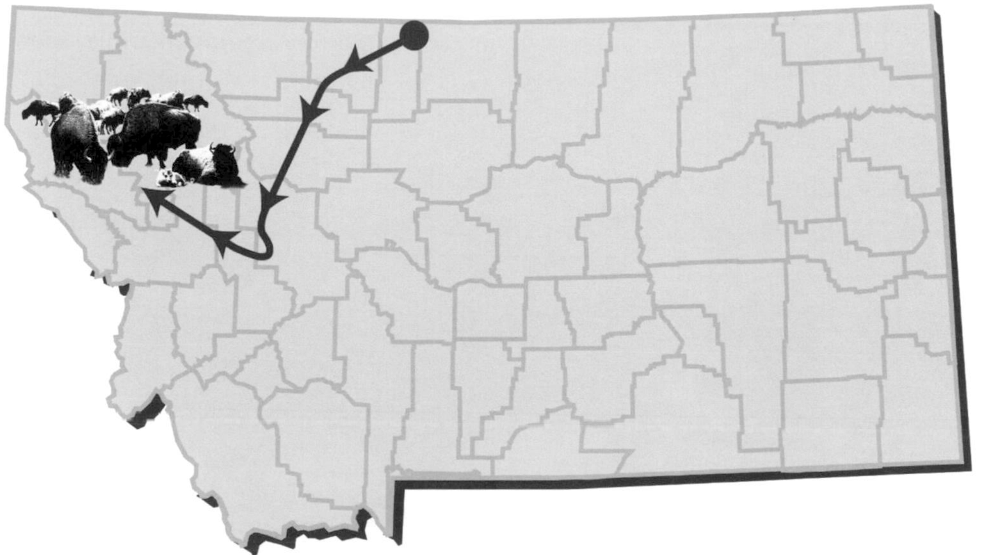

*The approximate 200-250 mile route followed by Walking Coyote in 1873 to bring buffalo back to the south end of Flathead Valley. (Illustration by Media Works, Bozeman, MT)*

***In 1900, an estimated 80 percent of the buffalo in existence owed their lineage to the herd begun by Walking Coyote and developed by Pablo and Allard.[20]***

*In 1890, former buffalo hunter Yellowstone Vic partnered with Dick Rock to trap and sell live elk and other species from their ranch on the Montana-Idaho border near Henry's Lake. They also had a moose named "Nelly Bly" that they raced against horses in harness races at fairs including the Chicago World's Fair.*

semi-domesticated or held in captivity. Michael Pablo maintained a few elk in a pen for display. He also had a pet mountain goat that entertained guests by walking a quarter of a mile on the top rail of a fence. Others broke elk or bison to harness and used them to pull sleighs and wagons. Buffalo were often used in rodeos until buffalo riding was outlawed by the Montana Legislature in the 1920s.

In 1890, former buffalo hunter Yellowstone Vic partnered with Dick Rock to trap and sell live elk and other species from their ranch on the Montana-Idaho border near Henry's Lake. They also had a moose named "Nelly Bly" that they raced against horses in harness races at fairs including the Chicago World's Fair. They shipped over 500 elk, deer, moose, antelope, bears, mountain lions and bighorn sheep in the first five years that they were in business. They sold to private collectors and zoos in the eastern United States.[21] News articles at the time lauded them for helping to preserve these species. They also trapped other animals for hides and furs. Live animals that they captured had to be taken from their ranch over 60 miles to railheads at either Three Forks or Monida, Montana.

In 1887, Jim Hill's Manitoba Railroad entered the state from the east. This later became the Great Northern Railway and reached Seattle in 1893. J. M. Kennedy of the northwestern Montana town of Libby told of the impact of being on the mainline.

> "Once after the construction of the Great Northern Railway through western Montana, west of Kalispell the business of killing deer and shipping the hides furnished profitable employment for many hunters, and the records of the Great Northern Railway show that in one season there were shipped out of the little village of Troy, on the western boundary line of Montana, more than ten thousand deer hides. The old timers in that region of the state refer to the period as "the deer skin age." It is said that deer hides in those days passed as currency. The settled price of a hide was twenty-five cents.

*Two Buffalo in Harness. c. 1880. (Courtesy Gallatin Historical Society, Pioneer Museum, Bozeman, MT - Donor: R. B. McCulloch)*

They were accepted at the grocery store and cobbler's shop, or at the restaurant, or in the newspaper office as the currency of the country. The editor of the little local paper at Libby once said that the gallant young swain who took his best girl to a dance in Libby paid the entrance fee in four deer skins."[22]

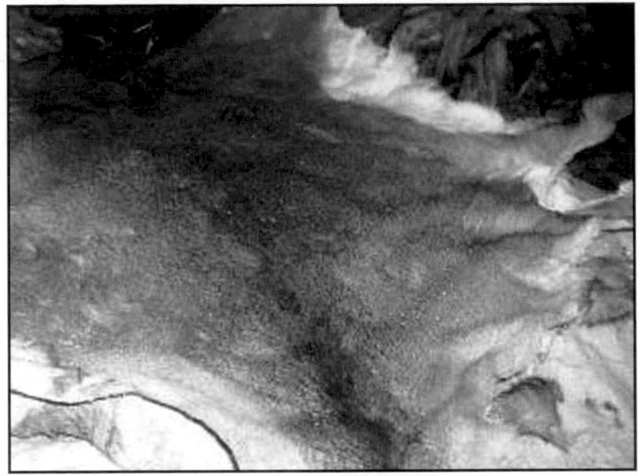

*Deer Hides were the "currency" of the day.*
*(Photographer unknown)*

Booming mining areas, particularly at Butte, but also at many other sites in western and central Montana swelled Montana's population to 132,159 by 1890. Montana was granted statehood on 22 February, 1889 a year during which some market hunters were arrested in the Madison River drainage for excessive killing of wildlife. Attraction to wildlife as a food item was summed up by Teddy Roosevelt when he said that it was much better than "embalmed beef." The method of preservation of meat at the time consisted mainly of putting it in barrels of brine, and smoking or drying it. Parties of Indians hunting off reservations were reported to be killing elk and deer. In 1889, wild fires were also reported in the Yellowstone NP area as well as in a number of other areas both in western Montana and the prairies of eastern Montana.

In 1893, the Legislature of the new state enacted a year long closed season on moose and elk. In 1895 lawmakers created the first Fish and Game Board to oversee the state's wildlife resources. They also established a 4 - month hunting season limiting big game hunters to 8 deer, 8 bighorn sheep, 8 mountain goats, 8 antelope, 2 moose and 2 elk.

The 1897 Legislature prohibited sale of game animals and birds and established daily limits on the number of game birds taken. The moose season was closed and would remain so for the next 48 years. Although the 25 counties in existence could hire game wardens to enforce these laws, not all did, which suggests early law enforcement was not very substantial or consistent. Some newspapers called game laws "a fraud upon the people" and "an imposition upon the taxpayers." Others complained that game laws discriminated against the poor man who could no longer shoot game or catch fish all year long "for the use of his table or the support of his family." Early game laws were not understood and newspapers could not agree whether seasons were open or closed in the early 1890s. Although market hunting was illegal and people were arrested for it on rare occasions, wild meat was commonly available in stores into the 1890s.

Railroad construction crews certainly harvested their share of wildlife encountered along their routes, but the impact of railways was much greater than that. Railways promoted settlement of land along their routes, prairie was plowed, and timber was cut for lumber, railroad ties and locomotive fuel. Timber was also cut for mines

***In 1895 lawmakers created the first Fish and Game Board to oversee the state's wildlife resources. They also established a four month hunting season limiting big game hunters to 8 deer, 8 bighorn sheep, 8 mountain goats, 8 antelope, 2 moose and 2 elk.***

*William Hruza's Meat Market, Livingston, MT. c. 1890s.* *(Courtesy Yellowstone Gateway Museum of Park County, Livingston, MT - William F. Whithorn Collection)*

and smelters. As much as 1,000 cords of timber per day was cut for mine supports, fuel and charcoal for smelters in the Butte area alone. Settlers hunted wildlife to make "ends meet" and for sale in markets of towns.

Large-animal populations of the state that had evolved over the previous 10,000 years under moderate hunting by humans were in desperate straits by 1890. Bison populations of North America were estimated at 300 to a couple of thousand. Perhaps 60,000 to 90,000 elk were left in North America, most in the vicinity of Yellowstone NP. George Bird Grinnell had said in the middle of the 1800s, "...never met a man of experience who did not agree with him that ... antelope were far more abundant than bison." By the turn of the century their number had dwindled to a few tens of thousands scattered over western portions of the continent. Disease, range competition and habitat destruction combined with market and subsistence hunting brought dark days for wildlife. The usual factors of germs, guns and increasing human populations wreaked havoc that also occurred on many other animal and human populations around the world.

At the close of the 19th century, two railroads stretched across the state on both northern and southern routes. Roads were unpaved, consisting



*(Courtesy Montana Historical Society, Helena)*

***Large-animal populations of the state that had evolved over the previous 10,000 years under moderate hunting by humans were in desperate straits by 1890.***

*Forests were exploited to provide wood to fuel the smelter at Anaconda, MT, shore up the mines in Butte, MT and provide ties for the railroads.* *(Courtesy World Museum of Mining, Butte , MT)*

of dusty or muddy ruts used by horses and carriages as well as ox-drawn freight wagons. Some bigger towns had electric companies which began to lighten the age-old darkness of night. The population of Montana had grown to 243,329 people in 1900; over 25 percent lived near the mining complex of Butte and Anaconda. Average wages ranged from $240 a year for farm labor to $720 per year for white-collar workers. Typical six-day work weeks of 60 hours left little leisure time or energy for recreation.

Human life expectancies of 47 years testified to the difficulties of life. Labor and nursing skills of women were critically important to maintaining healthy and productive families. Women would not be given respite from their critically important family nursing duties until discovery and subsequent availability of antibiotics in the 1940s. When these people thought of recreation to brighten their lives and also fatten their larders, thoughts turned to wildlife. Beginning in the 1870s, rod and gun clubs began to form in virtually every Montana community. These clubs were the sign of a broad-based social movement incorporating concepts of conservation (use wisely and keep for future use) that would have dramatic effects on the state over the next century.

***Beginning in the 1870s, rod and gun clubs began to form in virtually every Montana community. These clubs were the sign of a broad-based social movement incorporating concepts of conservation (use wisely and keep for future use) that would have dramatic effects on the state over the next century.***

***Helena Rod and Gun Club - 1888.*** *(Courtesy Montana Historical Society, Helena)*

# Footnotes

[1] Roe, F. G. 1970. The North American buffalo: A critical study of the species in its wild state. University of Toronto Press, Toronto, Canada. Vol. 1: 520 pp.

[2] Vaughan, J. C. 1957. Colonel Alfred Jefferson Vaughan: The frontier ambassador. Montana Historical Library, Helena. 469 pp.

[3] Madsen, B. M. and B. D. Madsen. 1998. North to Montana! Utah State University Press, Logan. 298 pp.

[4] Callaway, L. L. 1930. Montana's game in Vigilante days. Montana Wildlife: Biennial Report 1929-1930. Montana State Fish and Game Dept. 17-20.

[5] Malone, M. P. and R. B. Roeder. 1976. Montana, a history of two centuries. University of Washington Press, Seattle. 352 pp.

[6] Messiter, C. A. 1890. Sport and adventures among the North American Indians. R. H. Porter, London. 368 pp.

[7] Angler. 1883. The big game and the Park. Forest and Stream 20(4):68

[8] Ibid. Callaway, L. L. 1930.

[9] Lockwood, J. A. 2004. Locust. Basic Books, New York. 294pp. And: Riley, C. V., A. S. Packard Jr., C. Thomas. 1878. First annual report of the United States Entomological Commission for the year 1877 relating to the Rocky Mountain Locust. Government Printing Office, Washington D.C. 294 pp.

[10] Blakely, Charles Greenleaf. Personal papers. Haynes Collections, Renne Library Archives, Montana State University, Bozeman.

[11] Bradley, J. H. 1961. The march of the Montana column. Edited by E. L. Stewart. University of Oklahoma Press, Norman. 179 pp.

[12] Ibid. Malone, M. P. and R. B. Roeder. 1976.

[13] Farr, W. E. 2003. Going to buffalo: Indian hunting migrations across the Rocky Mountains. Part 1. Montana the magazine of western history 53(4):1-21 and Part 2: 2004. 54(1):26-43.

[14] Hornaday, W. T. 1889. The extermination of the American bison. Smithsonian Institution Press, Washington, D.C. 548 pp.

[15] Ibid.

[16] Mueller, G. D. 1982. Winter of calamity, 1886-87. In Montana Weather compiled by Carol Cunningham. Montana Magazine Inc., Helena. 70-75. This is the winter that produced the famous Charles M. Russell painting, "Waiting for a Chinook" or "Last of the Five Thousand", depicting a starving cow in a blizzard.

[17] Smith, V. G. 1997. The champion buffalo hunter. The frontier memoirs of Yellowstone Vic Smith. Editor: J. Prodgers. Two Dot Press, Helena, MT. 257 pp.

[18] Bartlett, W. A. 2001. The Pablo-Allard herd: origin. Chapter 4 in: "I will be meat for my Salish." Salish Kootenai College Press and Montana Historical Society Press, Salish Kootenai College, Pablo, MT. 69-101.

[19] Meagher, M. M. 1973. The bison of Yellowstone National Park. National Park Service Monograph 1:161 pp.

[20] Haynes, F. 1970. The buffalo. University of Oklahoma Press, Norman. 244 pp.

[21] Smith, V. G. 1997. The champion buffalo hunter: The frontier memoirs of Yellowstone Vic Smith.

J. Prodgers, Editor. Two Dot Press, Helena, MT. 257 pp.

[22] Kennedy J. M. 1920. The game warden. Biennial report of the Montana Game and Fish Commission, Helena. 54-56.

# Chapter 3

# A New Century, A New Time

As calendars flipped over to the 20th century Montana's wildlife assets were in dismal condition. The buffalo were gone. Elk were scarce and found only where protected by mountains and what few laws existed. Deer were seldom seen in many areas. George Bird Grinnell, in his efforts to document wildlife numbers, said that in the middle of the 19th century it was generally agreed that pronghorn antelope were several times more abundant than buffalo. Fifty years later, in the first decade of the 20th century, antelope too, were making their way to possible oblivion. Audubon or badlands bighorn sheep of the Missouri and Yellowstone River breaks had been so abundant that a party of mountain men killed 26 of them at the mouth of the Musselshell River in a two hour period in 1822.[1] Unregulated exploitation brought them to extinction in 1916.[2] Additionally, hunting and diseases brought into Montana by domestic sheep and livestock eliminated most of the other bighorn populations scattered about the state.

The Legislature of the new state of Montana was busy passing laws that could be enforced. In 1901, legislation established an Office of the State Game Warden[3] with W. F. Scott appointed to protect and oversee the fish and wildlife resources of the state. The first badge for Montana Game Wardens was of copper and bore on its backside the message that it was contributed by the Anaconda Copper Mining Company. To many this was a sign of the "copper collar" that the company held around the social neck of Montana.

Although the federal government had established some forest reserves that would become our national forests as well as creating Yellowstone NP, federal agencies that now manage these resources did not yet exist. The U.S. Army

*W. F. Scott was the first head of the Montana Fish and Game Department in 1901. The first Badge for Montana Game Wardens was of copper and bore on its back the message that it was contributed by the Anaconda Copper Mining Company.*

President Theodore (Teddy) Roosevelt, February 24, 1903. *(Library of Congress, Prints and Photographs Division. [reproduction number LC-USZ62-7220 DLC])*

was managing Yellowstone NP after an inadequately funded civilian staff could not control poaching and stealing of artifacts. From 1901-1908 President Teddy Roosevelt set aside 70 percent of Montana forest lands as national forests bringing complaints from some Montana residents. However, the conservation message that President Roosevelt and his supporters brought found acceptance in Montana. He received 53 percent of the vote of Montanans in 1904. While less than his national plurality of 59 percent, it did indicate popular support.

The American Bison Society was formed in 1905 with William Hornaday as president and Theodore Roosevelt as honorary president. It immediately began efforts to preserve bison. In 1906, it persuaded Congress to create the Wichita Mountain Refuge in Oklahoma and provided 15 bison to stock it. Then attention was turned to Montana where the Pablo-Allard herd was by far the largest herd left in the United States.

The Society worked with Senator Joseph Dixon of Montana to persuade Congress to purchase a block of land for the National Bison Range. The appropriation passed in 1908 only a short time before the Flathead Reservation was opened to homesteading, which would have eliminated the opportunity. This society obtained the first bison for the range.[4]

Not everyone approved of efforts to conserve bison:

> "Why ... people should take an interest in the buffalo and why any intelligent person should care for the preservation of these moth eaten, ungainly beasts, when their place might much better be taken up by modern blooded cattle, beautiful to look at, are conundrums no one answered." This quote was attributed to the Indianapolis Star.[5]

*A portion of the Pablo Bison Herd on its range, Flathead Indian Reservation, Montana, 1908-1909 ready for shipment to Canada.*[5]

*above: National Bison Range Sign and right: Bison Grazing on the National Bison Range, Moiese, MT - 2007.* *(Photos courtesy Brent N. Lonner)*

Bison were often shot from trains, but not in Montana. They were decimated before railroads existed in the state.

Two railroads crossed the state at the beginning of the

century. These were joined in 1909 by the Chicago, Milwaukee, St. Paul and Pacific ("Milwaukee") line across the central portion of Montana. All three railroads aggressively promoted settlement of areas along their lines. Land in the Gallatin Valley, given as land grants to the railroad, was soon converted into farm lands generating business for the Northern Pacific Railroad. The "Campbell System"[7] of dry land farming was seized upon by the railroads as a way to encourage development and traffic along their rail lines. This system involved deep plowing and allowing half of the land to lie fallow each year to conserve water. This would optimistically allow farming semi-arid lands of the "Great American Desert." These real estate promotions started the great Montana homesteading land rush as the century turned.

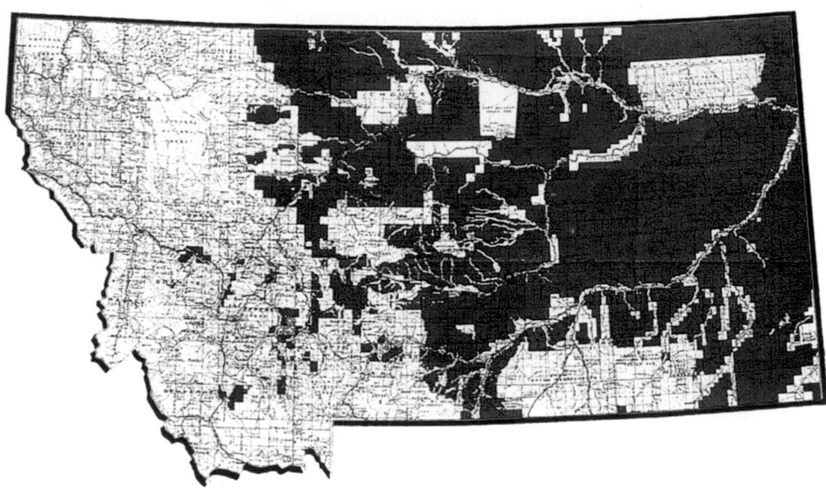

*The colored area indicates land open for homesteading in 1911 under the enlarged Homestead Act of 1909.* (Courtesy Montana Historical Society, Helena)

*Courtesy Montana Historical Society, Helena*

The Newlands Reclamation Act in 1902 stimulated construction of irrigation projects along the Yellowstone, Milk and Sun Rivers. Dams were also constructed on the Sun and Milk Rivers. Congress passed the Enlarged Homestead Act in 1909 increasing acreage homesteaders could claim from 160 to 320 acres. Jim Hill and his Great Northern Railroad advertised "Come to Montana and get a free home." This brought a phenomenal land rush. More homestead claims were filed in Montana than any other state or territory. The Northern Pacific Railroad also sold over 10 million acres of its enormous land grant to join the rush. Wheat production and number of farms expanded over four-fold in less than a decade. Homesteaders soon found that 320 acres were not enough to make a living. World War I provided a final boost to the land rush and the great Montana plow-up and sod busting era.

However, World War I brought a burst of patriotism that stimulated heavy enlistments in the Army. This was combined with a severely exaggerated population estimate by the military resulting in almost 10 percent of Montana's male population serving in the Army. Most of these men did not return to the hard life of a

***Abandoned Farm Madison Co., Montana June 1939. Photo by Arthur Rothstein*** *(Library of Congress, Prints & Photographs Division, FSA/OWI Collection [LC-USF34-0272633-D])*

“The Lacy bill that the Senate on April 18, 1900 passed has saved 5,000 or more game birds in this city alone, for the city of Butte is a butcher shop on game birds. I am pleased to say there has not been a game bird offered for sale in our markets this fall.”

—Thomas Curtis, county game warden for the Butte area, 1900.

prairie homesteader. Drought started in 1917 and spread across the state in the following years, forcing bankruptcies and abandonment of homesteads that began the depopulation of Montana's Great Plains.[6] Homesteaders harvested any wild food they encountered to survive as they also plowed up native habitat. Many men were to tell the story in both World War I and World War II, “I grew up on a Montana cattle ranch and never tasted beef until I joined the Army.” They ate wildlife rather than cut the profit margin by eating beef. Montana ranches were noted for high-quality short horn cattle, but by 1910, 5.3 million domestic sheep also grazed the plains, mountain meadows and alpine tundra.

Montana allowed women to vote in 1914 and elected the first woman to serve in the U.S. Congress. At about the same time women began to speak out forcibly against use of highly toxic strychnine and arsenic compounds being used to control wild scavengers and predators that were killing their poultry.

The early 20th century was a time of great labor strife in Butte. Strikes with high-pitched and occasional bloody battles, occurred as the national labor movements fought for recognition. Then the influenza epidemic of 1918-1919 swept across the state leaving an estimated 5,000 deaths in its wake.[7] With all of these social disruptions, poaching consistently served as a source of wild meat to feed families of idled workers as well as those who had been injured or families whose “bread winners” had died.

Even though wildlife had legal protection, it continued to suffer devastating impacts at the hand of man. Montana had forbidden sale of game animals and birds in 1877 and again after statehood in 1897. Congress passed the Lacy Act on April 18, 1900 prohibiting interstate transport of wildlife for sale. Thomas Curtis, a county game warden for the Butte area at the time commented,

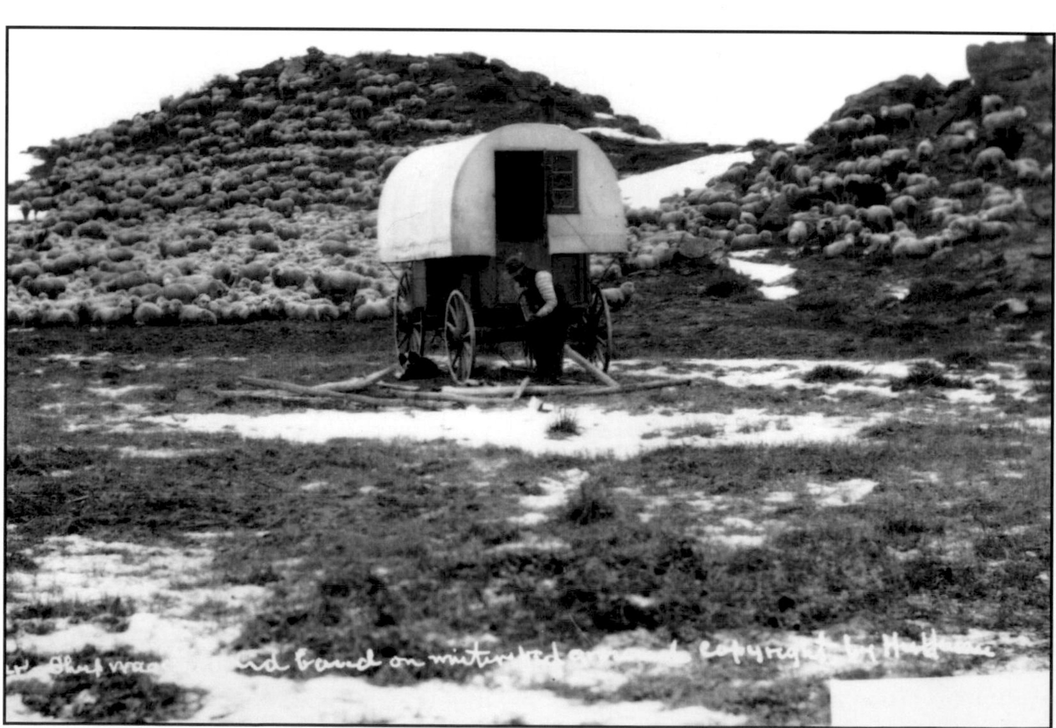

*Sheep Herder Winter Camp and Home. Photo by L. A. Huffman.*
*(Courtesy Montana Historical Society, Helena)*

"The Lacy bill that the Senate passed has saved 5,000 or more game birds in this city alone, for the city of Butte is a butcher shop on game birds. I am pleased to say there has not been a game bird offered for sale in our markets this fall."

***Hunter's Camp near Boulder Montana. c. 1890.***
*(from the 1909 Montana Fish & Game Biennial Report)*

***Goose Hunters***
*(from the 1918 Montana Fish & Game Biennial Report)*

Others made opposing observations. L. M. Mills of Saco, in the northeastern portion of the state, commented,

"The law is a dead letter. It affords no protection. Game birds and deer are fast being exterminated in this country, as no one makes any secret of killing game birds at all times of the year and deer are hunted with dogs."

J. F. Swarbuck of Adel commented in 1900,

"The sale of meat is the cause, I think of the destruction of more game and fish than any other, than all other combined. There are some who have not visible means of support other than the rod and gun, and who use them the year around, even boast of killing and the catches they make."[8]

In this turn-of-the-century environment of long working hours, low cash income, labor strife and poor travel conditions, the citizen rod and gun club movement slowly began to make their influence felt. The Gallatin County Sportsman's Club was formed in 1878 and other communities also formed rod and gun clubs.

***Butte Butcher Shop. c. 1910. Photo by Dusseau and Thomson.***
*(Courtesy Ken Hamlin Photo Collection)*

*Marcus Daly, one of the copper kings, apparently first introduced ring-necked pheasants on his estate in the Bitterroot Valley before 1900.*

The political and social strength of these clubs grew as the population grew. Their first order of business was to create a legal and law enforcement environment that reduced human impacts so wildlife populations might have a chance to succeed.

Small farmsteads and heavy grazing by horses, cattle and sheep had damaged much of the habitat of native game birds. Small amounts of free time and travel by foot or horses made replacement of native game birds with species that could survive on small farms desirable. The possibility of a few pheasants or ducks for Sunday dinner was very appealing.

***Marcus Daly Summer Home Bitterroot Valley, Montana. c. 1941-1942. Photo by Averill Smith** (Courtesy Montana Historical Society, Helena)*

Marcus Daly, one of the copper kings, apparently first introduced ring-necked pheasants on his estate in the Bitterroot Valley before 1900. The 1902 biennial report of the Montana Fish and Game Commission tells us, "These birds have been imported and turned loose year after year but their propagation has been anything but successful." In 1909, 200 pheasants were released near Choteau and over a 100 were released near Eureka in Lincoln County. Another 26 pheasants were released on the Tobacco Plains near Eureka, just south of Canada in Lincoln County. These efforts failed to establish them. The popularity of ring-necked pheasants for introduction continued and about 7,000 were released in Montana between 1909 and 1929. This is probably an underestimate because birds and eggs were readily available from commercial breeders in other western states for direct releases and from interested citizens who attempted to raise them for release. The 1917 Montana Legislature directed that one-third of license fees be used for propagating game birds and encouraging their release. Gambel's Quail were also planted unsuccessfully.[9]

Pheasants have been one of the most popular exotic or non-native species introduced into the state. This hybrid species has done well in new habitats created by farming. Selective forces of Montana's environment have helped shape the modern bird into one that can prosper in the state.

Members of Montana sportsmen's clubs frequently lamented the shortage of

***Pheasants at the Warm Springs Bird Farm Ready for Liberation** (Montana Fish and Game Department Photo)*

elk, deer, antelope and large mammals. Concerns were not purely for food on the table but also for esthetic reasons. Frequently mentioned was concern for the opportunity of their sons to hunt and enjoy nature. A poem circulated to rod and gun clubs expressing questions from a 12 year old boy to his parents reads in part:

> "And where is the big game
> that roamed around here
>
> When grandfather came
> here with you?
>
> I don't see one antelope,
> bison or deer.
>
> Didn't grandfather save me
> a few?"[10]

*Hunting: From One Generation to Another*
*(Photo from the 1903-1904 Montana Fish and Game Department Biennial Report.)*

***"And where is the big game that roamed around here***

***When grandfather came here with you?***

***I don't see one antelope, bison or deer.***

***Didn't grandfather save me a few?"[10]***

**—A poem circulated to rod and gun clubs expressing questions from a 12- year-old boy to his parents**

As smoke cleared from catastrophic forest fires during the summers of 1910 and 1911, thoughts of club members turned to restoration of elk. Historically, populations of elk were found from border to border, on the plains and in mountains. National forests set aside by Teddy Roosevelt provided extensive areas of potential elk habitat. But elk were in short supply. At this time only two regions of Montana contained elk. Most elk occurred around Yellowstone NP. These animals summered in the Park and moved down the Yellowstone and West Gallatin River drainages to winter ranges outside the Park. A smaller number still roamed the 4,000 square miles of rugged wilderness of the Sun River and South Fork of the Flathead River systems. The total number of elk in the state was estimated at between 5,000 and 6,000.

Many game preserves were established throughout the state to protect remnant wildlife populations. These preserves were established with good intentions, but did not take into account the biology of the species they were trying to protect. Most were abolished in later years. The general rationale for wildlife restoration was for esthetic reasons and to improve hunting opportunities.

Sportsmen's clubs stepped forward to take the initiative in expanding numbers and distribution of elk. These

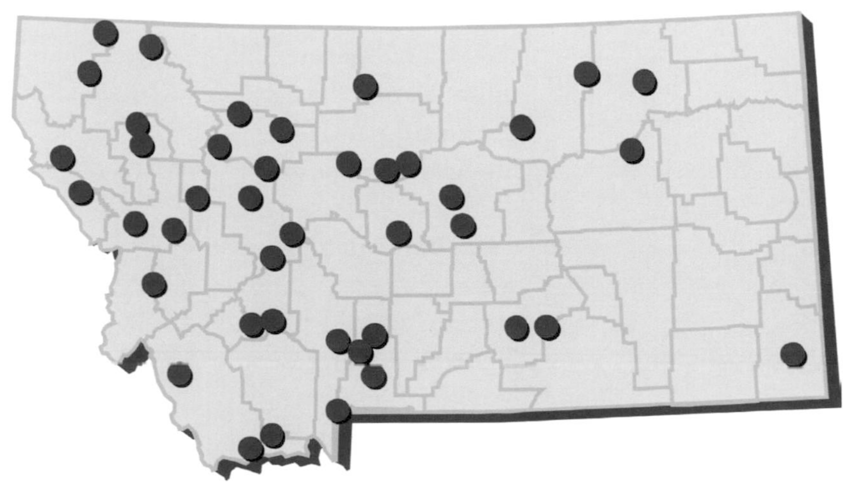

*Location of game preserves established in the early to mid 20th century to protect remnant wildlife populations.[11] (Illustration by Media Works, Bozeman, MT)*

clubs proposed that elk be trapped from existing herds and released on national forest lands. This was not a simple task because railroads were the only reasonable method for transporting elk. This required that elk be captured near a rail line and released where there were sidings that allowed trains to stop and unload. At that time the northern Yellowstone elk herd was the only herd that wintered near a rail line. Cost was also a problem because the small amount of money from the sale of hunting and fishing licenses was only sufficient to support a small number of existing game wardens and the growing fish planting program.

Sportsmen in Butte were first off the mark. Fund raising efforts got underway. The Northern Pacific Railroad agreed to transport elk for $5 a head to the Butte-Anaconda area. While $5 seems small today, then it represented a couple of days pay. Efforts bore fruit when a shipment of 25 elk was released in the Fleecer Mountain area, southwest of Butte, in March of 1910. Elk had been trapped north of Yellowstone NP near Gardiner, Montana where they had been fed during winter months. State Deputy Game Warden P. W. Nelson

*The sportsmen in Butte were the first off the mark. Fund raising efforts got underway. The Northern Pacific Railroad agreed to transport the elk for $5 a head to the Butte-Anaconda area. While $5 seems small today, then it represented a couple of days pay.*

*A crowd gathered to watch a release of elk trapped just north of Yellowstone National Park near Gardiner, Montana and transported by rail in cattle cars to the Mount Fleecer area southwest of Butte, MT. c. 1910. (Courtesy Jim McLucas Photo Collection)*

Montana Fish and Game Wardens Cinnabar Mt. about 1910 to 1912
NELSON
MORGAN
FROHMAN
McCORMACK


*Five Montana game wardens supervised citizen led trapping and transporting of elk near Gardiner for the first efforts to restore elk in Montana. c. 1910-1912. (Courtesy Jim McLucas Photo Collection)*

*Elk captured for restoration in a corral trap north of Yellowstone National Park near Gardiner, MT. c. 1912.* *(Courtesy Fred Martin Photo Collection)*

supervised the effort. Trapped elk were hauled on sleighs to the rail stock yard pens, loaded into a cattle car, and transported to Butte. At Butte, the car was switched to a train of the Oregon Short Line to cover the last 28 miles to Divide where they were released.

Interest in transplanting elk swelled with this successful transplant. In 1912, 540 elk were captured in a trap near Gardiner and shipped to various locations in the state. Included were a group of 31 elk to start a herd in Glacier National Park (NP). Rail trips took 18 hours to the Deer Lodge area, 24 hours to Hamilton and up to 30 hours to the Thompson Falls area near the Idaho border.

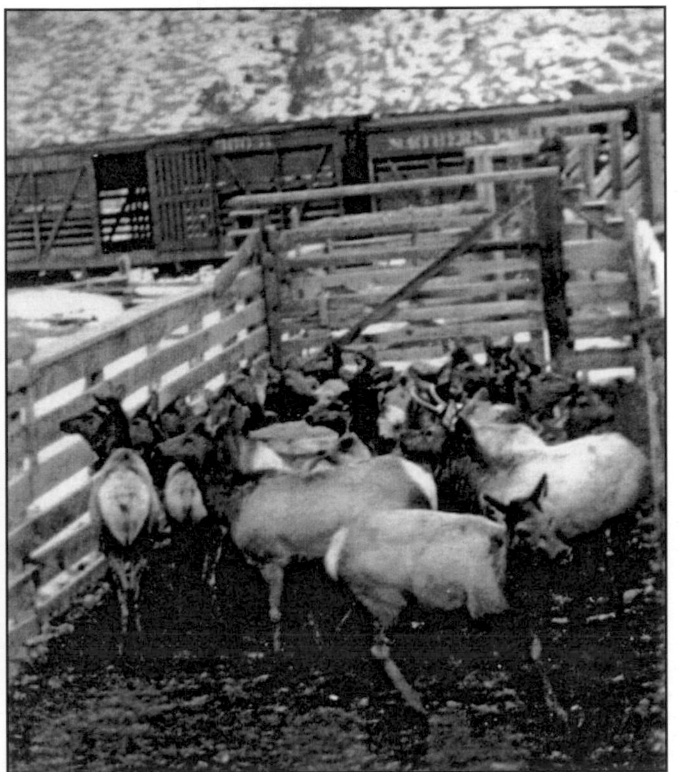

*Elk in a holding corral ready for shipment north of Yellowstone National Park near Gardiner, MT. c. 1912.* *(Courtesy Jim McLucas Photo Collection)*

Local rod and gun clubs often held elk in livestock pens from a few days to as long as a month before release. Mortality of elk during transplant operations was less than ten percent. Game wardens supervising these opera tions received many more requests for transplants of elk than they were able to fill in 1912. Trapping and transplanting operations

***In 1912, 540 elk were captured near Gardiner and shipped to various locations in the state. Included were a group of 31 elk to start a herd in Glacier National Park. Rail trips took up to 30 hours.***

continued through World War I and by the end of 1919 another 413 elk had been moved to new homes. All of these animals came from the Gardiner area with the exception of 75 that were trapped on the National Elk Refuge at Jackson Hole, Wyoming. Of these, 54 were released on a ranch near Dillon in Beaverhead County in 1915. Twenty-five elk were released on the National Bison Range at Moiese in 1916 supplementing a total of 21 from the Jackson Hole herd released in 1911, 1912 and 1915. This group increased rapidly and by 1924 surplus elk were available from the Bison Range. A state transplant was made in 1928 with 29 elk obtained from the National Bison Range. Before 1920, most elk transplants included sites west of the Continental Divide. Elk transplants east of the Divide included two at Mount Fleecer southwest of Butte, two at Bull Mountain north of Whitehall, one in the Highwood Mountains east of Great Falls and one near Billings.

By 1931 efforts put forth by sportsmen's clubs in transplanting elk began to show results. William Rush, who was a scientifically trained wildlife specialist for the U.S. Forest Service, estimated 15,000 elk in Montana with an annual hunter harvest of 1,144 in 1931. This estimate brought Montana to second place in North America in elk population numbers. Only Wyoming with large Yellowstone NP and Jackson Hole elk herds had more. Rush estimated that there were 7,500 in an area that corresponds to the Bob Marshall, Great Bear and Scapegoat Wilderness complex. The Sun and South Fork of the Flathead River drainages held the majority of elk. Northwestern Montana had an estimated 2,500 elk; The Bitterroot area 1,100 and the Butte-Helena area 2,300. The Gallatin drainage outside of Yellowstone NP was home to an estimated 700 elk.[12]

*William Rush, who was a scientifically trained wildlife specialist for the U.S. Forest Service, estimated 15,000 elk in Montana with an annual hunter harvest of 1,144 in 1931. This estimate brought Montana to second place in North America in elk population numbers.*

Pronghorn antelope were another species whose plight attracted attention. This species is a native of North America with no close relatives and is found no where else in the world. Fleetest of North American animals, originally they were more abundant than bison. In 1922-1924, even after numbers had increased slightly, there were only about 30,000 pronghorns left on the continent. Montana's share was 3,000. The 1911 Montana Legislature established the Snow Creek Preserve for pronghorns in what is now Garfield County. Because the area had not yet been surveyed, it eventually proved to be smaller than intended. An effort to convince Congress to make it a federal preserve failed. Portions of it now lie under Fort

*Pronghorn antelope were another species whose plight attracted attention. This fleetest of North American animals had originally been more abundant than the bison.*

***Pronghorn antelope populations were at very low numbers as the 20th century began.*** *(Courtesy Robert Cooney Photo Collection)*

Peck Reservoir or are in the Charles M. Russell National Wildlife Refuge.

Ambiguous feelings seen today about the role of the federal government in Montana's wildlife management affairs were also held early in the 20th century. State Game Warden, J. L. DeHart expressed his views in 1918,

> "Personally, I am unalterably opposed to any plan of giving the federal authorities supervision of big game in Montana. I do not believe that any of the natural resources of this state should be placed under the supervision of the federal government."

However, the federal government was not always looked upon so harshly by sheep and cattlemen. The message of Wallis Huidekope in 1919 was that,

> "During fiscal year 1919 the sum of $22,544 expended by the federal government in our state toward the maintenance of a professional trapper, with a total catch of 1,640 animals, divided as follows: 4 bear, 94 bobcats, 1,494 coyotes and 48 grey wolves. The stockmen of Montana should be particularly pleased as over 146 grey wolves have been cleaned up on the prairie country within a radius of 90 miles of Miles City."

Initial efforts to restore pronghorns were made by the Boone and Crockett Club and the U.S. Biological Survey, which trapped 3 buck and 6 doe pronghorn in an elk trap near Gardiner in 1911 and moved them to the National Bison Range at Moiese. The herd grew to 64 animals, but a hard winter and predators wiped out this herd in 1921-1922. The American Bison Society became interested in the plight of pronghorns and initiated several efforts. One effort was the first continental census of these speedsters in 1922-1923.Restoration of this species was another focused effort. Pronghorn handling techniques were primitive and their biology was poorly understood. The U.S. Biological

*Early Montana fish and game commissioners and department heads such as J. L. DeHart were assertive in their beliefs that the state had the primary responsibility to manage its wildlife correctly. (These beliefs were asserted in the 1918 Montana Fish and Game Department's Biennial Report.)*

***"Personally, I am unalterably opposed to any plan of giving the federal authorities supervision of big game in Montana. I do not believe that any of the natural resources of this state should be placed under the supervision of the federal government."***

—State Game Warden, J. L. DeHart in 1918

*"The present census records surviving herds in 44 districts, mainly in the eastern and central parts of the state, with a total of approximately 3,000 animals. As in many other states, the antelope situation here is precarious..."*

—Chairman of the Montana Fish and Game Commission, Thomas Marlowe, in 1924

Survey and American Bison Society captured pronghorn fawns in Nevada and raised them over winter until they became yearlings. Crates specifically designed for them were designed and built. Eight were transplanted in to the National Bison Range in 1924 by the U.S. Biological Survey and Permanent Wildlife Protection Fund of William Hornaday in the second attempt to start a pronghorn population.[13] By 1926 this attempt also failed and they were gone.[14]

The precarious situation of pronghorns was expressed in comments made in 1924 by Thomas Marlowe, Chairman of the Montana Fish and Game Commission:

> "The present census records surviving herds in 44 districts, mainly in the eastern and central parts of the state, with a total of approximately 3,000 animals. As in many other states, the antelope situation here is precarious..."

*Photograph taken September 1924 in an enclosure built for captured pronghorn antelope fawns, adjoining a house in Reno, Nevada, where they were held before transporting for restocking.* [13]

He also stated that predators would have to be severely controlled to bring back pronghorn.

B. W. Hogan of Ashland stated:

> "...in 1910 there were only 3 antelope in the entire Custer National Forest. These were well protected by ranchers and have increased to the present herd."

He indicated that the herd was about 250 in 1924-1925.[15] Technological change and social policy had an effect upon Montana pronghorns. During Prohibition, bootleggers running the Whoop-Up trail between Great Falls and Canada, used their "high powered automobiles to pursue and kill antelope," and citizens were powerless to prevent it. At the time, rod and gun clubs in Conrad and Brady were very interested in pronghorn preservation. Many remnant herds owed their existence to a few ranchers that were often aided by local sportsmen.[14] James Weaver, a Deputy Game Warden, from Lewistown stated,

> "The antelope is a game animal without a home. The natural habitat has been taken over by dry-land farmers... Barbed wire fences now enclose much of the territory where the herds once grazed before cultivation and intensive cultivation of the soil entered into the scheme of things."[16]

W. F. Sullivan, who became chairman of the Montana Fish and Game Commission in 1933, provided a home for pronghorns. He established a pronghorn preserve on his ranch on the east side of the Highwood Mountains at the foot of Square Butte. The herd of 700-800 was a popular attraction for passengers on a train that ran through the area.[17] Pronghorn hunting in the state was prohibited from 1903 to 1943 except in a couple of counties during 1935 and 1936.[18]

Beaver were also being transplanted and their numbers were increasing. Trapping beaver for pelts increased during the 1920s and was limited to damage control, usually for protection of irrigation ditches. Legal trapping took 9,714

*Beaver trapper - Old Vinger Ranch in Front of Bunkhouse, Grass Range, MT. (Courtesy Montana Historical Society, Helena)*

beaver pelts for the fur market in 1926. A fur raising industry also developed in the state during this period. Farms for beaver, fox and mink were in operation in the state of which silver fox and mink were most commonly raised. High demands and prices for beaver coupled with decreasing populations in other states made them an attractive target for fur farming. The U.S. Forest Service and the state cooperated with fur farming efforts.[19]

One philosophy behind restoration efforts was expressed by State Game Warden DeHart in a speech made to the Billings Commercial Club in 1919,

> "Our idea is to make an open park of all the wild lands of this state, a place in which our people of all classes can find pleasure and maintain their strength, where the well and strong can enjoy an outing that will keep them well and make them stronger, where those who are starting on the road to battered nerves and inability to meet the demands they are called upon to face, can strengthen their hold on all those things that fit men to meet the requirements of their every day battle with the world."[20]

*Beaver began to respond to protection and transplanting, permitting almost 10,000 to be trapped for sale in 1926. (Montana Fish and Game Department photo)*

***"During fiscal year 1919 the sum of $22,544 expended by the federal government in our state toward the maintenance of a professional trapper, with a total catch of 1,640 animals, divided as follows: 4 bear, 94 bobcats, 1,494 coyotes and 48 gray wolves. The stockmen of Montana should be particularly pleased as over 146 gray wolves have been cleaned up on the prairie country within a radius of 90 miles of Miles City."***

**—Wallis Huidekope in 1919**

*In 1919 a professional trapper took almost 1,500 coyotes for predator control. Photo taken near Birch Creek - Big Sandy, MT. (Courtesy Don Brown Photo Collection)*

# Footnotes

[1] Potts, D. T. 1826. Letter from Daniel T. Potts to Robert Potts. In: The first known man in Yellowstone, Editor J. Bagley. 2000. Old Faithful Eyewitness Publishing, Rigby, ID. 273-280.

[2] Thompson, K. 1950. Audubon sheep. In: Couey, F. M. 1950. Rocky mountain sheep of Montana. Montana Fish and Game Bulletin. 2:90.

[3] The title State Game Warden is equivalent to today's title of director or head of department. The law enforcement officers under his supervision were known as Deputy Game Wardens.

[4] Dary, D. A. 1989. The buffalo book. Ohio State University Press, Columbus. 384 pp.

Kraft, E. 2006. Untold tales of bison range trails. Stoneydale Press, Stevensville, MT. 18-23.

[5] Dary, D. A. 1989. The buffalo book. Ohio State University Press, Columbus. 238. This author attributes the quote to records of the American Bison Society files and the stated newspaper. The statement referred to the people of Boston but obviously meant the American Bison Society which was formed in New York City.

Photo, 1909. Excerpted from the Second Annual Report of the American Bison Society.

[6] James Hill "The Empire Builder" controlled both the Great Northern and Northern Pacific Railroads during this time period.

Malone, M. P. and R. B. Roeder. 1976. Montana, a history of two centuries. University of Washington Press. 352 pp.

[7] Ibid.

[8] Quotations of Curtis, Mills and Swarbuck. 1900. Annual report of Game and Fish Commissioners of the state of Montana, December 1, 1900.

[9] Information is from the biennial reports of the Montana Fish and Game Commission, 1910 to 1929.

[10] Excerpted from the 1918 Report of the Montana Fish and Game Commission, Helena. The three verse poem is "Dedicated to the fathers of boys in the states still inhabited by grouse, quail and deer."

[11] Biennial report, 1941-1942. Montana Fish and Game Commission, Helena. 9 pp.

[12] Rush, W. M. 1932. The elk situation in Montana. Biennial report of the Montana Fish and Game Department. 1931-1932. 7 pp.

[13] Nelson, E. W. 1925. Status of the pronghorned antelope, 1922-24. U.S. Department of Agriculture Bulletin 136, Government Printing Office, Washington. 69 pp.

[14] Kraft, E. 2006. Untold tales of bison range trails. Stoneydale Press, Stevensville, MT. 32-33.

[15] Ibid. Nelson, E. W. 1925.

[16] Weaver, J. A. 1932. Antelope increase on game preserves. Biennial report of the Montana Fish and Game Department. 1931-1932. 8 pp.

[17] Sullivan, W. F. 1934. Those antelope. Biennial report of the Montana Fish and Game Department. 1933-1934. 13-14.

Ibid. Weaver, J. A.

[18] Compton, H., J. Egan and R. Trueblood. 1971. Pronghorn antelope. Chapter 8 in Game Management in Montana. Edited by T. W. Mussehl and F. W. Howell. 81-87.

[19] Atwater, M. M. 1932. Fur farming in Montana. Biennial report of the Montana Fish and Game Department. 1931-1932. 13 pp.

[20] DeHart, J. L. 1920. Fish and wild game protection. Biennial report of the Montana Fish and Game Department, Helena. 1919-1920. 8-11.

## Chapter 4

# A WILL FOR WILDLIFE
# Out of Drought, Depression and Despair

Collapse of the nation's economy, beginning in 1929, had a profound affect on Montanans. The 1930s also brought a severe drought that spanned much of the decade. In a number of counties as much as 25 percent of the population was on welfare.[1] Many residents were forced back to a frontier economy. Slender gains resulting from previous efforts in wildlife restoration now provided food for desperate families. Trapping furbearers furnished a little cash to supplement the largely barter and trade economy of rural communities. The multi-year drought dried up many waterfowl habitats. K. F. Roahen, the U.S. Game Management Agent for Montana, commented on the situation in 1932:

"During the last few years, and including the season 1931, the drought throughout the United States and Canada, with the drainage of marsh areas for commercial purposes, has taken the majority of breeding grounds away from our waterfowl...it is a miracle that any birds have been able to survive."[2]

*Homestead Cabin, Custer Co., MT, June 1939. Photo by Arthur Rothstein.* *(Library of Congress, Prints & Photographs Division, FSA/OWI Collection [LC-USF34-027867-D])*

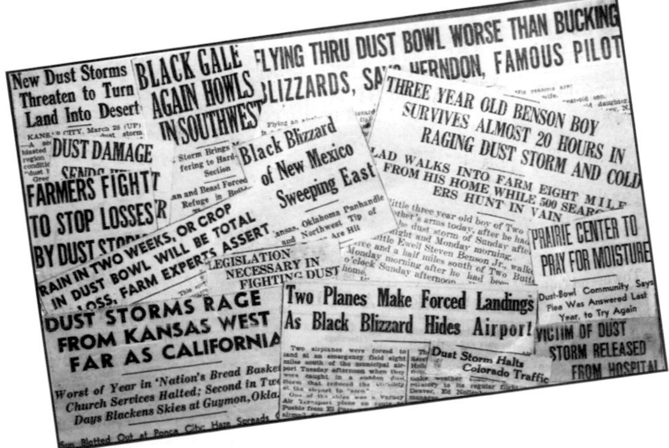

New Dust Storms Threaten to Turn Land Into Desert

BLACK GALE AGAIN HOWLS IN SOUTHWEST

DUST DAMAGE

Black Blizzard of New Mexico Sweeping East

THREE YEAR OLD BENSON BOY SURVIVES ALMOST 20 HOURS IN RAGING DUST STORM AND COLD

LAD WALKS INTO FARM EIGHT MILES FROM HIS HOME WHILE 500 SEARCHERS HUNT IN VAIN

PRAIRIE CENTER TO PRAY FOR MOISTURE

LEGISLATION NECESSARY IN FIGHTING DUST

DUST STORMS RAGE FROM KANSAS WEST FAR AS CALIFORNIA

Two Planes Make Forced Landings As Black Blizzard Hides Airport

VICTIM OF DUST STORM RELEASED FROM HOSPITAL

Dust Storm Halts Colorado Traffic

Worst of Year in 'Nation's Bread Basket'; Church Services Halted; Second in Two Days Blackens Skies at Guymon, Okla.

*Dust Storm Headline Montage.* *(Library of Congress, Prints & Photographs Division, FSA/OWI Collection [LC-USF34-003181-ZB])*

*"Approximately 90 percent of the water areas of Montana were dry during the past summer, all of which were formerly great nesting areas."* [2]

—K. F. Roahen, U.S. Game Management Agent, 1931.

*A dried up wetland area in central Montana. c. 1930s.*
*(Courtesy Don Brown Photo Collection)*

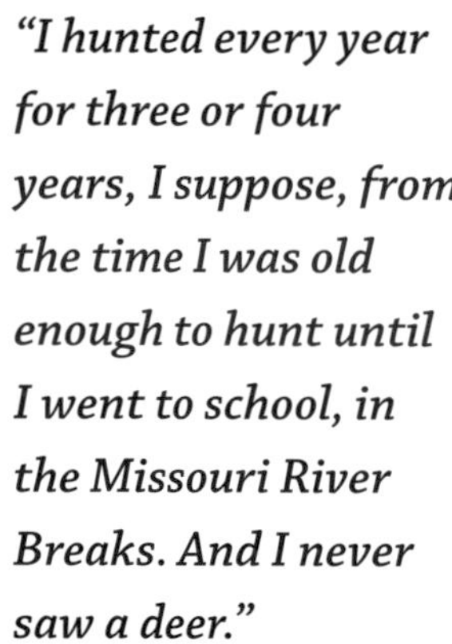

*"I hunted every year for three or four years, I suppose, from the time I was old enough to hunt until I went to school, in the Missouri River Breaks. And I never saw a deer."*

—Don Brown, hunter from Big Sandy in the 1930s

Bison in Yellowstone NP had grown from an estimated 50 animals at the turn of the century to about 1,100.[3] Officials offered to cull 50 bison from the park to help feed destitute families in Montana.[4]

Subsistence hunting hit wildlife populations very hard. Some farm families were forced to trap and can ground squirrels and prairie dogs to survive.

Bob Greene lived in Lewistown, "I did a lot of hiking and walking in the woods and out all the time. And if we ever saw a deer track, we were amazed."[5] Don Brown grew up in Big Sandy and hunted in the 1930s,

"I hunted every year for three or four years, I suppose, from the time I was old enough to hunt until I went to school, in the Missouri River Breaks. And I never saw a deer."

Rocky Mountain Locusts had become extinct by 1900, but during the 1930s other species of grasshoppers and Mormon Crickets replaced them. Plagues of these voracious insects wrought devastation

*A deer hunting party in Beaverhead Co., 1937. Montanans heavily relied on wildlife for food during the 1930s.*
*(Courtesy Ken Hamlin Photo Collection)*

in eastern Montana and neighboring states. They stripped crops from the fields with rangeland and gardens devastated alike. Attempts at defense against the wingless crickets included ditches filled with crude oil and solid metal fences. Baits of sodium arsenite, molasses and grain or sometimes

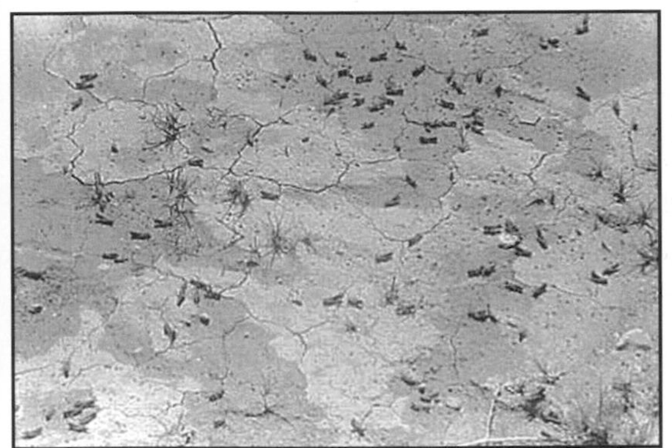

*Grasshoppers, Richland Co., Montana, June 1939. Photo by Arthur Rothstein. (Library of Congress, Prints & Photographs Division, FSA/OWI Collection [LC-USF33-003195-M5])*

*Rancher cleaning a cricket trap, Big Horn Co., Montana, June 1939. Photo by Arthur Rothstein. (Library of Congress, Prints & Photographs Division, FSA/OWI Collection ([LC-USF34-027411-D])*

***. . . grasshoppers and Mormon Crickets assumed their place in nature. Plagues of these voracious insects wrought devastation in eastern Montana and neighboring states.***

sawdust, arsenic and the banana odor of amyl acetate were mixed and then distributed by Low flying aircraft, various kinds of spreaders or even by hand. Not all workers wore protective face masks and rubber gloves. These poisons were spread over the landscape and decimated much of the wildlife that was trying to survive drought conditions in eastern Montana.

*Corn withered by heat and chewed by grasshoppers near Terry, Montana, June 1939. Photo by Arthur Rothstein. (Library of Congress, Prints & Photographs Division, FSA/OWI Collection [LC-USF34-005046-D])*

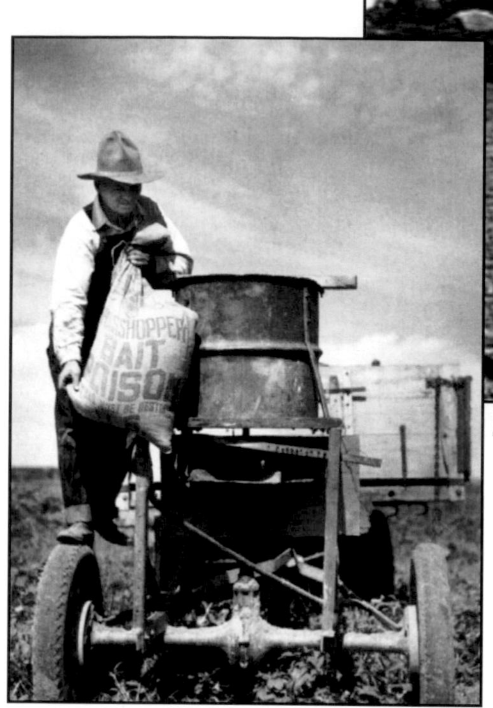

*Farmer loading a spreading machine with grasshopper poison near Forsyth, MT June 1939. Photo by Arthur Rothstein. (Library of Congress, Prints & Photographs Division, FSA/OWI Collection [LC-USF34-027794-D])*

*Spreading poisoned grasshopper bait. c. 1938.*

The grasshopper and Mormon cricket plague of 1938 was the last major infestation, but research to effectively combat them continued for many years. After World War II research concerning effects of a new class of safer chlorinated hydrocarbon pesticides was conducted on game birds. First of these research projects was one concerning Aldrin done in the early 1950s.[6]

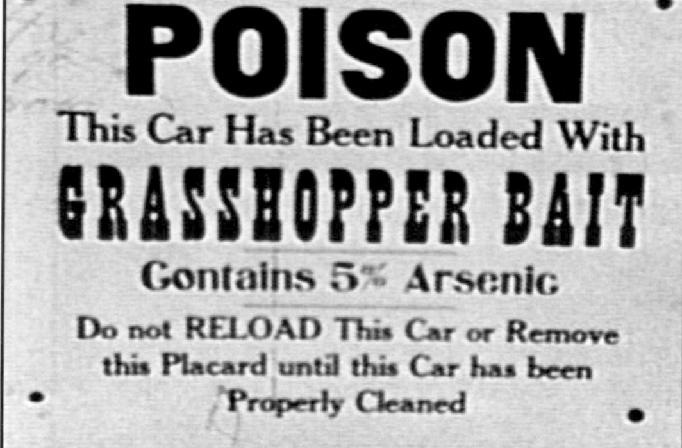


*Sign on the side of railroad box car loaded with Poison grasshopper bait. c. 1938.*

At the national level during the 1930s, a very committed group of conservationists was becoming influential enough to enact major programs that would have a revolutionary impact across the country including in Montana. Carl Shoemaker, an Oregon publisher and previously a lawyer that had served on the Oregon Fish and Game Commission, knew his way around Washington D.C. He was appointed head of the special conservation committee of the U.S. Senate.

While he was attending the 2nd North American Wildlife Conference in 1937, discussions with J. N. "Ding" Darling and other leading conservationists led to memories of a failed proposal for an excise tax on firearms and ammunition of 10 years before. Darling had resigned as chief of the U.S. Biological Survey in 1935 and in 1937 was head of the newly formed National Wildlife Federation. Their goal was to provide a source of money for wildlife conservation that could be used for research and scientifically based wildlife management programs.

Immediately after this meeting Shoemaker drafted proposed legislation that melded the idea of an excise tax on firearms and ammunition needed for wildlife research and scientific management. After thirteen drafts he had a proposal suitable for presentation to interested people.

His proposal had strong support from members of the public, rod and gun clubs, conservation organizations, state wildlife agencies and the U.S. Biological Survey. Next he met with representatives of the firearms industry. Charles Horn of the Federal Cartridge Company, T. E. Doremus of the DuPont Co., M. Hartley Dodge and C. K. Davis of the Remington Arms Company. They quickly supported the proposed law, but Mr. Horn did insist on a change for reducing the amount set aside for administration of the program from 10 percent to 8 percent. (Actual administration costs have run about 5 percent over the entire history of the program.)

*Poster promoting the North American Wildlife Conference in 1936 where discussions were instrumental in the establishment of the Pittman-Robertson Act. (Courtesy Wildlife Management Institute, Washington, DC)*

*Carl Shoemaker, principle author of national legislation resulting in the Pittman-Robertson Act. (Courtesy National Wildlife Federation)*

*Carl Shoemaker, an Oregon publisher and lawyer that served on the Oregon Fish and Game Commission, drafted proposed legislation in 1937 that melded the idea of an excise tax on firearms and ammunition for wildlife research and scientific management.*

With popular support in hand, Shoemaker approached Senator McNary of Oregon who immediately agreed to sponsor the bill. Senator Key Pittman of Nevada, who was chairman of the Special Committee on Wildlife, added his support as a sponsor. Shoemaker then presented the bill to Representative Willis Robertson of Virginia, chairman of the House Select Committee on Conservation of Wildlife Resources. Robertson penciled in a non-diversion clause, which was the most important change to the bill. This change reads "...and which shall include a prohibition against the diversion of license fees paid by hunters for any other purpose than the administration of said State fish and game department ...." This meant that any state that agreed to the program

*Senator Key Pittman of Nevada, co-author of the 1937 Pittman-Robertson Act for Federal funding of Wildlife Conservation. (Courtesy U.S. Senate Historical Archives, Washington, DC)*

*Representative Willis Robertson of Virginia, co-author of the 1937 Pittman-Robertson Act for Federal funding of Wildlife Conservation. (Courtesy U.S. Senate Historical Archives, Washington, DC)*

had to spend all money collected from hunters on their wildlife resources. The bill passed through the Senate with reasonable speed. However, it was delayed somewhat in the House of Representatives until garden and women's club members in Illinois prevailed upon Representative Scott Lucas to show haste in getting it passed. The bill, now called the Pittman-Robertson Act (P-R) was signed into law by President Roosevelt on September 2, 1937, less than four months after its initial introduction. Within a year 43 states had agreed to provisions of P-R[7], although Montana was not yet among them.

*The Pittman-Robertson Act was signed into law on September 2, 1937 beginning a new era in wildlife management in the United States.*

Hunters and sportsman clubs immediately began their campaign to win acceptance of P-R in Montana. As the campaign intensified, sportsmen invited Carl Shoemaker to Butte to speak to the Montana Wildlife Federation in January 1939. Two more years of intense lobbying, correspondence and discussion followed. Steve Arnold, a Republican rancher who represented Stillwater County, facilitated much of this exchange of ideas. Mr. Arnold introduced the P-R Assent Act into the 1941 Legislature. The debate that followed focused largely upon possible intrusions into state's rights. The bill passed both houses of the Legislature and then was signed by Governor Sam C. Ford. This made Montana the 47th of 48 states to accept federal funds under P-R.[8]

Acceptance of P-R meant change for the Montana Fish and Game Department. Ira Gabrielson, Chief of the U.S. Biological Survey in charge of administering the act, put in place a policy that personnel hired to carry out projects supported by P-R funds had to be "trained and competent."[9] This meant a radical change from previous practices of hiring game wardens as political patronage. Inclusion of college-educated wildlife managers into law enforcement agencies created a potential for bureaucratic conflict. Professor Joe Severy, a botanist on the faculty in the School of Forestry at the University of Montana in Missoula, had been appointed to the Montana Fish and Game Commission. He made finding a qualified individual who

*The Pittman-Robertson Act imposes a federal tax on firearms and ammunition and provides 3 dollars for each state dollar to states for scientifically based wildlife management activities.*

75TH CONGRESS, 1ST SESSION—CH. 899—SEPTEMBER 2, 1937

[CHAPTER 899]

AN ACT

To provide that the United States shall aid the States in wildlife-restoration projects, and for other purposes.

*Be it enacted by the Senate and House of Representatives of the United States of America in Congress assembled*, That the Secretary of Agriculture is authorized to cooperate with the States, through their respective State fish and game departments, in wildlife-restoration projects as hereinafter set forth; but no money apportioned under this Act to any State shall be expended therein until its legislature, or other State agency authorized by the State constitution to make laws governing the conservation of wildlife, shall have assented to the provision of this Act and shall have passed laws for the conservation of wildlife which shall include a prohibition against the diversion of license fees paid by hunters for any other purpose than the admin-

*Beginning language of the 1937 Pittman-Robertson Act to promote wildlife conservation by federal funding to individual states.*

*Montana State Capitol in Helena. c. 1930s.* *(Courtesy Hilger-McLucas Photo Collection)*

could successfully run the new program a personal task.

In the winter of 1934-35 the U.S. Forest Service conducted a survey of back-country elk winter ranges of the upper Sun River. This survey by Robert F. Cooney and L. J. Howard was one of the earliest biological surveys of the newly designated Bob Marshall Primitive Area and neighboring territory. Professor Severy had remembered Cooney as a student and U.S. Forest Service range specialist. He invited Bob to go with him to meet with Bruce Neal, Deputy Game Warden for the Sun River area and an influential individual in the state Fish and Game Department.[10] Bob "hit it off" with Mr. Neal and Professor Severy had his man to head up the new Wildlife Restoration Division as the first state Big Game Manager. This was before the Montana Legislature accepted P-R funds.

*Professor Joe Severy, a botanist on the faculty in the School of Forestry at the University of Montana and Chairman of the Fish and Game Commission, hired Robert Cooney as Montana's first wildlife biologist. c. 1941.*

Although P-R with its excise tax on firearms and ammunition was passed in 1937, Congress did not appropriate all of the taxes collected to the states until 1956. The basic formula for allocation of money includes area, number of hunting licenses sold and the population of a state. Each state must provide one dollar of matching funds for every three dollars of federal funds received. A reluctance of Congress to release the money kept funds in

***. . . Steve Arnold, a Republican rancher representing Stillwater County, introduced the P-R assent act into the 1941 Legislature. The debate that followed focused largely upon possible intrusions into state's rights. The bill passed both houses of the Legislature and then was signed by Governor Sam C. Ford. This made Montana the 47th of 48 states to accept federal funds under the P-R Act.***[8]

*Robert F. Cooney was the first Big Game Manager and Coordinator of the Montana Fish and Game Department's Wildlife Restoration Division. c. 1941. (Montana Fish & Game Department Photo)*

*Bob Cooney began efforts to build a management program with an initial budget of $100,000 provided by the P-R act.*

short supply during the startup years. Bob Cooney began efforts to build a management program with an initial budget of $100,000 provided by the P-R Act.

A new wildlife restoration program would build upon achievements of the previous 40 years. The elk transplanting program was began in 1910 and was maintained throughout the 1930s. This major cooperative effort between sportsmen, ranchers, U.S. Forest Service and the Montana Fish and Game Department had found new homes for 1,364 elk trapped just outside of Yellowstone NP near Gardiner. Railroads were still a major means of transportation for restoring elk. Areas receiving transplants included the Crow Indian Reservation, Big Belt Mountains, Judith Mountains, and a number of sites in Beaverhead County as well as other areas.

*The National Bison Range at Moiese, established in 1908, helped set a precedent for the federal wildlife refuge system.*

Introduction of pheasants had become a major program during the 1930s after the game bird farm constructed at Warm Springs in 1929 came into full production. Production rapidly rose from 6,148 pheasants planted in 1930 to over 15,000 per year by the end of the decade.[11] A second game bird farm at Billings was added. During grasshopper infestations in 1936, the Department closed hunting seasons on all native birds, in part, because farmers considered birds as allies when they ate insects.[12]

The National Bison Range at Moiese, established in 1908, helped set a precedent for the federal wildlife refuge system. Drought conditions in the 1930s brought new impetus to increasing the refuge system. In 1935 the federal government created the Charles M. Russell Game Range, which includes much of the Missouri River Breaks and Red Rock Lakes National Wildlife Refuge in the Centennial valley for trumpeter swans. Other areas continued to be added to the National Refuge system.

Late in the 1930s diligent work by game wardens, acceptance of game laws by the justice system and support by the general population had improved wildlife law enforcement to a level consistently supportive of wildlife recovery. This opened the door to a vigorous program of wildlife restoration and rebuilding Montana's wildlife legacy.

Environmental disaster brought on by drought in the 1930s ended as snow and rain came. A new era clearly was beginning for Montana's wildlife resource. Restoration of the resource had been carried about as far as it could under laws passed early in the century and with the

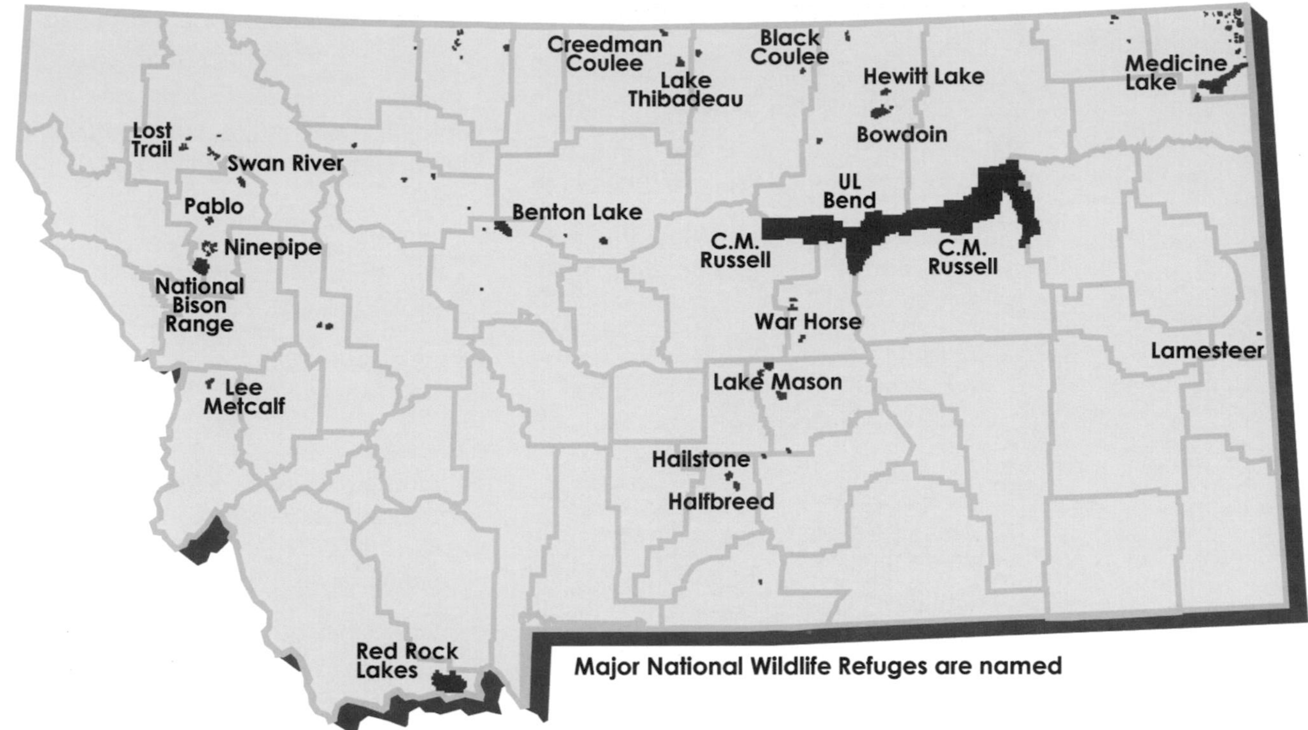


*Montana's National Wildlife Refuge system had its beginnings with the establishment of the National Bison Range in 1908.* (Illustration by Media Works, Bozeman, MT)

funding that these laws provided. A new approach using biological science with some additional funding was just beginning. These breezes of hope for wildlife in 1940 were met by storms of war already raging in both the far east and Europe. Soon these storms were to engulf the United States as well.

*After the bombing of Pearl Harbor on December 7, 1941 the United State was thrust into WW II. "Just as in the First World War, military enlistments and the draft took disproportionately high numbers of Montana youths. Roughly forty thousand were in uniform by 1942, about the same number had served in the earlier war."*[13] *"In WW II, Montana suffered the second highest percentage of combat deaths in the nation, with the loss of 1,829 lives. More than 57,000 Montanans served their country in active military service during WW II, including record numbers of Native Americans living in Montana.* [14] (Photo courtesy National Archives)

*. . .breezes of hope for wildlife in 1940 were met by the storms of war already raging in both the far east and Europe. Soon these storms were to engulf the United States as well.*

# Footnotes

[1] Murphy, M. 2003. Hope in hard times. Montana Historical Press, Helena. 242 pp.

[2] Roahen, K. F. 1934. Migratory bird problems. Biennial report of the Montana Fish and Game Dept. 1933-1934. 10.

[3] Meagher, M. M. 1973. The bison of Yellowstone National Park National Park Service Monograph. 161 pp.

[4] Ibid. Murphy, M. 2003.

[5] Brown, D. L. 2004. Videotaped interview with Harold Picton, Terry Lonner and Tom Manning.

Greene, R. 2004. Videotaped interview with Terry Lonner.

[6] Eng, R. L. 1952, A two-summer study of the effects on bird populations of chlordane bait and aldrin spray as used for grasshopper control. Journal of Wildlife Management 16(3):326-337.

[7] Williamson, L. L. 1987. An account of enacting the Pittman-Robertson act. Evolution of a landmark law. In: Kallman, H. et al. Editors. Restoring America's wildlife. U.S. Fish and Wildlife Service, Government Printing Office, Washington, D.C.

[8] Montana Standard March 5, 1941.

[9] Ibid. Williamson, L. L. 1987.

[10] Cooney, R. F. 1999. Videotaped interview with Harold Picton.

[11] Hendricks, J. F. 1930. Rearing game birds in captivity. Biennial report of the Montana Fish and Game Dept. 1929-1930. Helena. 42. Biennial report of the Fish and Game Commissions, Helena. 1937-1938.

[12] MacDonald, K. F. 1936. Great strides in game management in Montana. Biennial report of the Montana Fish and Game Commission, Helena. 1935-1936. 9.

[13] Malone, M. P. and R. B. Roeder. 1976. Montana: A history of two centuries. University of Washington Press, Seattle. 352 pp.

[14] Merrill-Maker, A. 2006. Montana Almanac, 2nd. Edition. Insider's Guide, Guilford, CT. 375 pp.

***Lookout platform on top of Larch Hill was used as part of the Sun River elk migration study by Lloyd McDowell. Photo taken November 21, 1943.***
***(Montana Fish and Game Photo)***

Chapter 5

# The War Years and Then Life Renews

World War II had begun both in Europe and in the Pacific but the United States would not enter it until December 7, 1941. Legislation allowing Montana's participation in P-R took effect in July of 1941. One of the first tasks to be undertaken when Montana received the first $100,000 under the this act was an attempt to find out just what wildlife resources Montana actually had. Drought and depression had been devastating, particularly in eastern Montana. Bob Cooney, head of the new Montana Fish and Game Department's Wildlife Restoration Division, contacted Professor P. L. Wright of the University of Montana in Missoula to draw up a wildlife inventory plan. Five students from this University and one from Montana State College in Bozeman were hired as "Fieldmen" to conduct the survey. Faye Couey with help from Walt Mauritson took the area north of the Missouri River. Merle Rognrud and Bill Bergeson marched west in the center of the state, covering counties between the Yellowstone and Missouri Rivers. Jim Beer and Hector LaCasse surveyed counties south of the Yellowstone River. Equipped with a 7x7 foot tent, a cook kit, a purchase book for camp groceries and supplies, they started on the first systematic wildlife survey of eastern Montana. They contacted agriculture and soil conservation offices in every county. Sportsman clubs and landowners were contacted for assistance. As Rognrud put it, ". . .they were sent

***Montana Fish & Game Crews were sent out in the summer of 1941 to conduct border to border inventories of the state's wildlife.***
***(Courtesy Robert Cooney Photo Collection)***

out and with their backs against the North Dakota line and started working their way west". Every 6 miles each two man crew ran sampling transects and recorded everything related to wildlife observed. Thus, each township on their route was sampled. Merle and Bill Bergeson reached White Sulphur Springs by late summer. The six man crew then met in Helena in September to tabulate their results.

*Much of the wildlife inventory travel in the mountains was done on snowshoes.*

However, the expeditions were not without problems. Merle had checked out a loaded pickup in Helena. It had tents, saddles, axes and even a chainsaw. When they got to Glendive a telegram was waiting for them. They had a truck load of equipment intended for a new grizzly bear study in western Montana, not supplies for the prairies of eastern Montana. After an exchange of equipment by Railway Express they were able to get their survey underway.

Surveys in mountain areas were also conducted. A six man crew was established to survey the Middle and South Forks of the Flathead River. Surveys were conducted during winter when elk occupied winter ranges. Working in pairs, they traveled a total of 4,106 miles in a 6-month period with the majority of travel completed on snowshoes.[1] Similar surveys were conducted in all major big game areas of the state.

*Merle Rognrud looking for mountain goats on top of the Continental Divide at the head of N. F. of the Sun River near Switchback Pass - July, 1946. (Courtesy Merle Rognrud Photo Collection)*

For example, winter treks covered 120 miles of the South Fork of the Flathead from the Blackfoot Valley to Coram near Glacier NP. First, a 350-mile round trip was necessary to leave a vehicle at Coram for their return. Weather was not always kind after snowshoeing began. Rognrud recalls a section where trees around them were banging at frequent intervals. This

*U.S. Forest Service Crew cabin used for winter snowshoe surveys in the western mountains of Montana - 1942. (Courtesy Robert Cooney Photo Collection)*

meant temperatures were at least - 40 °F causing frozen trees to develop splits in their trunks. The men would stop at U.S. Forest Service cabins that had been stocked with food by a pack string during the previous summer. Occasionally summer crews had not been careful and flour bins were infested with flour weevils. This gave winter crews the choice of no breakfast pancakes and biscuits for lunch or cooked weevils in both or attempting to strain out most of the insects for a little more palatable repast. Changes in temperature sometimes brought snow that stuck to snowshoes, necessitating carrying a branch to whack the snowshoes every third step. Isolated by miles of wilderness and without communication, broken snowshoes meant an on the spot repair job by one means or another.

***Winter snows were often deep and temperatures well below zero while conducting wildlife surveys on snowshoes in Montana's western mountains.***
*(Courtesy Robert Cooney Photo Collection)*

The 1940s were years in which elk and other wildlife were in short supply and it was necessary to gather as much information as possible about elk and other wildlife residents of the areas. The only way to find out about elk and their winter range condition was to go out and look.

Surveys of the Little Belt Mountains covered 5,539 miles most of which was by vehicle, but 1,818 miles were on foot and 240 miles on horseback. While miles covered were not reported it is clear from information that similar efforts were made in the Cabinet-Yaak, Bitterroot, Sun River, Thompson River, Swan Valley, Madison River and Blackfoot River areas. Surveys were conducted for some special species including grizzly bears, mountain goats, bighorn sheep, moose and antelope. Surveys also covered eastern Montana and provided an information base for a new era of wildlife management based on science.[2]

Biological surveys were not the only projects to be undertaken by the new sparsely funded restoration division. In 1940, Barney Brannin, a rancher from Melville, proposed that mountain goats be introduced into the Crazy Mountains, a mountain range in south-central Montana that mountain goats had never naturally colonized. Local U.S. Forest Service officials supported the project. This began a new phase of transplanting that became an important element in restoration of Montana's wildlife resource.

Bob Cooney and members of the Forest Service began searching for an area that might serve as a source for mountain goats. They examined and rejected several areas in western Montana because of inaccessibility. Finally, a site in the Deep Creek area of the Rocky Mountain Front, 30 miles west of Choteau, was selected. Ranchers and the U.S. Forest Service provided access, horses and labor. The building of a mountain goat trap was completed high in the alpine near timberline on March 30, 1941.

***. . . winter treks covered 120 miles of the South Fork of the Flathead from the Blackfoot Valley to Coram near Glacier National Park. First, a 350-mile round trip was necessary to leave a vehicle at Coram for their return. Weather was not always kind after snowshoeing began. Rognrud recalls a section where trees around them were banging at frequent intervals. This meant temperatures were at least - 40 ° F causing frozen trees to develop splits in their trunks.***

*Crazy Mountains in south central Montana - site of the first mountain goat transplant in 1941. (Photo courtesy Martha A. Lonner)*

***In 1940, Barney Brannin, a rancher from Melville, proposed that mountain goats be introduced into the Crazy Mountains, one of the mountain ranges in south central Montana that mountain goats had never naturally colonized.***

Cooney reported,

> "Our first catch of four goats was made two weeks after the pen was set. A week later we caught eight more. They were taken off the mountain in individual crates perched rather precariously upon a two-wheeled cart. The goats were then transported approximately 300 miles by pickup to the Crazy Mountain range in central Montana and released."

Even though our nation entered World War II in December of 1941, trapping and transplanting of mountain goats continued in spring of 1942.

> "Due to heavy snowdrifts in the area, it was impossible to reach the trap with the two-wheeled cart as had been done the previous year. Anticipating this, crates were built that could be packed on horses. These were found to be satisfactory for the six mile trip."

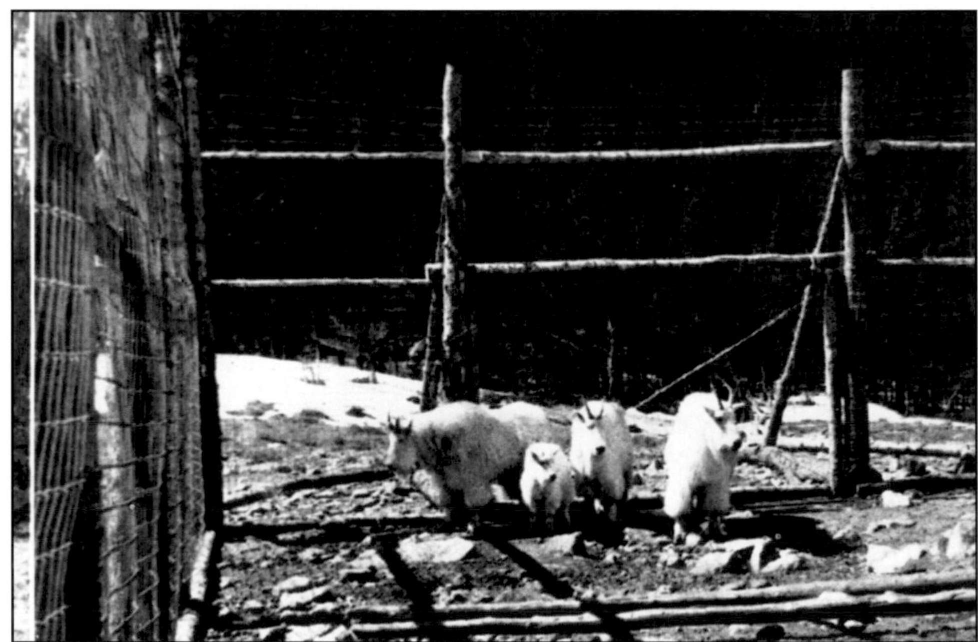

*The first mountain goat trap was built by Montana Fish & Game near timberline west of Choteau, Montana in March of 1941. (Courtesy Jim McLucas Photo Collection)*

*Hilary Gollehon, a local rancher, assisted with trapping and transplanting mountain goats by horse from the Deep Creek trap west of Choteau, MT. c. early 1940s.*
*(Courtesy Robert Cooney Photo Collection)*

*"Due to heavy snowdrifts in the area, it was impossible to reach the trap with the two-wheeled cart as had been done the previous year. Anticipating this, crates were built that could be packed on horses. These were found to be satisfactory for the six mile trip."*

After WW II began, Mr. Cooney attempted to volunteer for military service. He was refused because the authorities felt that he had a job "essential to the war effort." In 1942, defeat followed defeat for the U.S. and allied forces. Contingency plans called for wildlife to be a food supply if the United States was invaded and the population and troops were forced to retreat from the coast. The value of wildlife resource as an alternate food source was well recognized after it had helped many families to survive the disaster years of the Depression. Even after the tide of war turned, wildlife was viewed as a food supply that would free up beef and other meats for use by the military and starving populations in liberated countries. Military ammunition available to hunters was of little value because rifles of many hunters could not use .30-06 military cartridges and full-jacket bullets were ineffective for wildlife. Hunters developed a variety of ways of modifying military bullets to expand when they hit game animals. Overall, hunting was reduced by gasoline rationing and because a large proportion of

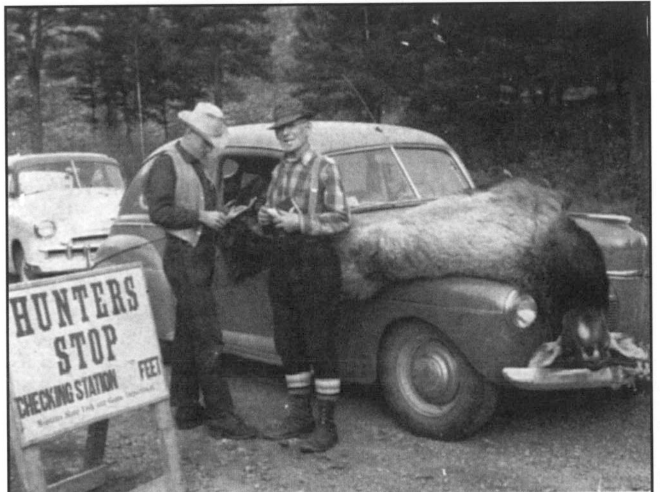


Because of the limited access to the Gallatin Canyon, hunter check stations have long provided effective methods of checking game harvest there. Fish and Game Department Photo.

*Original Photo Caption*

*Wildlife was viewed as a major asset during and after WW II, providing an alternate food source to enhance our national security.*

*. . .wartime hunting in Montana did allow continuation of the long standing practice of some ranchers furnishing employees transportation and free time to go elk hunting. Elk and other game taken during these hunts was used to feed harvest and branding crews, allowing ranchers to avoid killing their cash crop of cattle to feed hired hands.*

Montana hunters were serving in the military. However, wartime hunting in Montana did allow continuation of the long standing practice of some ranchers furnishing employees transportation and free time to go elk hunting. Elk and other game taken during these hunts was used to feed harvest and branding crews, allowing ranchers to avoid killing part of their cash crop of cattle to feed hired hands. Elk hunts in the Gardiner area just north of Yellowstone NP were often used to feed workers, as hunters could take a train to Gardiner saving war-short gasoline and tires.

The drop in hunting activity during the war meant a dramatic drop in hunting license sales, which reduced funds available for wildlife work. Gasoline, tire rationing and poor condition of rural roads made field work difficult. Faye Couey lived in a rented cabin about 20 miles from town conducting a pioneering study of the Sun River bighorn sheep herd. Here is an excerpt from his field notes:

> "On Jan. 3, (1943) a storm came up for 3 days and dropped 44" of snow and 30 degrees below zero. Then came a Chinook wind rising the temperature by 60 degrees, putting a crust on the snow. ...we were short of vegetables. Stecker – a resort owner at the mouth of the canyon, had parsnips and we dug some with a pick. A good mess of water cress was found in French Gulch below us but the whitetail deer found it and cleaned it out. We ran out of eggs but Mrs. Allan had some storage eggs which were kind of strong but ok for baking."[3]

THE RELATION OF PHEASANTS TO AGRICULTURE IN THE YELLOWSTONE AND BIG HORN RIVER VALLEYS OF MONTANA

By
Robert W. Hiatt *

Field Work by William R. Bergeson

Wildlife Restoration Project
Montana 1-R

After a short time in northwestern Montana, Faye Couey and his wife Evelyn moved to Billings to conduct wildlife and range surveys in eastern Montana from 1943 to 1944. Travel was by car and occasionally by airplane as the pioneer biologist tried to cover the eastern two-thirds of the state.

Food shortages of WW II also affected wildlife in other ways. The country was striving for an absolute maximum in food production in its effort to help feed the world. Irrigated land of the Yellowstone and Big Horn River valleys developed very large pheasant populations. Pheasants were eating corn seedlings. This led to poisoning of pheasants to maintain local crop production. A high population of pheasants had also developed on irrigated land along the Milk River in northern Montana. Large numbers of these pheasants were live-trapped to control damage. They were released in the Helena Valley, where bird hunters had better access to them.

Rains again come to Montana during the late 1930s reviving agriculture and the Montana economy. Moderate weather continued for several decades. Wartime and post war demands for minerals and timber products brought wealth. Per capita income rose to levels that put the state within the top 10 states nationwide. During WW II, snow and rain also prevented Japanese incendiary bombs attached to balloons that rode prevailing winds from Japan from starting forest fires when they came down within the state. In 1997 a hunter in Beaverhead County found one of these bombs and carried it for some distance before setting it down. The bomb was later detonated by Montana Air National Guard bomb disposal experts. This demonstrated that some of these bombs are still present in backcountry areas. (They are still extremely dangerous and should not be disturbed. Report their location to law enforcement officials so that they can be safely disposed.)

World War II ended and soldiers returned to their civilian careers. Don Brown, Merle Rognrud, Bill Bergeson, Bob Greene, Jim McLucas, Dick Weckworth and Ken Greer were but a few of these. The GI bill enabled many veterans to go to college and some decided to study wildlife ecology and management. Money available because of the P-R Act provided wildlife jobs for these newly trained, competent and educated veterans. These young men had literally "been trained to fight" and they were to bring revolutionary changes to much of society. Changes from dire poverty of the Depression to burgeoning economic prosperity after the war and change from a relatively isolated rural society to a cosmopolitan one were as dramatic as any period in our nation's history.

After WW II, thoughts in Montana again focused on wildlife restoration. Faye Couey made a trip to Wyoming to obtain a pronghorn trap. They later erected it near Gardiner, hoping to trap some of the Yellowstone NP pronghorn herd. This effort in 1945 was unsuccessful. Plans also called for transplanting and restoring bighorn sheep and mule deer.

Jim McLucas, a Marine Corps veteran from Butte, was initially hired to do predator control work. This job evolved into the state's big game trapping and transplanting expert. Wynn Freeman, a navy veteran, who earned

***The return of veterans from WW II brought substantial changes to both society and wildlife management.***

***During WW II, snow and rain also prevented Japanese incendiary bombs attached to balloons that rode prevailing winds from Japan from starting forest fires when they came down within the state.***

*Type 97, 12 Kg, Thermite Incendiary Bomb (Japanese WWII Balloon Bomb) was found by a hunter in 1997 in Beaverhead Co, MT.*
*(Photo courtesy Montana National Guard)*

*The Montana Fish and Game Department established research assistantships at both Montana State University and the University of Montana to meet the need for wildlife personnel that had Master of Science degrees with substantial field research experience.*

a Master of Science degree in Wildlife Management after the war, was hired as the statewide waterfowl biologist in 1948 by the Montana Fish and Game Department. In 1963 he became administrator of the department's Game Management (now Wildlife) Division. Wynn insisted upon thoroughly trained professionals eschewing the "good old boy" approach so common in previous eras. He teamed up with a combat infantry veteran, Professor Don C. Quimby of Montana State University, to formulate and establish a policy that mandated any new biologists hired had to have a Master of Science degree that included field research. The Montana Fish and Game Department then established research assistantships for wildlife graduate students at both Montana State University and the University of Montana to carry out this goal. Research these graduate students conducted provided the basis for Montana's wildlife restoration and management decisions.

*Jim McLucas was hired by the Montana Fish & Game Department to do predator control and also trap and transplant big game. c. 1947. (Courtesy Hilger-McLucas Photo Collection)*

These efforts were combined with establishment of the Montana Cooperative Wildlife Research Unit in 1950 at the University of Montana in Missoula. The unit is a cooperative effort among the U.S. Fish and Wildlife Service, university faculty and students, and the Montana Fish and Game Department. Universities helped provide scientific expertise that enabled the state fish and game department and not the federal government to become the leader in wildlife decisions made within the state. This high level of education and application of science gave state wildlife managers

*Wynn G. Freeman had a distinguished career as a wildlife professional with the Montana Fish & Game Department from 1948 until his death in 1978. He was a strong advocate of hiring highly trained professional wildlife biologists. (Montana Fish & Game Photo)*

*Don C. Quimby came to Montana State College (Montana State University) in 1948 and created a program in fish & wildlife management. He worked closely with the Montana Fish & Game Department in training fish & wildlife students with graduate degrees. He retired in 1975. (Photo courtesy Don C. Quimby family)*

an advantage in dealing with federal and other agencies, a critical step that permitted Montana to control its own wildlife future.

Full-time research efforts by the Montana Fish and Game Department began in the mid-1950s with headquarters at Montana State University in Bozeman. Several early mule deer studies concerned food habits. This required development of extensive plant collections and a means to identify plant fragments. Work on furbearer food habits imposed similar needs as well as methods for determining age and condition of animals such as mink.[4] Additional data collections were needed to support a furbearer management program. Ken Greer, a U.S. Army Air Corps Pilot during WW II, was asked to establish a furbearer laboratory in 1955 under the fur section of the Department. It was located on the Montana State College campus in Bozeman. During 1957 it became the Wildlife Investigations Laboratory.[5] Soon after that it also became headquarters of the Montana Fish and Game Department's Research Section. Other support services were added during the infancy of this laboratory. It was one of the few state operated wildlife research laboratories in the nation.[6] Its pioneering work has advanced knowledge in many areas including food habits, reproduction, age determination, disease, parasites, structure of populations and many other subjects for

*Montana Hall at Montana State University, Bozeman.*
*(Photo courtesy Terry N. Lonner)*

*Main Hall at the University of Montana, Missoula.*
*(Photo courtesy Terry N. Lonner)*

*Ken Greer, first supervisor of Montana's Wildlife Research Laboratory, examines a portion of the 8,000 prepared mink specimens. c. 1957.*
*(Montana Fish & Game Photo)*

***The need for detailed information about mink and other furbearers led to the establishment of a state furbearer research laboratory on the Montana State College (University) campus in Bozeman in 1955.***

*This building at Montana State College (now Montana State University) in Bozeman housed the Wildlife Laboratory and the Research Section for the Montana Fish & Game Department. It was initially started by Ken R. Greer as a furbearer laboratory in 1955 and he pioneered it into one of the first and finest wildlife laboratories in the nation. c. 1965.* (Courtesy Kenneth R. Greer Photo Collection)

*A wildlife food habits examination table in the state's Wildlife Laboratory as described to the left. c. 1965.* (Courtesy Kenneth R. Greer Photo Collection)

Montana's diverse wildlife species and populations. Research and monitoring of diseases such as brucellosis, chronic wasting disease, west nile virus and avian flu has been expanded or added to services provided by Montana's Wildlife Laboratory.

***Creative cooperative approaches among agencies, universities, agriculturalists, hunters and other citizens were developed to use wildlife biology and ecology to solve environmental problems and gain the broadest possible benefits for society.***

Although P-R was not yet fully funded by Congress, the long planned program of wildlife restoration in Montana began in earnest. World War II was over, soldiers returned and a hunting public was rejuvenated to provide interest, support and funds to continue wildlife restoration and management programs. The new approach included not only wildlife restoration on a massive scale but also liberalized hunting seasons to harvest expanding wildlife populations and make them available to the people. Both old and new ideas were tested by scientific research and many were discarded. Range and habitat evaluation programs were begun. Creative cooperative approaches between agencies, universities, agriculturalists, hunters and other citizens were developed to use wildlife biology and ecology to solve environmental problems and gain the broadest possible benefits for society.

*Montana Fish & Game personnel, university students, faculty, and ranchers on a field trip to discuss range conditions as they relate to wildlife and livestock. c. 1960s.* (Courtesy Robert Cooney Photo Collection)

# Footnotes

[1] Anon. 1942. Flathead game management unit. 1941-1942 Biennial Report. Montana Fish and Game Commission, Helena. 46-47.

[2] Anon. 1942. Various reports for game management units. 1941-1942 Biennial report. Montana Fish and Game Commission, Helena. 48-66.

[3] Diary of Faye Couey courtesy of the family. "Storage eggs" were eggs that were sealed by dipping in "water glass or liquid glass" (sodium silicate) which coated them, preventing spoiling for 6 to 9 months. This method was used when refrigeration was not available.

[4] Greer, K. R. 1957. Some osteological characters of known-age ranch minks. Journal of Mammalogy. 38:319-330.

Mitchell, J. L. 1961. Mink movements and populations on a Montana river. Journal of Wildlife Management. 25:48-54.

[5] Craig, Vernon, editor. 1958. The Laboratory in Management. Montana Wildlife, August 1958. 28-31.

[6] Greer, K. R. 1999. Videotaped interview with Harold Picton and Terry Lonner.

## Fish and Game Commission Estimates One Montana Deer Hunter in Nine Was Successful in 1946 Season

By DON JEWELL

**Despite a 1.33-to-1 ratio of deer to hunters in Montana, state fish and game commission experts estimate less than one hunter in nine who tramped the woods and trails of the Treasure state returned home with his prize during the recent big game season.**

According to figures released by A. A. O'Claire, state fish and game warden, approximately 1,764 deer were killed in the six special deer hunting areas specified by the wild life commissioners during the 1946 season. No definite estimate on the total state-wide kill, however, will be available until completion of the 1946-47 big game census.

While 572 more deer were taken during the 1946 season than were shot in 1945 in the six areas, there were 1,068 less elk shot last year. The elk figure, however, is expected to climb since the Gardiner area is not yet closed. Last year hunters took 2,094 elk in the area, compared with 156 shot thus far.

Game commission spokesmen explain the difference is due to the fact that weather within Yellowstone National park has been relatively mild and elk were, therefore, not pushed out to hunting areas until recently.

BIG HORN RAM—One of the most difficult species of big game to build back in Montana and other western states as well is the Big Horn ram. Every effort is being made by the Montana fish and game commission to increase its numbers. The above speciment was photographed in the Gardiner area.

*(Courtesy Don Brown)*

*Canada geese raised at the Warm Springs Game Bird Farm for transplanting. c. 1955*
*(Courtesy Robert Greene Photo Collection)*

*Preparing trapped elk for transplanting. c. 1960. (Courtesy Jim McLucas Photo Collection)*

*Beaver in cages ready for transplanting. c. 1942. (Courtesy Robert Cooney Photo Collection)*

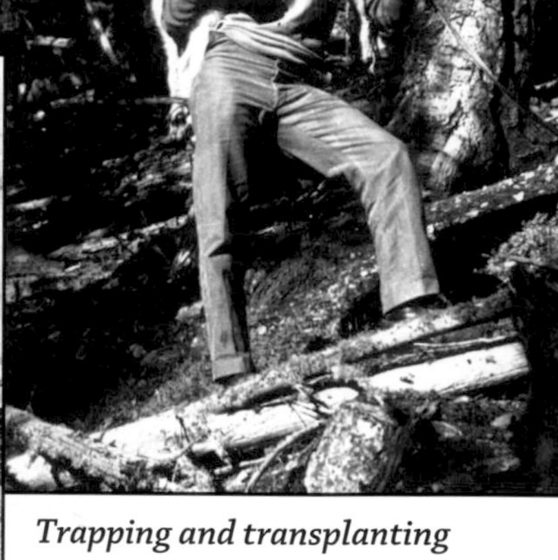

*Trapping and transplanting mountain goats. c. 1948.*
*(Courtesy Jim McLucas Photo Collection)*

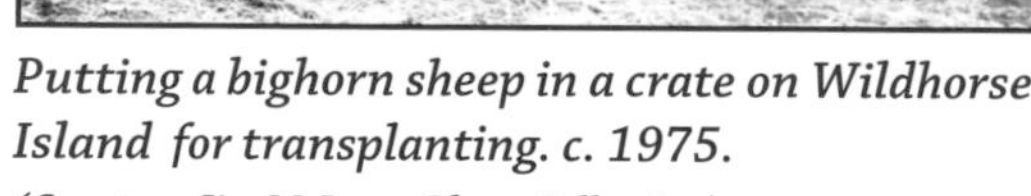

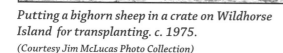

*Putting a bighorn sheep in a crate on Wildhorse Island for transplanting. c. 1975.*
*(Courtesy Jim McLucas Photo Collection)*

*Releasing a trapped antelope. c. 1948.*
*(Courtesy Robert Cooney Photo Collection)*

*Liberating pheasants from one of Montana's 4 Game Bird Farms. c. 1950.*
*(Montana Fish and Game Photo)*

*Trapping mule deer for transplanting. c. 1948.*
*(Courtesy Jim McLucas Photo Collection)*

PART II

# The Restoration

**Montana Counties**

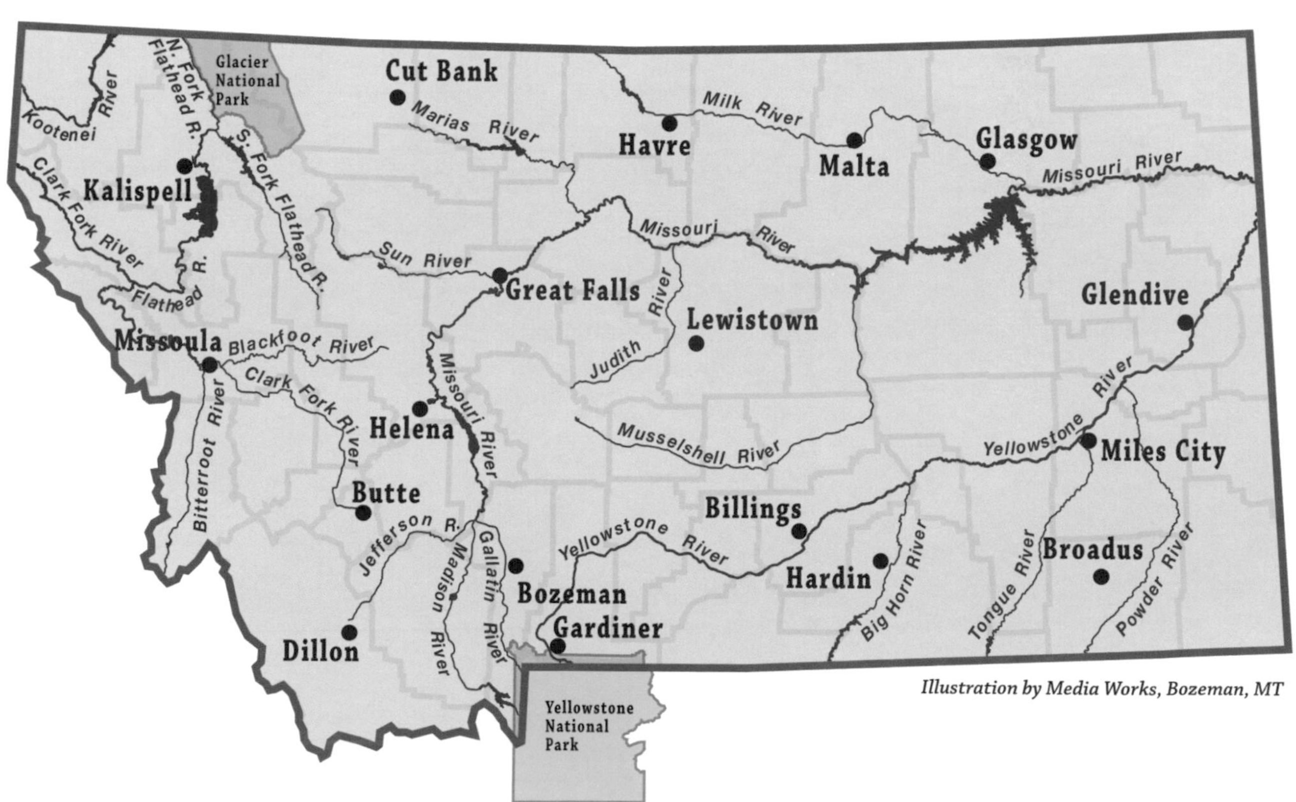


**Some Montana Rivers and Towns**

Chapter 6

# Birds and More Birds

Agriculture came with settlement of the plains and heavily impacted habitat of native birds. Irrigation and relatively small new grain fields created a new environment with much potential for small game, but one which native grouse could not adapt. Over 100,000 new farm ponds created between 1930 and 1960 provided new homes for waterfowl. They also increased aquatic habitat for a diversity of other wildlife during dry seasons that often provided watered swales with more stable vegetation.

## RING-NECKED PHEASANT

*(Phasianus colchicus)*

Ring-necked pheasants were one of the most popular exotic or non-native birds introduced into the Montana. Often referred to as a "chink," it appears to be a blend of the Chinese ring-necked pheasant, English black-necked pheasant and Mongolian pheasant with other varieties. It has become "fine tuned" to local habitats over more than 50 generations that it has been here. Males are distinguished by their ringed neck and longer tail feathers. Each cock may have a harem of several hens which will raise one brood of chicks per year. They will re-nest if their nests are destroyed before the last week of incubation. As ground nesters, suitable sites are in alfalfa fields as well as shrub and weedy areas along edges of fields. Wheat and barley are major foods for this agriculturally adapted bird. Winter, with deep snow potential for burying food and cover, combined with cold temperatures is a critical period. Artificial feeding of birds in winter usually harms more than it helps. It produces high concentration of birds vulnerable to predators, disease and vehicle traffic. Annual mortality is typically high as it is with most small game birds and other animals. Only about 30 percent of pheasants survive to an age of 1 year. Agricultural practices like

*The ring-necked pheasant introduced to Montana is a hybrid of several other pheasant species from Europe and Asia.*

those that reduce the number and size of fence rows along fields reduce pheasant habitat substantially in many areas of Montana.

Pheasants became of great interest for introduction after their first successful introductions to Oregon in 1881 and New Jersey in 1887. It is not known when these birds were first introduced into Montana, but it apparently occurred before 1895. Success of self-sustaining populations was closely tied to development of irrigated agriculture in the state.[1] Some of the first releases were made before 1900 by Marcus Daly at his home in the Bitterroot Valley near Hamilton. In the Montana Fish and Game Department's 1902 biennial report it stated, "These birds have been imported and turned loose year after year but their propagation has been anything but successful."

***About 894,000 pheasants were raised and planted in Montana by the state between 1929 and 1982.***

***Pheasants being released that were raised at the Warm Springs Game Bird Farm. c. 1960.*** *(Montana Fish and Game Photo)*

In 1909, 200 pheasants were released near Choteau in Teton County and 100 near Eureka in Lincoln County. Later another 36 were released on the Tobacco Plains near Eureka in an unsuccessful effort to establish them. Popularity of the birds for introduction continued and about 7,000 were released in Montana between 1909 and 1929. This may be an underestimate because birds and eggs were readily obtained from commercial breeders by private individuals. The official program used birds from commercial breeders in other western states for transplants and introductions by interested citizens who attempted to raise and release them.[2]

In 1929, the Montana Fish and Game Department established a bird farm at Warm Springs to produce pheasants for transplanting around the state. Production began in 1930 and grew rapidly to about 15,000 birds planted per year. Additional game farms were built at Billings and Fort Peck with a smaller experimental operation at Moiese. By 1946, over 37,000 pheasants were planted per year. Birds were generally distributed evenly around the state in 48 counties that were considered to have pheasant

***Pheasant pens at the Montana Fish & Game bird farm in Warm Springs.*** *(Great Falls Tribune, March 6, 1955)*

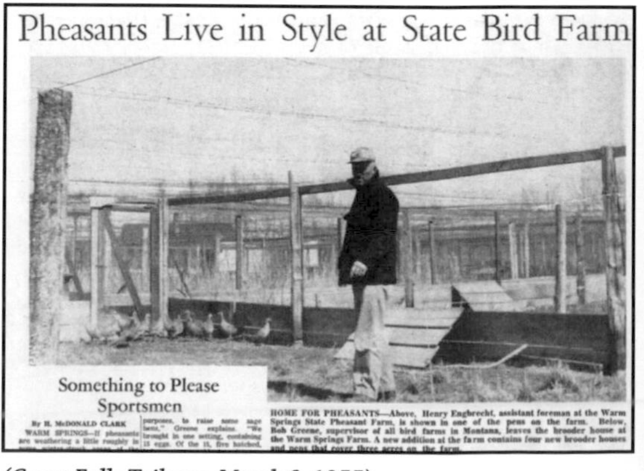

Pheasants Live in Style at State Bird Farm

Something to Please Sportsmen

HOME FOR PHEASANTS—Above, Henry Engbrecht, assistant foreman at the Warm Springs State Pheasant Farm, is shown in one of the pens on the farm. Below, Bob Greene, supervisor of all bird farms in Montana, leaves the brooder house at the Warm Springs Farm. A new addition at the farm contains four new brooder houses and pens that cover three acres on the farm.

*(Great Falls Tribune, March 6, 1955)*

habitat. By 1954 over half a million game farm pheasants had been released. The total number of planted pheasants was 894,142 by 1982 when transplanting was discontinued. This total does not include birds resulting from a program that distributed eggs to 4-H clubs for incubation and release. This program included paying 50 to 75 cents to local clubs for each pheasant raised and released in the field, although the program was not regarded as being particularly successful.

Some sportsman clubs also carried on their own pheasant rearing programs. Other clubs concentrated upon providing over-wintering habitat for the birds. The game bird farm program evolved into "put and take" hunting where many birds were planted each year and a few were shot by hunters. Studies showed that only a small percentage of planted pheasants were taken by hunters, implying a cost of over $40 per bird taken. Planting was thus an inefficient use of money. The result was closure of game bird farms and elimination of pheasant planting. Today, as well as in the past, fortunes of Montana's widespread pheasant populations are directly tied to the fluctuations in quality of habitat as agricultural practices and land uses change.[3]

*Pheasant eggs from the Warm Springs Game Bird Farm.* *(Courtesy Robert Greene Photo Collection)*

The ring-necked pheasant introduction program became a cause for concern of the newly created Wildlife Restoration Division of the Montana Fish and Game Department. Success of the program brought a need for trapping and transplanting pheasants to control some populations on irrigated farmlands during World War II. Where food production was a high priority land owner complaints about crop damage triggered control efforts. Dense pheasant populations in irrigated valleys of the Milk and Yellowstone Rivers provided 5,677 birds for some transplants from 1941 to 1948. About 92% of the birds were trapped in various areas along the Milk River Valley. Major recipients of these birds included the Fort Peck area, the Fairfield Bench northwest of Great Falls and the Helena Valley.[4] Poisoning was also used to reduce numbers of pheasants in the Billings and Hardin areas.[5]

During the late 1940s estimated pheasant densities in areas such as the Fairfield Bench were as high as those of the more famous pheasant habitats in South Dakota. Increases in strip

***Success of the program brought a need for the trapping and transplanting of ring-necked pheasants to control dense populations on irrigated farmlands during World War II.***

*Montana sportsman often got involved with raising and releasing pheasants. c. 1950s.* *(Montana Fish and Game Photo)*

*The popularity of pheasants in the Flathead Valley was shown by the "Chink Hunters Ball" that was held each year to celebrate the opening of the pheasant season.*

farming and other changes in agricultural practices have since reduced the amount of critical over-wintering cover for pheasants. Arsenic grasshopper baits had been widely used during the 1930s with negative impacts upon game birds. Heavy use of persistent pesticides in the 1950s and 1960s undoubtedly also impacted populations before their use was discontinued in the 1970s.

Popularity of pheasants in the Flathead Valley was shown by the "Chink Hunters Ball" that was held each year to celebrate the opening of pheasant hunting. This hugely popular celebration induced the Montana Fish and Game Commission to delay start of the actual hunt until noon the next day to allow celebrants a few hours to recover from previous evening events.

Pheasants remain a popular part of Montana's fauna. Recent efforts to increase their abundance have focused upon improving winter cover and other habitat conditions necessary for them to survive.

**Pheasants transplanted from Montana's Game Bird Farms and the number of counties (of 56) receiving them; 1930-1982.**

| Year(s) | Number | Number of Counties | Year | Number | Number of Counties |
|---|---|---|---|---|---|
| 1930 | 6,146 | 55 | 1957 | 35,444 | 52 |
| 1931 | 8,720 | 52 | 1958 | 31,403 | 44 |
| 1932 | 4,856 | 52 | 1959 | 34,739 | 37 |
| 1933 | 10,162 | 52 | 1960 | 7,827 | 21 |
| 1934 | 9,970 | 48 | 1961 | 7,042 | 22 |
| 1935 | 9,275 | 45 | 1962 | 8,585 | 22 |
| 1936 | 10,572 | 48 | 1963 | 9,747 | 20 |
| 1937 | 11,035 | 46 | 1964 | 7,554 | 19 |
| 1938 | 15,556 | 51 | 1965 | 8,536 | 17 |
| 1939 | 23,118 | 55 | 1966 | 8,300 | 19 |
| 1940 | 27,733 | 56 | 1967 | 8,610 | 17 |
| 1941 | 29,608 | 52 | 1968 | 8,087 | 19 |
| 1942 | 36,845 | 55 | 1969 | 8,674 | 20 |
| 1943 | 9,685 | 31 | 1970 | 7,707 | 19 |
| 1944 | 20,869 | 43 | 1971 | 8,824 | 19 |
| 1945 | 8,035 | 28 | 1972 | 9,930 | 21 |
| 1946 | 37,019 | 53 | 1973 | 8,227 | 18 |
| 1947 | 46,513 | 54 | 1974 | 4,366 | 16 |
| 1948 | 38,196 | 53 | 1975 | 6,701 | 19 |
| 1949 | 27,743 | 52 | 1976 | 9,627 | 19 |
| 1950 | 30,728 | 46 | 1977 | 7,832 | 18 |
| 1951 | 32,794 | 48 | 1978 | 7,715 | 17 |
| 1952 | 33,723 | 54 | 1979 | 7,533 | 24 |
| 1953 | 25,675 | 52 | 1980 | 5,275 | 22 |
| 1954 | 36,533 | 49 | 1981 | 2,722 | 11 |
| 1955 | 37,014 | 39 | 1982 | 1,353 | 10 |
| 1956 | 33,659 | 44 | TOTAL | **894,142** | |

**1942 Ring-necked Pheasant Distribution**

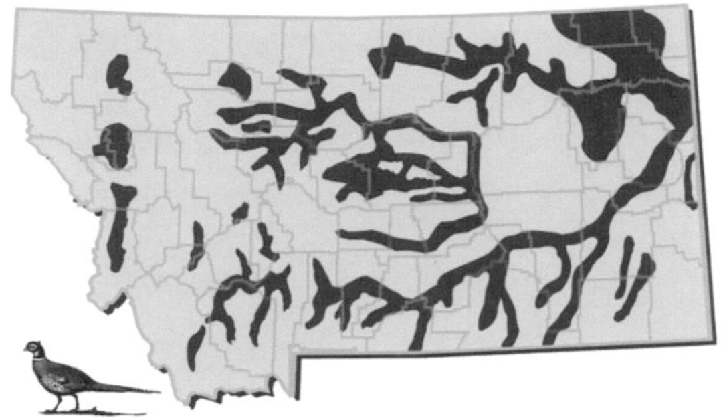

**1970 Ring-necked Pheasant Distribution**

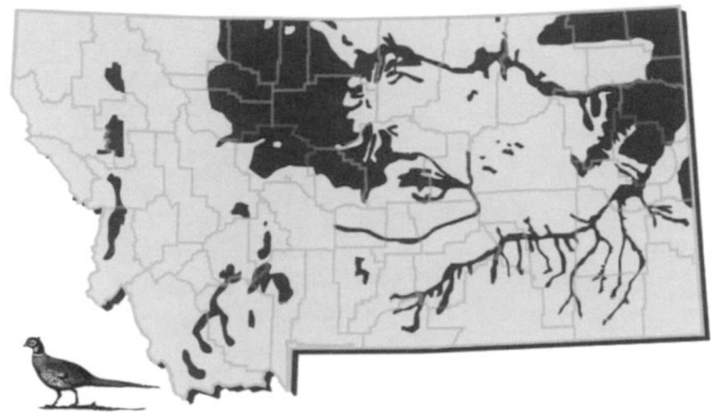

**2008 Ring-necked Pheasant Distribution**

They lay large clutches of 12 - 18 eggs. Their high reproductive rate corresponds to high annual mortality, typical among game bird species. They often form coveys of 15 or more birds. In summer coveys may represent a family group which remains together during winter. Heavy grazing, herbicides and consolidation of grain fields tend to reduce their habitat.

Hungarian partridge originated in central Europe and were brought to the eastern United States in the 1870s, but when they were first brought to Montana is not certain. A dead partridge was found in Sanders County (northwest Montana) in 1915.[6] Partridges had first been successfully introduced in North America from plants near Calgary, Alberta in 1908-1911. The birds may have dispersed from these transplants entering northern Montana between 1914 - 1921. They were reported to occupy northern counties in 1922. The Montana Fish and Game Commission first expressed interest in these birds in 1914 and authorized purchasing them in 1921. The first shipment of 1,000 birds arrived from Europe by boat in 1923 and were distributed to 45 counties. Another 2,000 arrived in 1924, 2,000 in 1925 and 1,000 in 1926. At least another 600 were obtained from Europe after 1926.[7] Game bird farms occasionally raised a few partridges. For example, the game bird farm program furnished 25 that were released in one county

***The Montana Fish and Game Commission authorized the purchase of Hungarian partridge in 1921 with the first shipment of 1,000 birds arriving from Europe by boat in 1923.***

## GRAY OR HUNGARIAN PARTRIDGE

*(Perdix perdix)*

Gray or Hungarian partridge or "hun" is another popular non-native bird that was introduced into Montana. It favors a cool, moderately dry climate with a mixture of cultivated and non-cultivated land. Grain, weed seeds and insects are preferred foods of the "gray bullet" or "feathered fox".

*Since its introduction in the 1920s the gray or Hungarian partridge has become the most widely distributed upland game bird in Montana.*

in 1932 and 52 were released in three counties in 1933. Artificial propagation efforts were of small scale and short duration. In 1943, 12 gray partridge were trapped in the Milk River valley for release in the Helena Valley and another 30 from the same area were taken to the Fort Peck Game Bird Farm for breeding stock.

Statewide wildlife surveys, one of the first tasks undertaken after the Wildlife Restoration Division was formed in 1941, were continued after World War II. Three crews with two men each started at the North Dakota border and headed westward, conducting surveys in every township. By summer's end, they reached central Montana. During these surveys, newly wed wives saw their husbands disappear for several months at the beginning of summer into prairies and mountains of Montana, not to reappear until fall.[8] These surveys revealed that Hungarian partridges had the most extensive distribution of any game bird in Montana. By the late 1940s, many considered it common in grassland areas of the state. Partridge were abundant on prairies along the northern border, in central Montana and in grassland areas of the western intermountain valleys. In contrast, pheasants were more restricted to irrigated areas, along streams and intermountain valleys. Currently gray partridge occupy ranges of ring-necked pheasant and sharp-tailed grouse and overlap into that of sage grouse and lower elevation summer habitats of blue grouse. They are likely to be encountered in all but forested and mountainous habitats.

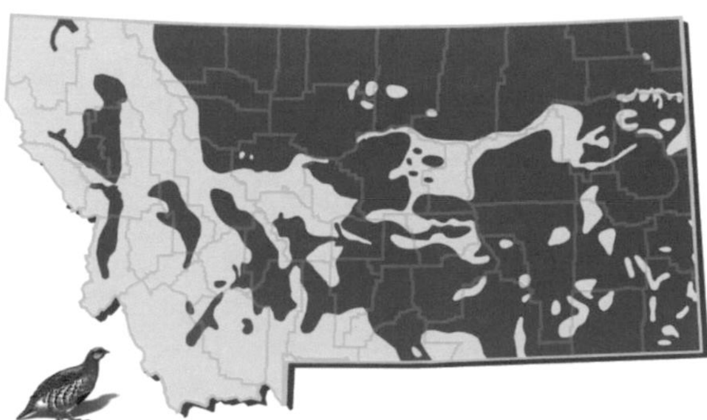

**1942 Hungarian Partridge Distribution**

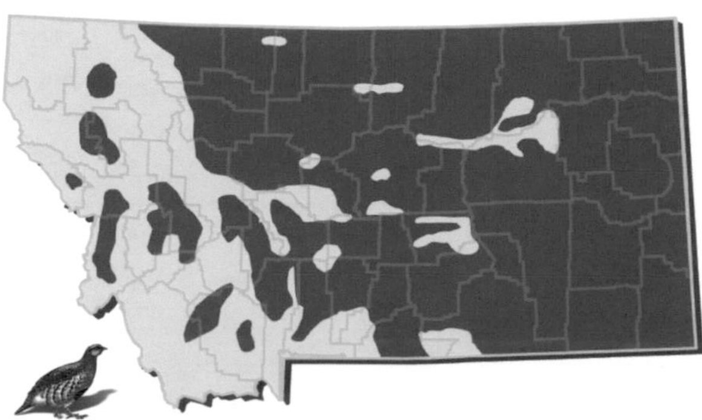

**1970 Hungarian Partridge Distribution**
(not updated since 1970)

## CHUKAR PARTRIDGE

(*Alectoris chukar*)

Chukar are native to southern Europe and a belt that extends eastward across mid-eastern countries of Eurasia to China and Mongolia. Transplanted chukar populations in the western United States occur in semi-arid habitats with steep rocky terrain and an abundance of cheatgrass. In Montana, habitat of annual grasses blends with sagebrush-juniper or sagebrush-bitterbrush. Free water must be available and chukars tend to be limited to areas of low snow cover. Chukars feed on green grasses and forbs and switch to seeds and insects as green plants mature. Berries and grain are important in fall and winter.[9]

Chukars were also raised on state operated game bird farms for release in Montana. Chukar introductions began in 1933 with a release along the Yellowstone River near Glendive. Sixteen counties received a total of 365 birds between 1933 and 1940. Overall, the state released 5,000 chukars in what was suspected as suitable habitat throughout the state after 1950. Most of 89 plants failed, and the program was discontinued in 1958. Transplants in the Big Horn canyon - Pryor Mountains area of south-central Montana are regarded as most successful, but remnant populations may still exist in a few other locations.[10] Chukars were intended to utilize habitats in arid areas not utilized by native species.

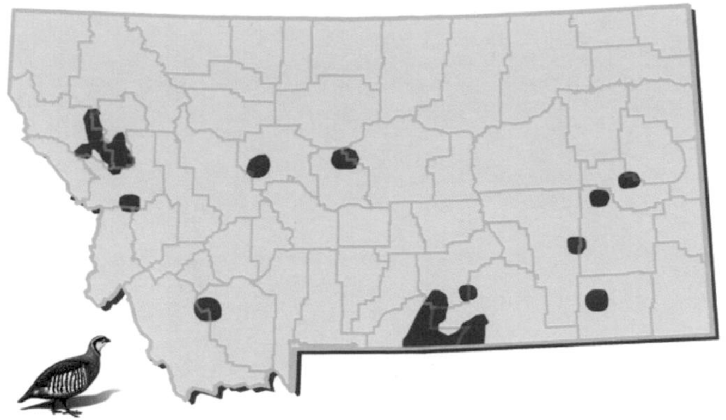

**1970 Chukar Partridge Distribution**
**(not updated since 1970)**

***Chukar partridges are found in only a few areas within Montana.***

## OTHER EXOTICS

During mid-Twentieth Century, the U.S. Fish and Wildlife Service operated an exotic species office in Washington, DC and encouraged states to introduce species from other continents to utilize under-used habitats. They also made a number of unsuccessful attempts to introduce other non-native bird species into Montana. "Official" plants of game farm reared Gambel's Quail *(Callipepla gambelii)* were made in the 1930s in a dozen counties across the state. These totaled over 500 birds. Additionally, Green pheasants *(Phasianus versicolor)*, Amherst pheasants *(Chrysolophus amherstiae)*, silver pheasants *(Lophura nycthemera)* and other varieties were released in small numbers, but all of these introductions failed.[11]

## MERRIAM'S TURKEY

(*Meleagris gallopavo merriami*)

Historical records suggest that wild turkeys were not native to Montana. South Dakota was probably the westward limit of eastern wild turkeys and Merriam's or western wild turkeys were limited to Colorado and elsewhere in the southwest.[12] If turkeys had ever been present in Montana, they certainly were extirpated by the end of the 19th century.

Merriam's turkey occupy habitats that include open stands of ponderosa pine with small open parks and grassland. These stands typically include stands of deciduous trees and shrubs along drainage bottoms. Preferred foods include seeds, fruits, berries, leaves and insects. Grass is an important food item and ponderosa pine seeds are a preferred food when available. Domestic grain is also used when available and may be particularly important during years of poor pine nut production.[13]

***Historical records suggest that wild turkeys were probably not native to Montana.***

*Bob Greene, long-time supervisor of the Montana Bird Farm Program, releasing a Merriam's Turkey near the Marias River north of Valier, Montana. February 22, 1985. (Courtesy Robert Greene Photo Colliction - photo by Gary Olson)*

***Merriam's Turkey have expanded their distribution in a spectacular fashion since their first introductions in 1954 near Lewistown in central Montana and in 1955 in the Long Pines area of southeastern Montana.***

Attempts to introduce wild turkeys in Montana date back to 1939. At least six attempts by private individuals using farm-reared turkeys of eastern stock (*Meleagris gallopavo silvestri*) and one of Rio Grande Turkeys *(Meleagris gallopavo intermedia)* failed to establish populations. In the 1950s the Montana Fish and Game Department noted successful plants of wild-trapped Merriam's turkey in Wyoming and South Dakota. Non-native Merriam's turkeys were first transplanted into Montana on November 13, 1954 in Lime Kiln Gulch in the Judith Mountains near Lewistown. The birds from Colorado were an exchange for mountain goats. Three additional transplants of turkeys received from Wyoming were also made. On January 27, 1955 some wild turkeys from Wyoming were released at Capitol Rock in the Long Pines near Ekalaka. Beaver Creek near Ashland received turkey transplants in October 1956 and January 1957. These transplants were followed by others using turkeys trapped in the wild from the Long Pines and other areas in Montana. By 1965, 19 such plants had been completed extending across Montana to the Bitterroot and Flathead areas.[14] Private individuals, particularly in the Flathead valley area, brought the eastern variety into the state. Some of these stocks have established robust populations, especially where they have access to farmsteads and human-supplied food.

Additional transplants were also made during the remainder of the 20th century. Natural colonization was rapid, spreading these popular birds widely across the state. The big bird has clearly found a home in Montana and has become common from border to border.

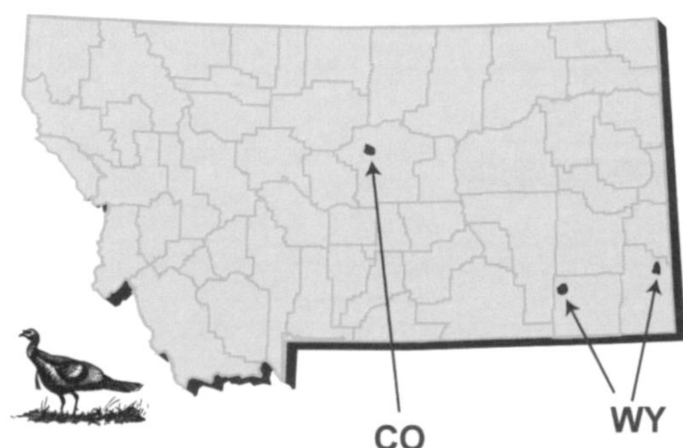


**1954 – 1956 Merriam's Turkey Transplants**

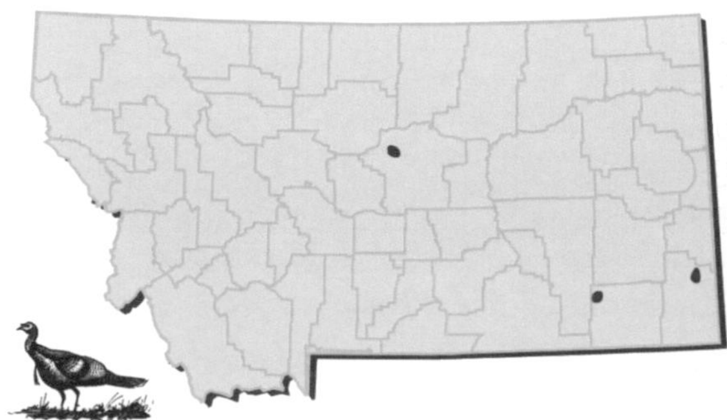

**1956 Merriam's Turkey Distribution**

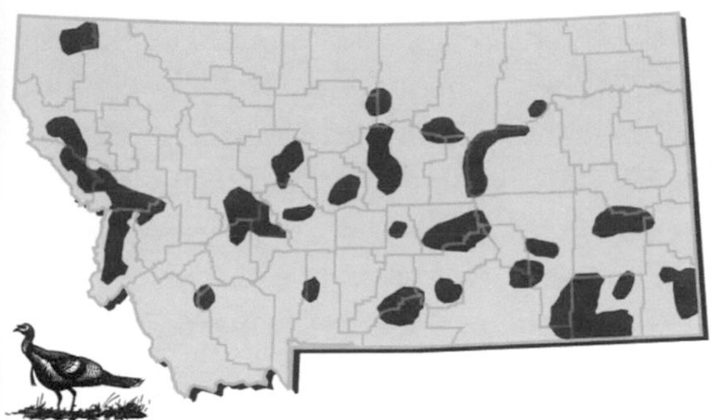

**1970 Merriam's Turkey Distribution**

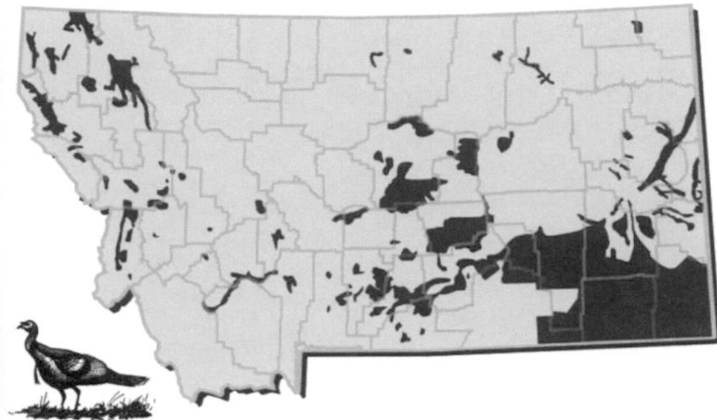

**2008 Merriam's Turkey Distribution**

## SAGE GROUSE

*(Centrocercus urophasianus)*

Sage grouse are largest of two native species of prairie grouse. Big sagebrush is a critical component of their habitat. They feed upon leafy materials such as herbaceous plants and leaves of sagebrush. Sagebrush is particularly important as a winter food and may comprise 90 percent or more of their winter diet. Grasses make up 60 percent of their diet during summer.[15] "Sage hens" use leks or "strutting grounds" for springtime mating rituals. Sagebrush is also important in providing security cover for raising broods and protection from weather in winter. Sagebrush control efforts, heavy grazing by livestock, plowing native prairie lands and prairie fires were major factors in reducing sage grouse habitat in the 20th century and continues in the 21st century.

Captain Meriwether Lewis commented about sage grouse on June 5, 1805 while in the vicinity of the Marias River,

> "I saw a flock of the mountain cock, or a large species of heath hen with a long pointed tail which the Indians informed us were common in the Rocky Mountains. I sent Shields to kill one of them, but he was obliged to fire a long distance at them and missed his aim."[16]

It took several more encounters before they were able to kill one. His more detailed descriptions made later make it clear that Lewis was referring to sage grouse. Early accounts indicate they were abundant in many parts of the state at the end of the 19th century. Sage grouse were targets of market hunting, which had severe impacts on populations in many areas. A 1925 comment stated:

> "Sage hen hunters familiar with this region in the past, state that the Sage-hen was formerly abundant in the sagebrush plains about Silver Bow. It is probably entirely extinct in the region."[17]

***Sagebrush control efforts, heavy grazing by livestock, plowing native prairie lands and prairie fires were major factors in reducing sage grouse habitat in the 20th century and continues in the 21st century.***

The situation was different in other areas:

> ". . . grouse are plentiful throughout this section and are found in large number on and between Rosebud Creek and Tongue River."[18]

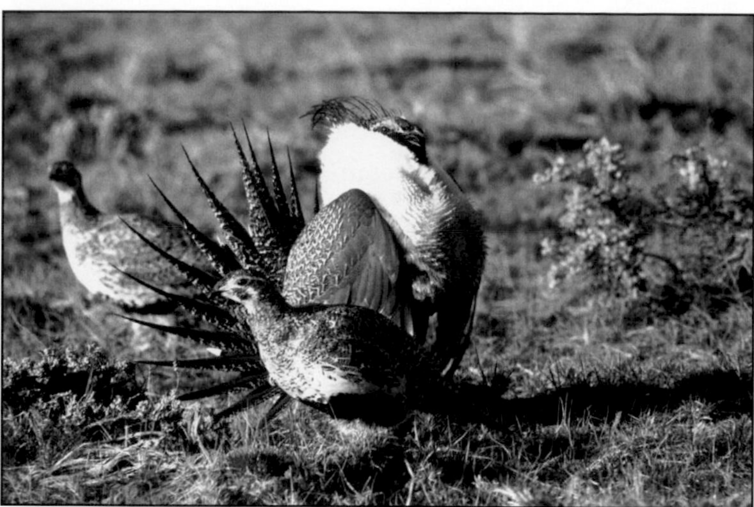

*Sage Grouse on a "strutting ground" near Wilsall, MT. c. 1973.*
*(Photo courtesy Terry N. Lonner)*

Their very abundance was sometimes viewed as a problem:

> "Mr. Garner also stated that they wanted some relief from the sage hen in the northern part of Fergus County, that the sage grouse had become pests, and something must be done in the matter."[19]

***Human impacts upon sage grouse habitat continued to grow throughout the 20th century.***

"Honyockers" or homesteaders of the plains came into Montana during the second decade of the 20th century but were mostly gone by 1920. Native prairie grouse had been heavily impacted by presence of these homesteaders. In the 1920s, the Montana Fish and Game Commission expressed an interest in trying to restore the birds to some areas believed to have been historic sage grouse range from which they had been eliminated. In 1925, Commission minutes report that, "Tom Gilmore paid $2.00 per bird to trap 25 sage grouse for liberation in a western area of state for experimental purposes. Sent to T. N. Marlowe in Missoula."[20] There are no records of the fate of this effort or evidence of sage grouse populations resulting from it. In fall of 1942, 242 sage grouse were trapped in Carter County near Ekalaka and transplanted to seven other areas that appeared to have suitable habitat.[21] The largest number, 72, were released near Brown's Lake in the upper Blackfoot River drainage near Ovando. An additional 62 were released in the Silver Flats area north of Helena. The Helena area received another 38 that were released along the Missouri River in a lower portion of the Helena Valley. The lower Bitterroot Valley south of Missoula received a plant of 31 sage grouse. A plant of 26 sage grouse was made in the Pipestone-Moose Creek-Rochester Basin area south of Butte. A small plant of 7 was made in the Vaughn area west of Great Falls. An area near Joliet (southwest of Billings) received 6 birds. History tells us that none of these introductions met with much success.

*Loading crates of Sage Grouse on a train for transplanting from eastern Montana to western Montana. c. 1940s. (Courtesy Robert Cooney Photo Collection)*

Human impacts on sage grouse habitat continued to grow throughout the 20th century. Comments of Neil Martin and researcher Duane Pyrah made in 1970 are still appropriate today:

> "Since sage grouse have not adjusted to patterns of land use which eliminate or seriously disturb any of their seasonal ranges, their existence depends upon man's ability and willingness to maintain vital habitat."[22]

A detailed sage grouse conservation program that focuses upon habitat conservation and restoration has been developed by state, federal, tribal and private entities.[23] This visionary program is now policy and is being carried out in the field.

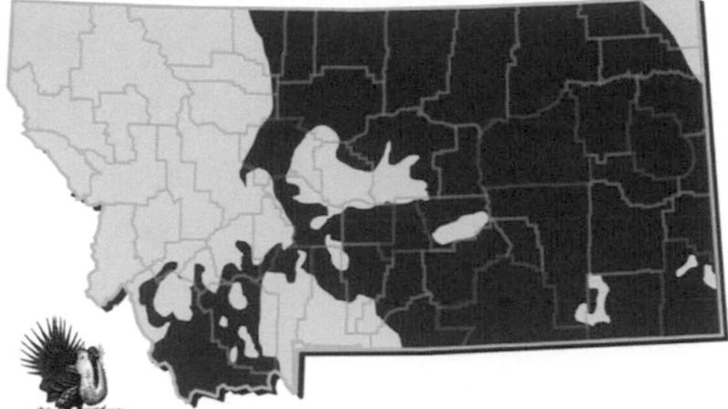

**Historical Sage Grouse Distribution**

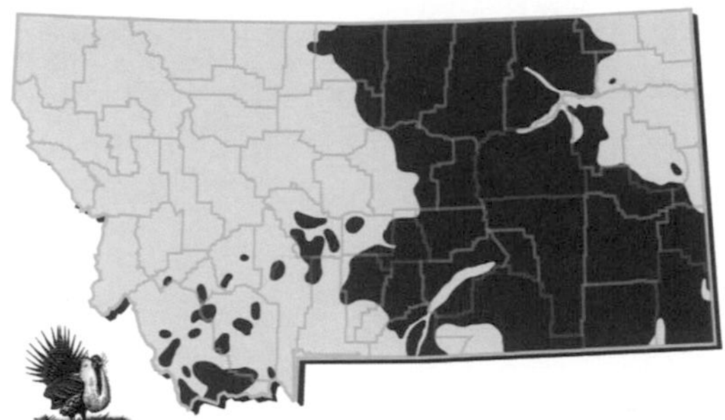

**1942 Sage Grouse Distribution**

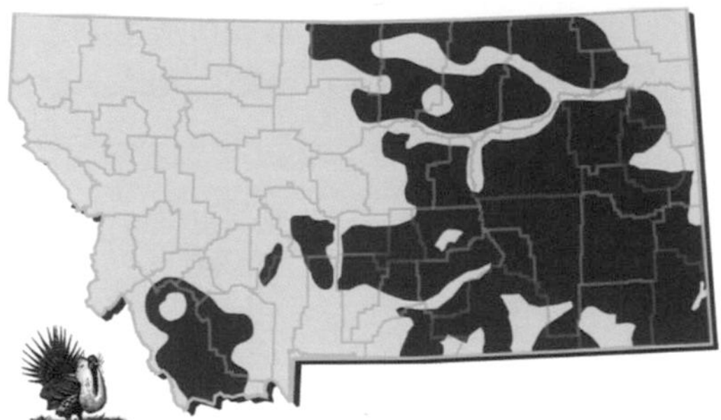

**1970 Sage Grouse Distribution**

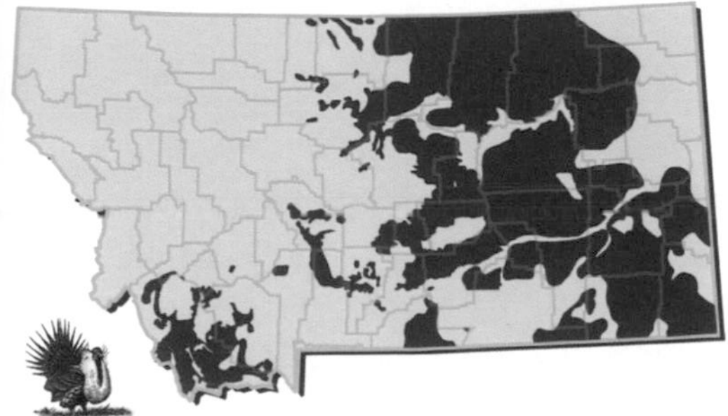

**2008 Sage Grouse Distribution**

## SHARP-TAILED GROUSE

***(Tympanuchus phasianellus)***

There are two subspecies of sharp-tailed grouse in Montana. The plains sharp-tailed grouse *(Tympanuchus phasianellus jamesi)* are native to grassland prairies east of the Continental Divide. Sometimes called "pintails" or "chickens", they are usually found where upland prairie habitat has not been modified by agriculture or other uses. Columbian sharp-tailed Grouse *(Tympanuchus phasianellus columbianus)* were originally widely distributed west of the Continental Divide, but its distribution has been reduced to only the Blackfoot River Valley.[24]

Courtship takes place on leks or "dancing grounds". They require grass, shrubs and trees to furnish both food and cover during various seasons of the year.

***Courtship takes place on leks or "dancing grounds".***

***Plains sharp-tailed grouse on a "dancing ground".***
*(Photo courtesy Harold Picton)*

The Montana Fish and Game Commission used transplants in efforts to enhance the status of sharp-tailed grouse. In February of 1942, six Plains sharptails were moved from Gallatin County to Flathead County.

Eight birds were moved from Phillips County to the Helena valley in February of 1943. Efforts resumed in 1972 with the transplant of 24 plains sharp-tailed grouse from Teton County to Wall Creek in Madison County, supplemented by six additional birds from Golden Valley County. Efforts at Wall Creek appear to have been successful.

Attempts have been made to reintroduce Columbian sharptails into historical ranges. Birds from Idaho were introduced on the National Bison Range at Moiese in 1973, 1974 and 1980. One bird was observed in 1981, but no additional sightings have been reported since. Seventy birds were transplanted to the Tobacco Valley in northwest Montana between 1987 and 1991. All birds that survived were from British Columbia and maintained the small remnant population for several years. By 1994, a population decline stimulated transplants of another 73 British Columbia birds in 1996 and 1997, but none have been seen since 2002.[25]

*Efforts resumed in 1972 with the transplant of 24 plains sharp-tailed grouse to Wall Creek in Madison County from Teton County, supplemented by six additional birds from Golden Valley County. Efforts at Wall Creek appear to have been successful.*

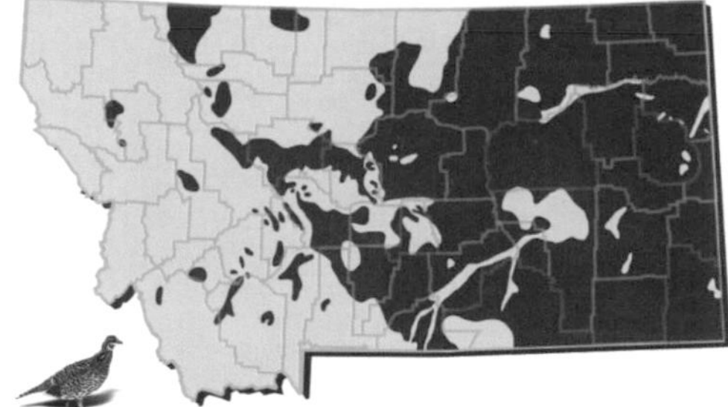

**1942 Sharp-tailed Grouse Distribution**

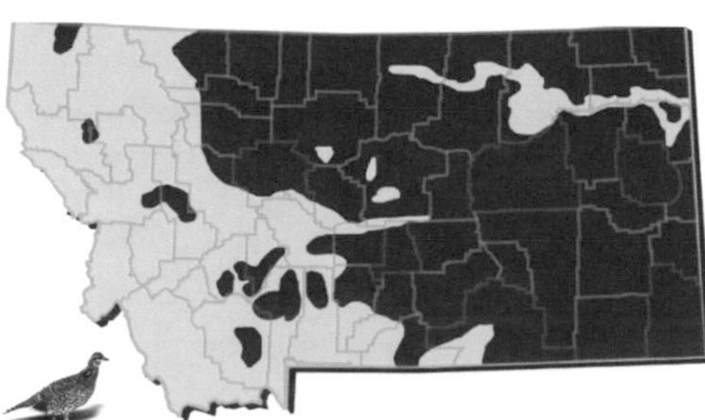

**1970 Sharp-tailed Grouse Distribution**
(not updated since 1970)

## FOREST GROUSE

Montana has three species of native forest grouse.

### Blue Grouse
*(Dendragapus obscurus)*

Blue grouse are widespread in coniferous forests of mountainous areas in western Montana as well as island ranges in the central portion of the state. Blue grouse range widely, summering in moist meadows often at lower elevations while wintering at high elevations in ridge top forests.

### Ruffed Grouse
*(Bonasa umbellus)*

Ruffed grouse have a similar distribution in mountainous areas but inhabit mostly bottom lands in the midst of deciduous trees and shrubs.

### Spruce Grouse
*(Dendragapus canadensis)*

Spruce grouse, "fool's hen" or Franklin's grouse are found in mid-elevation dense coniferous forests in western portions of the state.

During winter blue and spruce grouse survive by consuming conifer needles. In spring and summer they switch to a richer diet of green leaves, insects and berries to raise their young. The summer diet of ruffed grouse is similar to blue and spruce grouse, but ruffed grouse feed on buds of deciduous trees and shrubs in winter. Male blue grouse display during spring in open patches of coniferous timber. Each breeding male defends an area of one to two acres. Male ruffed grouse are active on their "drumming logs" in spring and usually stay, throughout the year, within a half mile of them.[26]

None of the forest grouse species have been transplanted within Montana. Their numbers fluctuate with climate and habitat conditions. Some forest management practices have had substantial impacts on these species. Results from a 1960s blue grouse ecology study in the Sapphire range of the Bitterroot Mountains in western Montana had a major influence on forest management practices that also benefited many other wildlife species. The influence of this study is discussed in chapter 18.

***None of the forest grouse species have been transplanted within Montana.***

*Male Blue Grouse displaying during the spring breeding season.* *(Montana Fish and Game Photo)*

*Female Ruffed Grouse.* *(Photo courtesy Brent N. Lonner)*

***A research project concerning the ecology of blue grouse had a major impact upon forest management practices.***

*Male Spruce Grouse.* *(Photo courtesy Terry N. Lonner)*

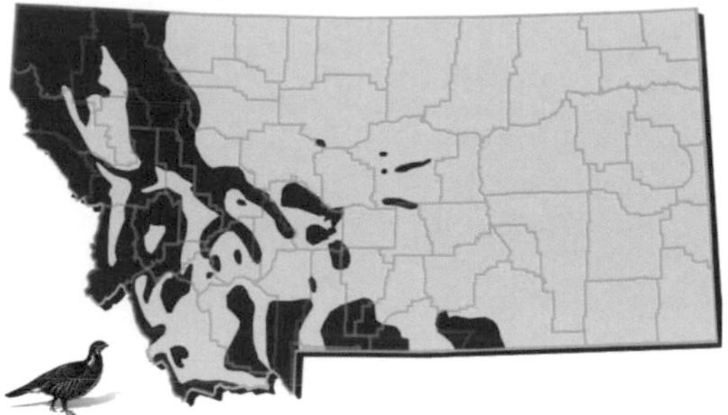

**1942 Blue Grouse Distribution**

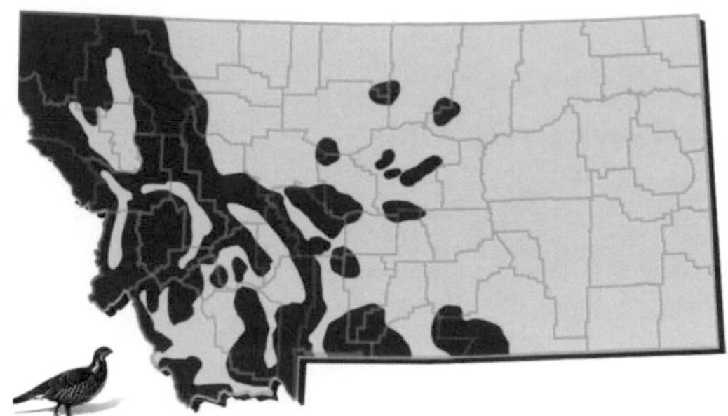

**1970 Blue Grouse Distribution**
(not updated since 1970)

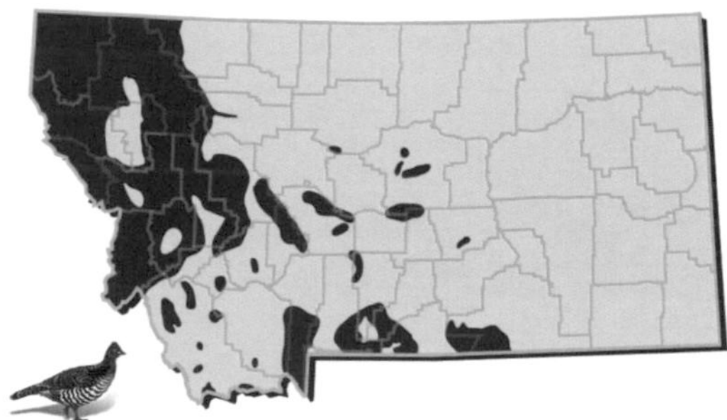

**1942 Ruffed Grouse Distribution**

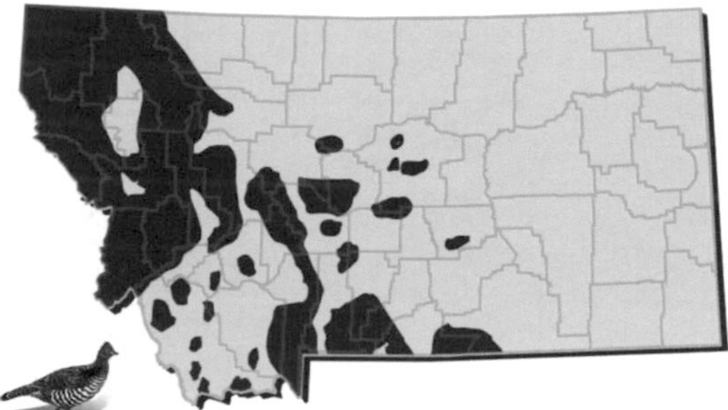

**1970 Ruffed Grouse Distribution**
(not updated since 1970)

**1942 Spruce Grouse Distribution**

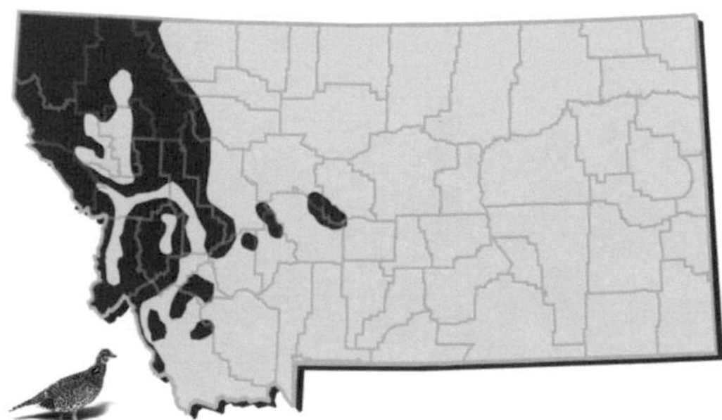

**1970 Spruce Grouse Distribution**
(not updated since 1970)

## WHITE-TAILED PTARMIGAN

*(Lagopus leucurus)*

White-tailed Ptarmigan are native to Montana and are classified as a game bird with a closed season. None of Montana's upland game birds closely resembles this bird. They live in alpine and subalpine habitats extending from Glacier National Park south along the Continental Divide in the Swan and Mission Mountain Ranges. Both sexes have white wings, belly and tail during the summer and turn all white in the winter.

*summer plumage* *winter plumage*

***White-tailed Ptarmigan are native to Montana and are classified as a game bird with a closed season.***

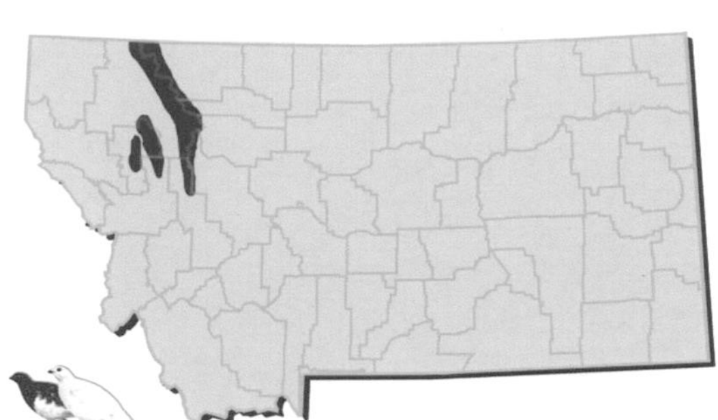

**1996 White-tailed Ptarmigan Distribution**

*White-tailed Ptarmigan (summer plumage) in Glacier National Park.*
*(Photo courtesy Brent N. Lonner)*

## WATERFOWL

*Adult Canada geese at the Warm Springs Bird Farm used to produce goslings for restoration efforts in Montana. c. 1952.* (Courtesy Robert Greene Photo Collection)

Most of the effort to restore waterfowl populations after the disastrous drought years of the 1930s focused on reclaiming, improving and expanding habitat. However, Canada geese (*Branta canadensis*) and Trumputer Swans (*Cygnus buccinator*) were given special attention for restoration.

*"... at one time, believe it or not, the State of Montana had very few Canada geese and it became a project of the Fish and Game Department to increase the number of Canada geese."*

*—Bob Greene [5]*

Nesting Canada geese were uncommon in many parts of Montana before 1980. They were restricted to some areas on the large rivers and reservoirs as well as a few stock ponds with islands in Blaine, Phillips and Valley Counties in north central Montana.[27] Goose eggs were collected and hatched at the Warm Springs Game Bird Farm and when the young geese were about ready to fly they were taken to various places in the state for re-introduction. Many of these attempts were not very successful until a key research project in the 1960s was conducted by Dennis Surrendi, a student from Montana State University but working in Canada. He found that geese would return to nest in areas where they learned to fly.[28] His findings led to successful transplants of geese from Bowdoin National Wildlife Refuge to Medicine Lake National Wildlife Refuge, to Freezout Lake and to the Tongue River Reservoir. Later, many other areas experienced successful transplants using this concept. As Canada goose populations expanded, natural colonization enabled "honkers" to become a prominent member of Montana's waterfowl species.

*Research found that geese would return to nest in areas where they had learned to fly. This led to the first successful efforts to transplant Canada geese.*

Trumpeter swans were approaching extinction. In the1930s the federal government established the Red Rock Lakes National Wildlife Refuge in the Centennial Valley to enable the small existing population of swans to survive. Over the years the population increased and spread into nearby areas of Idaho's Henry's Fork of the Snake River and Yellowstone NP. By the end of the 20th century humans began additional efforts to help the big birds reclaim their heritage. Reintroductions at the beginning of the 21st century were made into such areas as the Mission Valley south of Polson and the Blackfoot Valley near Ovando. These efforts continue.

*Trumpeter swans transplanted on the Pablo National Wildlife Refuge in the Mission Valley south of Polson, MT in 2003.* (Photo courtesy Dale Becker)

# Footnotes

[1] Weigand, J. P. and R. G. Janson. 1979. Montana's Ring-necked pheasant. Montana Fish, Wildlife and Parks, Helena. Technical bulletin:178 pp.

[2] Janson, R., F. Hartkorn and R. Greene. 1970. Ring-necked pheasant. Chapter 18 in: Game Management in Montana. Montana Fish, Wildlife and Parks Dept., Helena. 153-159.

[3] Ibid. Weigand, J. P. and R. G. Janson. 1979.

[4] 1911-1956 Biennial reports of the Montana Fish and Game Dept., Helena.

[5] Greene, R. 1999. Videotaped interview with Harold Picton.

[6] Weigand, J. P. 1977. The biology and ecology of the Hungarian (European gray) partridge (*Perdix perdix*) in north-central Montana. Ph.D. Thesis, Montana State University, Bozeman. 385 pp.

Trueblood, R. and J. Weigand. 1970. The Hungarian partridge. Chapter 19 in: Game Management in Montana, Montana Fish and Game Dept., Helena. 151-145.

[7] Ibid. Weigand, J. P. 1977.

[8] Greene, R., K. Greene, F. Couey and M. Rognrud. 1999 and 2003. Videotaped interviews conducted by Harold Picton and/or Terry Lonner.

[9] Whitney, C. 1970. Chukar partridge. Chapter 21 in: Game Management in Montana, Montana Fish, Wildlife and Parks Dept., Helena. 175-179.

[10] Ibid.

[11] 1930-1940. Biennial reports, Montana Fish and Game Commission, Helena.

[12] Greene, R. and R. Ellis. 1970. Merriam's Turkey. Chapter 20 in: Game Management in Montana, Montana Fish and Game Dept, Helena. 167-173.

[13] Ibid.

[14] Jonas, R. 1966. Merriam's turkey in southeastern Montana. Technical Bulletin 3, Montana Fish, Wildlife and Parks Dept., Helena. 36 pp.

Rose, B. J. 1956. An evaluation of two introductions of Merriam's turkey into Montana. Master's thesis, Montana State University, Bozeman. 37 pp.

Ibid. Greene, R. and R. Ellis. 1970.

[15] Martin, N. and D. Pyrah. 1970. Sage grouse. Chapter 16 in: Game Management in Montana. Montana Fish and Game Dept., Helena. 135-141.

Wallestad, R. 1975. Life history and habitat requirements of sage grouse in central Montana. Montana Fish and Game Dept., Helena. 66 pp.

[16] Lewis, M. 1805. Entry for June 5, 1805. In: Vol. 4. The journals of the Lewis and Clark expedition, G. E. Moulton Editor. University of Nebraska Press, Lincoln. 258.

[17] Saunders, A. A. 1925. Some birds of southwestern Montana. The Condor. 14:25.

[18] First Biennial Report, Montana Game and Fish Commission 1934-1914. 27.

[19] Minutes of the Montana Fish and Game Commission November 23, 1925.

[20] Minutes of the Montana Fish and Game Commission July 19, 1925.

[21] Biennial Report 1942-1943. Montana Fish and Game Commission, Helena. 81, 86-88. Bird planting Log Book. Unpublished account ledger log book, Montana Fish and Game Dept.

[22] Ibid. Martin, N. and D. Pyrah. 1970.

[23] Montana Sage Grouse Working Group. 2002. Management plan and conservation strategies for sage grouse in Montana. Montana Fish, Wildlife and Parks, Helena. 159 pp.

[24] Thier, T. 2005. Personal communication with Harold Picton dated August 29, 2005.

[25] Ibid.

# Footnotes, cont.

[26] Mussehl, T., P. Schladweiler and R. Weckworth. 1970. Forest grouse. Chapter 17 in Game Management in Montana. Montana Fish and Game Dept., Helena. 143-151.

[27] Witt, D. and J. Salinas. 1971. Waterfowl. Chapter 23 in Game Management in Montana. Montana Fish and Game Dept. Helena. 185-193.

[28] Surrendi, D. C. 1970. The mortality, behavior and homing of transplanted juvenile Canada geese. Journal of Wildlife Management. 34:719-733.

*Mule Deer in a corral trap ready for transplanting. c. 1950.*
*(Courtesy Jim McLucas Photo Collection)*

Chapter 7

# Rocky Mountain Mule Deer

Rocky Mountain mule deer (*Odocoileus hemionus hemionus*) occupy rough terrain in the western U.S. and Canada. Adapted to highly variable climates, mule deer are sometimes called "black-tails" because of the black tip on their tail. However, this name is more appropriate for the closely related Columbian black-tailed deer *(Odocoileus hemionus columbianus)* of the west coast. Captain Meriwether Lewis provided the first detailed description and applied the name of mule deer because he was impressed by the size of 11 inch ears that he measured on a buck.

He also noted, "...we have rarely found the mule deer in any except the rough country; they prefer the open grounds and are seldom found in woodlands or river bottoms,..." [1]

Males of these two subspecies possess antlers like other members of the deer family (Cervidae). They are of bone rather than the fingernail or hoof like material forming horns of antelope, bison, bighorn sheep and mountain goats. Their antlers are shed annually during winter months and then regrown. Females or does typically begin breeding as yearlings and have one or two fawns. They feed on broadleaf plants, buds of shrubs and other concentrated and easily digestible foods. Mule deer in central and western Montana often migrate to high elevation summer ranges in mountain areas. Migrations of up to 10 miles are common but one of 90 miles has been recorded. Dispersals of over 100 miles are known for mule deer living on the

***". ... we have rarely found the mule deer in any except the rough country; they prefer the open grounds and are seldom found in woodlands or river bottoms, . . ."*** [1]

**—Captain Meriwether Lewis**

*"...so the MacKay's had an extra hay sled and lumber and we built a crate on it. We caught 161 mule deer, hauled them out. The first trip was with a horse and sled."*[3]

— Jim McLucas

prairie in eastern Montana. Captain Lewis sometimes referred to them as "jumping deer" because of their unique bouncing running gait called "stotting". This gait is very effective for escaping predators in a rough, rocky or small shrub habitat.

Mule deer were originally widely distributed across the state. By the beginning of the 20th century they were over hunted and nearly vanished from many areas of Montana including some smaller mountain ranges. Establishment of game preserves had enabled some populations to grow, sometimes causing damage to agricultural crops and bringing landowner complaints. They often prevented effective control of these populations. As management progressed and became more refined there was a demand for widespread restoration of mule deer populations.[2]

Yellowstone Vic Smith apparently shipped and sold live mule deer from the upper Madison River area along the Montana-Idaho border in the 1890s.[3] The first official transplant of mule deer was the introduction of 6 deer from the northern Yellowstone Park range in 1918 to the National Bison Range in Lake County to supplement an existing population of 13. By 1929, this population had increased to 145 and the Bison Range began to furnish mule deer for transplanting.[4]

*A typical wooden panel or "corral trap" used for capturing mule deer.*
*(Courtesy Jim McLucas Photo Collection)*

Mule deer traps were made of eight foot square wooden panel sections that could be dismantled and transported on a truck. Originally developed for elk, these traps were also effective for mule deer. Deer were often baited into traps with hay if weather was severe with limited access to natural foods. Funnel or wing fences could also be added which allowed men on horseback to drive deer into traps.

Transplanting mule deer began in 1942 and continued through the years of World War II. A total of 410 deer in 26 transplants were moved between 1942-1945. Many of these deer were moved from Lincoln and Flathead counties in the northwestern portion of the state to the Glendive area in southeastern Montana involving a tedious trip of over 600 miles under a wartime speed limit of 35 miles per hour. The speed limit was because of gasoline availability and particularly by the poor quality of tires available to civilians during the war.

Tasks of trapping crews were not always easy. The winter of 1949 was exceptionally severe. One 3-man trapping crew headed by C. H. Harkness went to the West Rosebud River at the foot of the Beartooth Range in Carbon County. Winds had destroyed several wooden-panels of the trap. Although a combination of deep snow and wind isolated the crew for long periods, they persisted, capturing 77 mule deer that were transported to Sarpy Hills in Bighorn County and to Fish Creek near Sidney in Richland County. In 1949, another trapping crew led by Frank

Lancaster faced difficult winter trapping conditions on the National Bison Range. Snow depths of 6 inches to 5 feet made trapping difficult. Deer were driven into the trap by men on horseback. Deer that avoided capture because of deep snow proved very difficult to capture in subsequent drives. However, the crew captured 81 deer during that tough winter and released them in what is now Lewis and Clark Caverns State Park (Morrison Cave). The National Bison Range furnished 674 mule deer for Montana's transplanting efforts. Another 168 came from the Crazy Mountains in south central Montana. The MacKay ranch in the Rosebud country of Carbon County furnished 169. As recalled by Jim McLucas,

> "...so the MacKay's had an extra hay sled and lumber and we built a crate on it. We caught 169 mule deer, hauled them out. The first trip was with a horse and sled."[5]

The Bull Mountains near the then booming coal mining town of Roundup received 430. Over 300 mule deer each went to the badlands along the Yellowstone River near Glendive and to the vicinity of Lewis and Clark Caverns. Other trapping operations were carried out along the Dearborn River and in valleys in north eastern parts of the Crazy Mountains. The trapping operations provided a total of 1,835 mule deer to start new herds in areas from which they had been extirpated.

> "...the deer are hard to handle because they never quit fighting. They've just got their legs going all the time...And they'd strip the clothes right off of you." [6]
>
> —Joe Gaab

*Crates built to haul and transport deer. c. 1950.*
*(Courtesy Jim McLucas Photo Collection)*

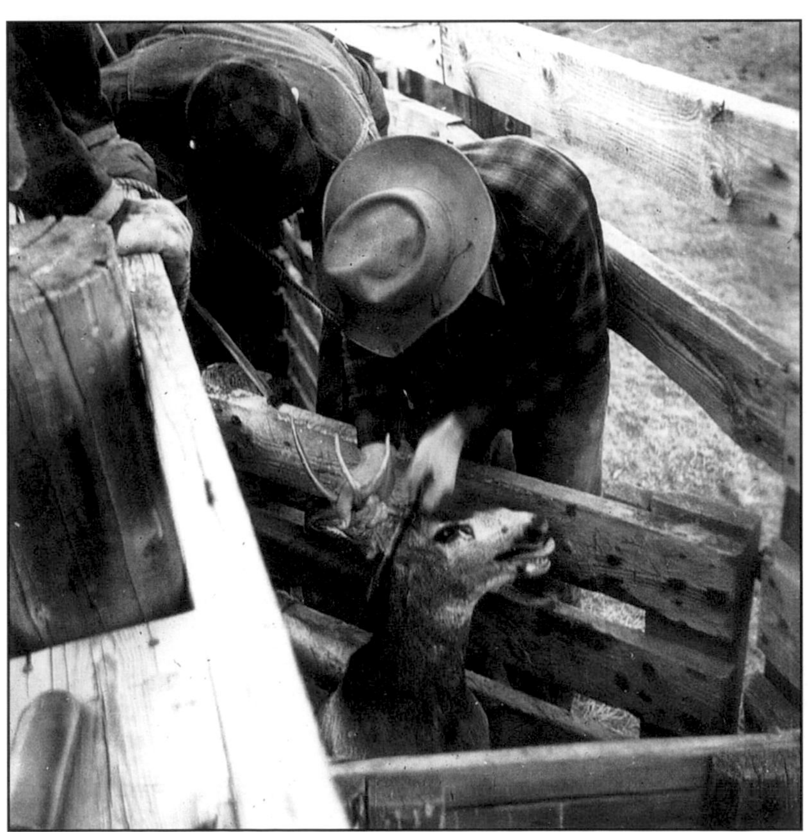

*George Feucht sawing off antlers of a trapped mule deer before loading it into a truck for transplanting to eastern Montana. January, 1948.*
*(Courtesy Merle Rognrud Photo Collection)*

*Mule deer in a holding pen ready for transplanting. c. late 1940s.*
*(Courtesy Jim McLucas Photo Collection)*

*"... deer are hard to handle because they never quit fighting. They've just got their legs going all the time... And they'd strip the clothes right off of you."*[6]

—Joe Gaab

Once animals were trapped and loaded in trucks it became a race against time to get them to the release site. Drives through the night were common. Winter weather and moonless nights contributed to an incident that occurred after a drive of over 300 miles described by Joe Gaab:

> "In the middle of the night...we had a guy with us that we contacted to take us out to where we were gonna plant them. Well, we opened the back end of the truck, pitch black and you couldn't see your hand in front of your face. Pretty soon the first deer went out, kerplunk and the second one jumped out, kerplunk, and about the third one I said we've got to move this truck. . .these deer are hitting into a pond or something. And sure enough that's what was happening. . . so we moved the truck and pointed them in a different direction."[6]

Mule deer steadily increased in numbers from the 1940s into the 1960s. By the late 1950s, they were so numerous that very liberal hunting seasons could not even control their numbers in most locations. Agricultural damage was common. On some winter ranges, particularly along mountain fronts, hundreds of deer died of starvation as they depleted winter food supplies.

Many factors were involved in rapidly expanding mule deer populations. Much marginal farm land was abandoned as the plains depopulated in the 1920s and 1930s. After disasters of the 1930s, some efforts were made to retire sub-marginal lands from crop production and resettle some impoverished farmers. This was the first resettlement program in the United States. Changes in the cattle industry tended to bring more attention to improving the quality of rangelands. In 1928, the Mizpah–Pumpkin Creek Grazing Association in eastern Montana became the first cooperative grazing district in the nation. This paved the way to improve quality of rangelands across the state.

Domestic sheep are also in the category of being open habitat concentrate feeders with food habits that overlap those of mule deer. Numbers of domestic sheep in Montana declined from over 4 million in the 1930s to fewer than 900,000 by the early 1970s.[7] Domestic sheep numbers continued to drop to about 300,000 in 2004.[8] Predator numbers were also maintained at a low level during those years of high sheep numbers. Changing times brought reduction of illegal hunting, improvement of range conditions, an absence of predators and reduction of range competition by domestic animals. These changes all influenced recovery of mule deer populations.

All 62 mule deer transplants went to sites that field surveys identified as areas with low mule deer populations and may have accelerated recovery of deer populations in some areas.[9] Programs removed deer from areas where they were causing agricultural problems and moved them to areas where they were highly desired. However, natural dispersal and re-colonization accounted for most of the mule deer re-population in the state.

By 1970 mule deer had re-colonized the entire state.[10] After a period of an excessive population high, mule deer populations now fluctuate in a more natural fashion.

*Since the beginning of the 20th century, mule deer have recovered and now inhabit the entire state of Montana.*
*(Photo courtesy Terry N. Lonner)*

## An annotated listing of Montana mule deer transplants; 1918 - 1951.

| Year(s) | Source | Number | Release Site |
|---|---|---|---|
| 1918 | Yellowstone National Park, Park Co. | 6 | National Bison Range, Lake Co. [1] |
| 1921 | Conley Ranch, Deer Lodge Co. | 17 | National Bison Range, Lake Co.[1] |
| 1929-1931 | National Bison Range, Lake Co. | 60 | shipped to 11 individuals in this time period [1] |
| 1942-1943 | National Bison Range, Lake Co. | 19 | Glendive Badlands, Dawson Co. |
| | National Bison Range, Lake Co. | 16 | Glendive Badlands, Dawson Co.[2] |
| | National Bison Range, Lake Co. | 14 | Cabin Cr., Fallon Co.[2] |
| | Crazy Mtns., Sweet Grass Co. | 9 | Bull Mtns., Musselshell Co. |
| | National Bison Range, Lake Co. | 20 | Glendive Badlands, Dawson Co.[3] |
| | National Bison Range, Lake Co. | 20 | Bull Mtns., Musselshell Co. |
| 1944-1945 | Crazy Mtns., Sweet Grass Co. | 36 | Glendive Badlands, Dawson Co. |
| | National Bison Range, Lake Co. | 9 | Bull Mtns., Musselshell Co. |
| | Lebo Ranch, Wheatland Co. | 3 | Bull Mtns., Musselshell Co. |
| | Voldseth Ranch, Meagher Co. | 13 | Glendive Badlands, Dawson Co. |
| | Lebo Ranch, Wheatland Co. | 3 | Glendive Badlands, Dawson Co. |
| | Voldseth Ranch, Meagher Co. | 6 | Bull Mtns., Musselshell Co. |
| | Grave Cr., Lincoln Co. | 15 | Bull Mtns., Musselshell Co. |
| | National Bison Range, Lake Co. | 41 | Glendive Badlands, Dawson Co. |
| | Fortine, Lincoln Co. | 11 | Stillwater River, Stillwater Co. |
| | National Bison Range, Lake Co. | 20 | Bull Mtns., Musselshell Co. |
| | Chris Orness Ranch, Sweet Grass Co. | 20 | Bull Mtns., Musselshell Co. |
| | National Bison Range, Lake Co. | 23 | Bull Mtns., Musselshell Co. |
| | Cooper Cr., Meagher Co. | 7 | Bull Mtns., Musselshell Co. |
| | Cooper Cr., Meagher Co. | 6 | Bull Mtns., Musselshell Co. |
| | National Bison Range, Lake Co. | 20 | Bull Mtns., Musselshell Co. |
| | Fortine, Lincoln, Co. | 20 | Bull Mtns., Musselshell Co. |
| | Crazy Mtns., Sweet Grass Co. | 18 | Fox Cr., Richland Co. |
| | Cottonwood Cr., Meagher Co. | 10 | Glendive Badlands, Dawson Co. |
| | Cooper Cr., Meagher Co. | 13 | Glendive Badlands, Dawson Co. |
| | Basin Cr., Sweet Grass Co. | 38 | Sarpy Cr., Bighorn Co. |
| 1946 | Ennis, Madison Co. | 2 | Lewis and Clark Caverns, Jefferson Co. |
| | National Bison Range, Lake Co. | 20 | Bull Mtns., Musselshell Co. |
| | National Bison Range, Lake Co. | 20 | Bull Mtns., Musselshell Co. |
| | National Bison Range, Lake Co. | 20 | Bull Mtns., Musselshell Co. |
| | National Bison Range, Lake Co. | 20 | Bull Mtns., Musselshell Co. |
| | National Bison Range, Lake Co. | 20 | Bull Mtns., Musselshell Co. |
| | Thronruds Ranch, Sweet Grass Co. | 35 | Cabin Cr., Fallon Co.[3] |
| | Thronruds Ranch, Sweet Grass Co. | 17 | Fox Cr., Sidney, Richland Co.[4] |
| 1947 | National Bison Range, Lake Co. | 20 | Bull Mtns., Musselshell Co. |
| | National Bison Range, Lake Co. | 40 | Bull Mtns., Musselshell Co. |
| | National Bison Range, Lake Co. | 20 | Bull Mtns., Musselshell Co. |
| | National Bison Range, Lake Co. | 40 | Bull Mtns., Musselshell Co. |
| | Crazy Mtns., Sweet Grass Co. | 24 | Sarpy Cr., Bighorn Co. |
| | Crazy Mtns., Sweet Grass Co. | 41 | Glendive Badlands, Dawson Co. |
| | Dearborn River, Lewis and Clark Co. | 20 | Lewis and Clark Caverns, Jefferson Co. |

## An annotated listing of Montana mule deer transplants; 1918 - 1951, cont.

| Year(s) | Source | Number | Release Site |
|---|---|---|---|
| 1947 cont. | Crazy Mtns., Sweet Grass Co. | 12 | Glendive Badlands, Dawson Co. |
| | Crazy Mtns., Sweet Grass Co. | 19 | Cabin Cr., Fallon Co. |
| | Crazy Mtns., Sweet Grass Co. | 9 | Sarpy Cr., Bighorn Co.[3] |
| | Dearborn River, Lewis and Clark Co. | 75 | Lewis and Clark Caverns, Jefferson Co. |
| 1948 | National Bison Range, Lake Co. | 27 | Lavina, Musselshell River, Golden Valley Co. |
| | National Bison Range, Lake Co. | 60 | Lewis and Clark Caverns, Jefferson Co.[2] |
| | National Bison Range, Lake Co. | 20 | Bull Mtns., Musselshell Co.[2] |
| | National Bison Range, Lake Co. | 14 | Lewis and Clark Caverns, Jefferson Co. |
| | MacKay Ranch, Carbon Co. | 52 | Sarpy Hills, Bighorn Co. |
| | Mackay Ranch, Carbon Co. | 33 | Glendive Badlands, Dawson Co.[3] |
| | MacKay Ranch, Carbon Co. | 7 | Billings Game Preserve, Yellowstone Co. |
| | MacKay Ranch, Carbon Co. | 20 | Sarpy Hills, Big Horn Co. |
| | MacKay Ranch, Carbon Co. | 20 | Fish Cr., Golden Valley Co. |
| 1949 | Mackay Ranch, Carbon Co. | 37 | Sarpy Hills, Bighorn Co.[3] |
| 1950 | National Bison Range, Lake Co. | 132 | Lewis and Clark Caverns, Jefferson Co. |
| | Reese Cr., Gallatin Co. | 5 | Lewis and Clark Caverns, Jefferson Co. |
| 1951 | National Bison Range, Lake Co. | 421 | Flathead Indian Reservation by the U.S. Fish and Wildlife Service [1] |
| Summary | **subtotal** | **1,331** | **by Montana Fish and Game Dept.** |
| | **subtotal** | **504** | **by U. S. Fish and Wildlife Service** |
| | **Total** | **1,835** | |

Annotations about the type of transplant are from field work reported in: Couey, F.M., D.L. Brown, L.E. Brown and K.E. Riersgard. 1950. Big game transplanting evaluation report eastern Montana. Montana Fish and Game Department, Helena. 93pp. Augmentation transplants supplement a population already existing in the area. 23 were released on the National Bison Range by their personnel in the first two decades of its operation.

[1] Kraft, E. 2006. Untold tales of bison range trails. Stoneydale Press, Stevensville, MT. 28-31.
[2] Small residual population in area, augmentation transplants
[3] Augmentation transplants
[4] No deer in area, restoration transplant.

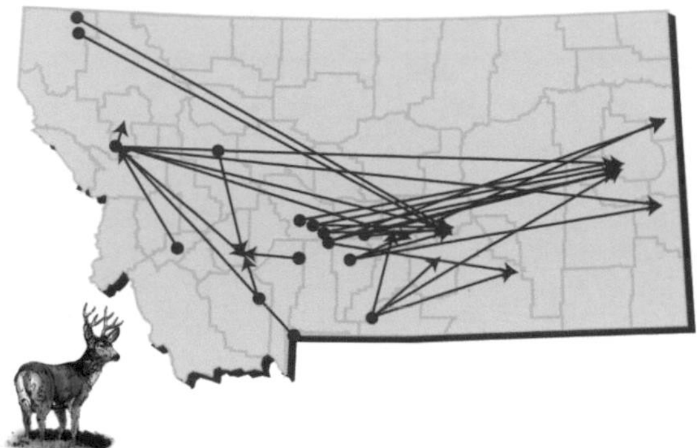
1918 - 1951 Mule Deer Transplants

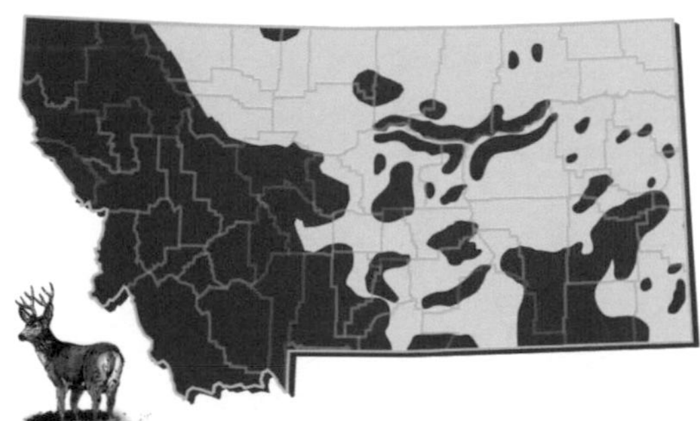
1942 Mule Deer Distribution

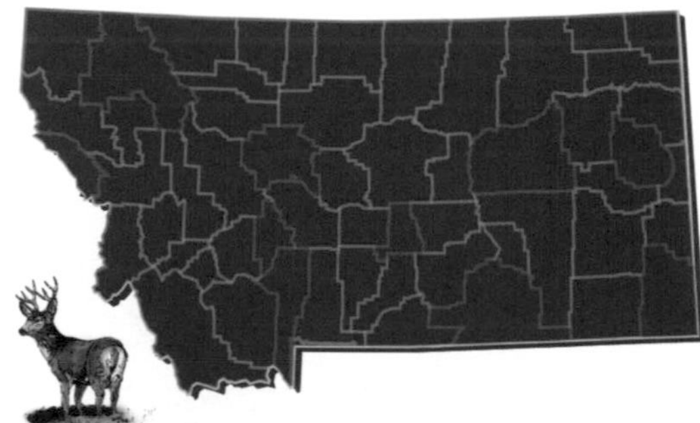
1970 Mule Deer Distribution

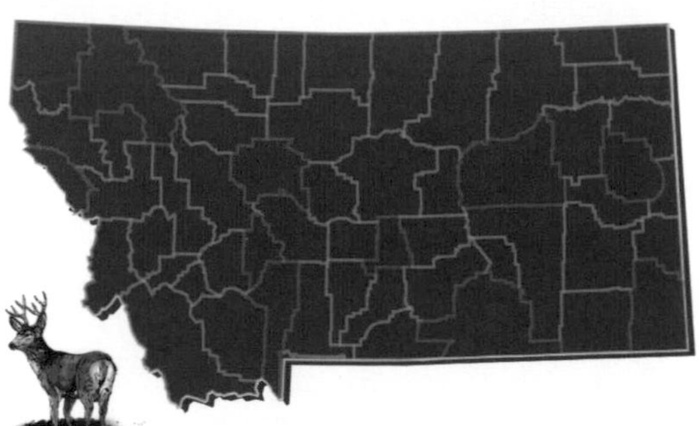
2008 Mule Deer Distribution

# Footnotes

[1] Burroughs, R. D. 1961. The natural history of the Lewis and Clark Expedition. Michigan State University Press, East Lansing. 128-132. Excerpt from Captain Lewis May 10, 1805.

[2] Egan, J. 1970. Mule deer. Chapter 6 in Game Management in Montana. T. W. Mussehl and F. W. Howell editors. Montana Fish, Wildlife and Parks Dept. Helena. 53-67.

[3] Smith, V. G. 1997. The champion buffalo hunter. Edited by J. Prodgers. Two Dot Press, Helena, MT. 256 pp.

[4] Kraft, E. 2006. Untold tales of bison range trails. Stoneydale Press, Stevensville, MT. 30-31.

[5] McLucas, Jim. 1999. Videotaped interview with Harold Picton and Jim Williams.

[6] Gaab, J. 1999 and 2003. Videotaped interview with Harold Picton or Terry Lonner and Tom Manning.

[7] Malone, M. P. and R. B. Roeder. 1976. Montana: A history of two centuries. University of Washington Press, Seattle. 352 pp.

[8] Merrill-Maker, A. 2006. Montana Almanac, 2nd. Edition. Insider's Guide, Guilford, CT. 375 pp.

[9] Couey, F. M., D. L. Brown, L. E. Brown and K. E. Riersgard. 1950. Big game transplanting evaluation report eastern Montana. Montana Fish and Game Dept., Helena. 93 pp.

[10] Ibid. Egan, J. 1970.

*Mule Deer Bucks. c. 1948. (Courtesy Jim McLucas Photo Collection)*

*Montana Fish & Game truck used for transplanting deer and other big game animals. c. 1950s.* *(Photo courtesy Harold Picton)*

# Chapter 8

# White-tailed Deer

White-tailed deer *(Odocoileus virginianus)* were observed by Lewis and Clark as they traversed Montana. They often referred to them as "common deer" indicating that they were the same species as those present in the eastern United States. David Thompson also noted them in northwestern Montana during his travels and fur trading operations in the early 1800s.

In eastern Montana, whitetails occupy stream bottom habitats with shrubs and deciduous forests. In western Montana both conifer and deciduous forest areas and valleys provide white-tailed deer habitat. Whitetails in Montana are slightly smaller than mule deer but have a higher reproductive potential. Their large white tails, raised as an alarm signal, are very distinctive. Whitetails are unusually tolerant of snow for an animal of their size, although increasing snow-pack influences migration and habitat selection in conifer forests in western Montana. A complex network of trails in areas of dense cover allows them to avoid predators and often move unseen in suburban areas. The relatively level bottomland habitat brings them into close contact with agriculture and humans. Whitetails often flourish in such environments.

In some areas, whitetails have summer and winter ranges separated by several miles. Although migrations of up to 30 miles have been recorded in northwestern Montana, they generally are not as migratory as mule deer. Unlike mule deer, whitetails are subjected to large scale die-offs due to EHD or epizootic hemorrhagic disease, a disease closely related to bluetongue

*Jim McLucas told of going out deer trapping after midnight to avoid some of the conflicts. It was a deep snow winter in the Thompson River country. Six deer were caught individually by forcing them into deep snow and then catching them by hand.*[3]

in cattle.[1] The disease is transmitted by a biting midge, an insect that inhabits moist meadows along streams. Although over half of a whitetail population may die during an outbreak, it has not prevented their success. Mule deer and cattle acquire an active immunity to the disease.

Historically, the first effort to move whitetails to begin a new population occurred in 1910 when four deer were moved from the city of Missoula to the newly established National Bison Range. By November of that year, these and two other whitetails that had been residents of the bison range vanished by either poaching or natural causes. In 1921, another group of 17 whitetails were brought to the National Bison Range from a ranch near Deer Lodge. Although these were relatively tame and not conditioned to predators such as coyotes, some managed to survive and establish a population.[2]

Whitetails were vulnerable to heavy subsistence hunting pressure in the early years of settlement of Montana. Heavy livestock grazing and agricultural practices degraded their habitat. By 1940 white-tailed deer were absent from most areas in eastern Montana that they had once inhabited although they remained abundant in forests of northwestern Montana. Operations to transplant whitetails began in 1945 when Lincoln County in northwest Montana and the Blackfoot River Valley in Missoula County served as source areas.

There were no biological obstacles to trapping and handling these deer, but other problems ensued. Source areas had abundant whitetails and managers perceived their range to be overused. Landowners were contacted, the situation explained, and permission obtained prior to the start of an operation. By the time operations actually started, some citizens became aroused against removal of "their deer" and delayed trapping, which forced abandonment of a few trap sites.

Jim McLucas told a story of deer trapping after midnight to avoid some conflicts. It was a deep snow winter in the Thompson River country and 6 deer were caught individually by forcing them into deep snow and catching them by hand.[3]

Eventually the trapping was completed. Corral traps of portable wooden panels were usually constructed and whitetails baited in with alfalfa hay. Most deer were transported from Lincoln county over 500 miles to release in the Stillwater, Rosebud and Boulder river drainages in Stillwater and Sweetgrass counties of south-central Montana. Whitetails trapped in Missoula County had a shorter journey to the Boulder River Valley near Big Timber. Other deer from Lincoln and Missoula Counties were released along

*White-tailed Deer Portable Trap* (Courtesy Jim McLucas Photo Collection)

the Missouri River in Broadwater County and Musselshell River in Wheatland County. The Boulder and Jefferson River areas in Jefferson County received transplants from Lewis and Clark, Powell and Sanders Counties. The Crazy Mountains received deer from Lincoln County. Powell County furnished a few to the Yellowstone River Valley in Treasure County.

Fifteen of 18 transplants went to areas where no white-tailed deer had been seen for years. Three other transplants went to areas were numbers of whitetails seemed critically low.[4] Transplants supplemented expanding remnant populations to occupy streamside habitats across the entire state.[5] Reintroductions were successful in accelerating the recolonization process that was naturally occurring. During the 1945 to 1952 operational period, 447 whitetails were given new homes. Natural colonization from supplemented populations reclaimed their original range in a dramatic fashion.

***For the first time on record the number of whitetails taken by hunters in 1996 exceeded those of mule deer. This punctuated the expansion of this species.***

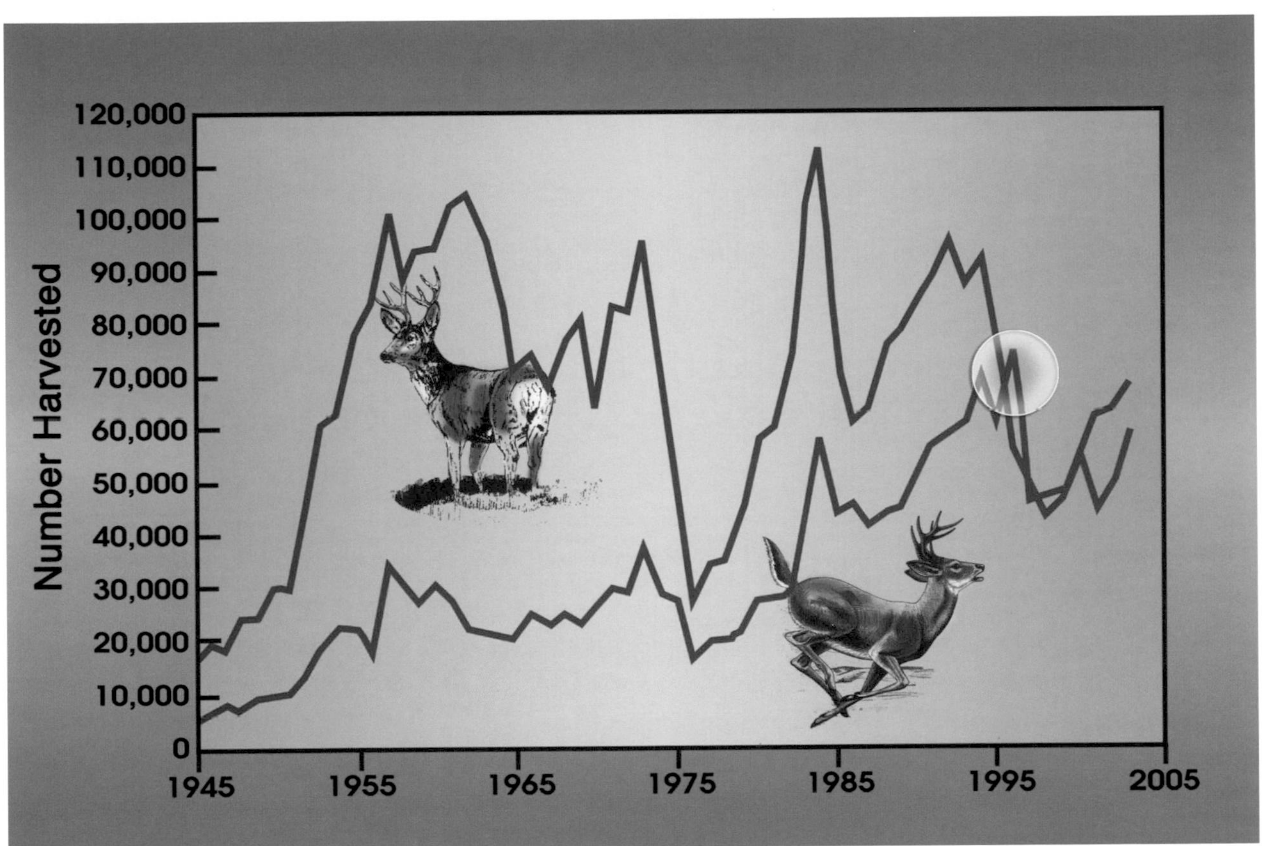


***For the first time on record in Montana more white-tailed deer were harvested than mule deer in the mid 1990s.***
*(Data from Research and Technical Services, Harvest Surveys Section, Montana Fish, Wildlife and Parks, Graph illustration by Media Works, Bozeman, MT)*

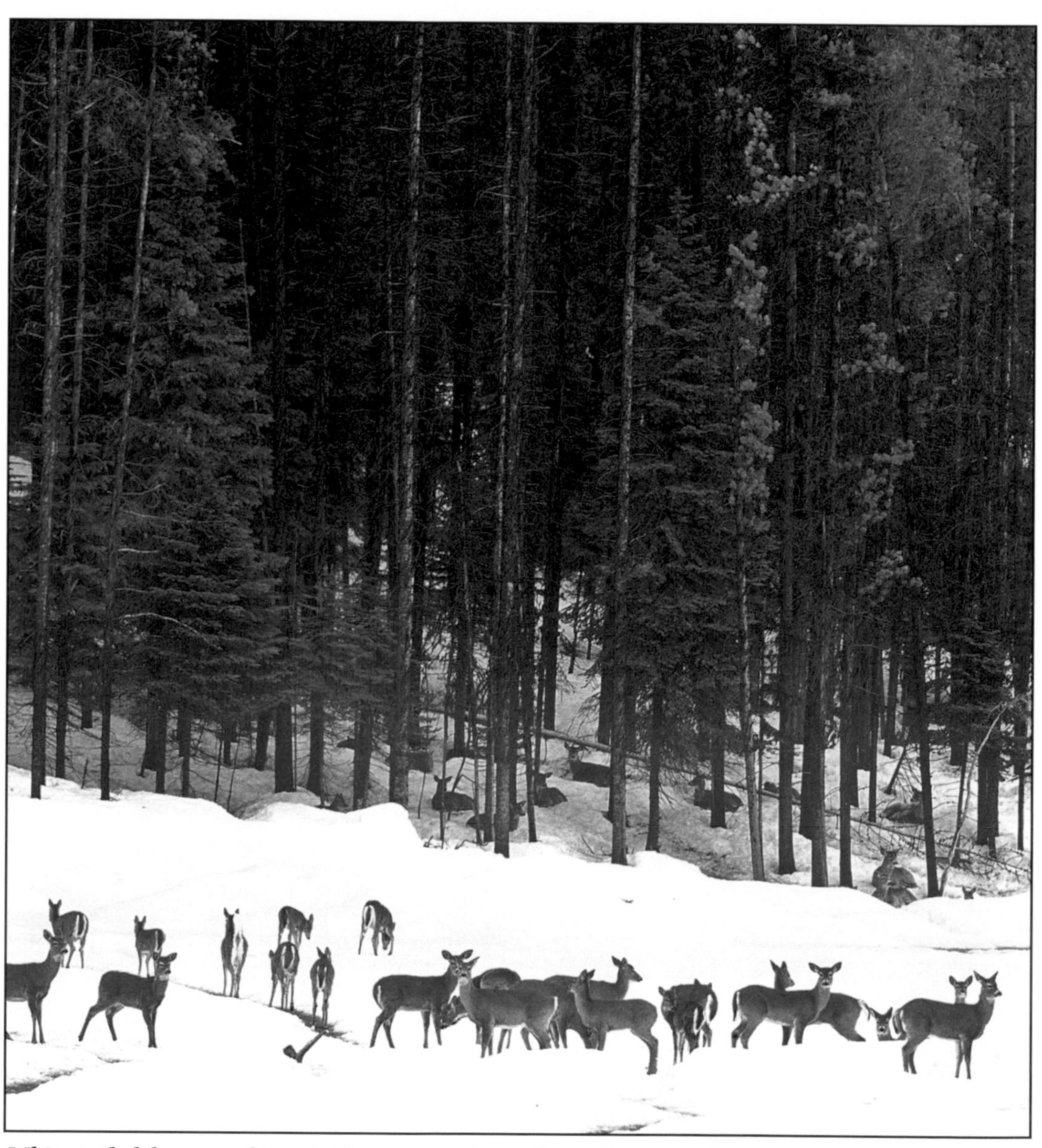

*White-tailed deer were historically common in northwest Montana, but are now common throughout the state, especially in association with agriculture and suburban areas.*
*(Photo courtesy DonaldMJones.com)*

An annotated listing of Montana white-tailed deer transplants; **1910 - 1951**.

| Year(s) | Source | Number | Release Site |
|---|---|---|---|
| 1910 | City of Missoula, Missoula Co. | 4 | National Bison Range, Lake Co.[1] |
| 1921 | Conley Ranch, Powell Co. | 17 | National Bison Range, Lake Co.[2] |
| 1944-1945 | Grave Cr., Lincoln Co. | 6 | Stillwater River, Stillwater Co. |
| | Bowser Lake, Flathead Co. | 11 | East Rosebud River, Carbon Co. |
| | Salmon Lake, Missoula Co. | 14 | Stillwater River, Stillwater Co. |
| | Graves Cr., Lincoln Co. | 3 | Stillwater River, Stillwater Co. |
| 1945-1946 | Bowser Lake, Flathead Co. | 52 | East Rosebud River, Carbon Co.[3] |
| | Bowser Lake, Flathead Co. | 21 | Stillwater River, Stillwater Co.[4] |
| | Murphy Lake, Lincoln Co. | 20 | Winnecook, Wheatland Co. |
| 1946-1947 | Fortine, Lincoln Co. | 20 | West Rosebud – Mystic Lake, Stillwater Co.[3] |
| | Fortine, Lincoln Co. | 21 | Crazy Mtns., Park & Sweetgrass Co.[3] |
| | Fortine, Lincoln Co. | 40 | Winnecook, Wheatland Co.[5] |
| 1947-1948 | Ant Flat, Flathead Co. | 20 | Boulder River, Sweetgrass Co. |
| | Murphy Lake, Lincoln Co. | 36 | Townsend, Broadwater Co. |
| | Lincoln, Lewis and Clark Co. | 38 | Townsend, Broadwater Co.[6] |
| 1948-1949 | Poorman Cr., Lewis and Clark Co. | 22 | Boulder River, Jefferson Co. |
| | Blackfoot River, Powell Co. | 20 | Boulder River, Jefferson Co.[7] |
| 1949-1950 | Thompson River, Sanders Co. | 51 | Jefferson River (Whitehall), Jefferson Co.[5] |
| 1950-1951 | Blackfoot River, Powell Co. | 25 | Jefferson–Ruby Rivers, Madison Co. |
| | Blackfoot River, Powell Co. (Copenhaver) | 6 | Yellowstone River (Myers), Treasure Co. |
| Summary | **subtotal** | **426** | **by Montana Fish and Game Dept.** |
| | **subtotal** | **21** | **by U. S. Biological Survey** |
| | **Total** | **447** | |

The annotation comments are from field survey reports in: Couey, F.M., D.L. Brown, L.E. Brown and K.E. Riersgard. 1950. Big game transplanting evaluation report eastern Montana. Montana Fish and Game Dept. Helena. 93pp. Augmentation transplants supplement an existing population of deer. 21 White-tailed deer were released on the National Bison Range by their personnel in its first two decades of operation.

[1] Planted in June but all white-tailed deer on the range were dead by the end of November.
[2] Kraft, E. 2006. Untold tales of bison range trails. Stoneydale Press, Stevensville, MT. 28-29. The 1921 transplant included 17 white-tailed deer and 17 mule deer.
[3] No white-tailed deer were present in area before transplant, mule deer were abundant before transplant.
[4] No white-tailed deer were present in area before transplant.
[5] Historic range but few or no white-tailed deer were known to be present before transplants.
[6] Very few white-tailed deer in area before transplant, augmentation transplant.
[7] Historical range but no white-tailed deer have been seen for several years, a few mule deer are present and an occasional moose.

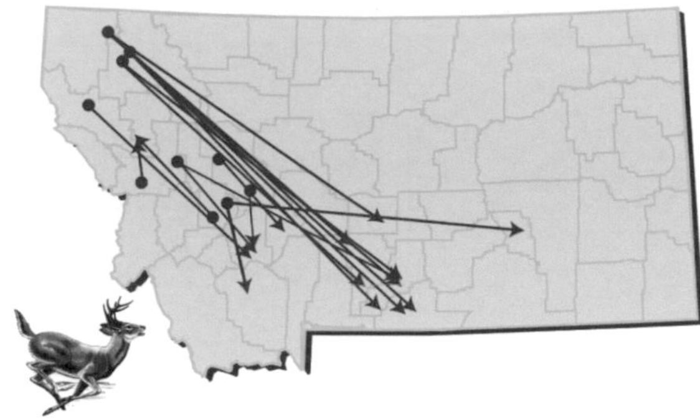

1910 - 1951 White-tailed Deer Transplants

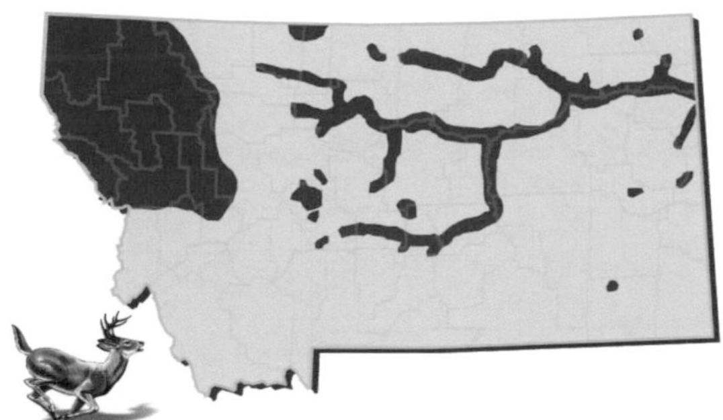

1942 White-tailed Deer Distribution

1970 White-tailed Deer Distribution

2008 White-tailed Deer Distribution

# Footnotes

[1] Feldner, T. J. and M. H. Smith. 1981. Epizootic hemorrhagic disease in Montana: Isolation and serologic survey. American Journal of Veterinary Research 42:1-:198-202.

[2] Kraft, E. 2006. Untold tales of bison range trails. Stoneydale Press, Stevensville, MT. 28-29. The 1921 transplant included 17 white-tailed deer and 17 mule deer.

[3] McLucas, Jim. 1999. Videotaped interview with H. Picton and Jim Williams.

[4] Couey, F. M., D. L. Brown, L. E. Brown and K. E. Riersgard. 1950. Big game transplanting evaluation report eastern Montana. Montana Fish and Game Dept., Helena. 93 pp.

[5] Allen, E. O. 1970. White-tailed deer. Chapter 7 in Game Management In Montana. Editors: T. W. Mussehl and F. W. Howell. Montana Fish and Game Dept., Helena. 69-79.

*A successful white-tailed deer hunt in Flathead County, Montana. c. early 1900s.*
*(Courtesy Robert Cooney Photo Collection)*

*These pronghorns were outside the trap when the gates closed, but were captured by nimble crewmen. c. 1950.*
*(Courtesy Robert Cooney Photo Collection)*

Chapter 9

# Pronghorn Antelope

Pronghorn antelope *(Antilocapra americana)* are native to North America and have no close relatives.

Several "sister" species existed during the ice age but vanished during great extinctions at the end of the last ice age. African antelope belong to the cattle family (Bovidae) whereas the pronghorn is a sole species in its own family, (Antilocapridae).

Pronghorns have an extraordinary number of adaptations for running. Their ability to process oxygen is five times greater than a domestic goat and several times that of a world class human athlete.[1] Speed of a pronghorn running over native prairie has been measured at 53 miles per hour.[2] This compares to 49 miles per hour attained by thoroughbred race horses on the smooth prepared track of the Kentucky Derby and 22 miles per hour for the best human sprinters. Specializations in their muscle cells, brain cooling mechanisms needed for long distance exertion, as well as adaptations such as a heart and lungs with two to three times the capacity of other mammals of equal size give pronghorn extraordinary endurance.[3] Males, or "bucks", weigh about 120 lbs. and does 110 lbs.

They differ from other horned animals by shedding their black horn sheaths each year in late fall. Both sexes have horns but bucks are larger. Bucks also can be distinguished by a black patch on their cheeks. Small hooves and other features of their

***Pronghorn antelope are native to North America and have no close relatives.***

*Pronghorns are found no where else in the world and are the second fastest land mammal on earth with speeds of over 50 mph. Only the African Cheetah is faster. For distances over a quarter of a mile, pronghorns would win over every other animal on earth.*

"sports car" design severely reduce their ability to tolerate snow and thus limit their distribution. Does give birth from 1 to 3 fawns in June. Pronghorns along with bison were the major large herbivores of short grass prairie and sagebrush grassland ecosystems prior to settlement. More abundant than bison, pronghorns were a major human food resource. Crow and Blackfeet tribes operated "corral" traps for pronghorns near Gardiner and also near Emigrant in the Yellowstone Valley as late as the early 19th century. Colonel Theodore Roosevelt wrote,

> "On my ranch it has always been the animal which yielded most of the fresh meat in the spring and summer."

This was common practice and summed up by a comment of E. W. Nelson that in 1884,

> "We killed antelope, deer or elk for ranch use throughout the year without a thought that the supply was not perpetual."[4]

Although pronghorn were originally more abundant on the Great Plains than bison, their numbers were dramatically reduced by the beginning of the 20th century. Montana's share of the population had been reduced to about 3,000.[5] Many people feared they would go the way of the bison. The National Bison Range was a possible haven for a new pronghorn herd and received one of the earliest transplants. [Elk were trapped at Gardiner and occasionally pronghorns would enter the trap because rangeland north of Yellowstone NP in Gardiner basin was severely depleted at this time.] In 1911, the Boone and Crockett Club and U.S. Biological Survey took advantage of this and transported 4 pronghorn bucks and 8 does by railroad and wagon to the National Bison Range. This small herd prospered and grew to 64, but a severe winter in 1921-1922 enabled predators to kill the entire herd.[5] Once again the National Bison Range was without pronghorn.

The American Bison Society made a second effort to restore pronghorns to the Bison Range, but knowledge needed to capture and handle them was minimal at the time. The society turned to the U.S. Biological Survey and a refuge area in Nevada. Young pronghorn fawns were raised in pens. After they had grown to about 3 months old, customized shipping crates were made for them. In 1924, eight of these fawns were shipped to the National Bison Range by railroad and truck to establish a new herd with help of the Wildlife Protection Society. This second attempt at establishing a population also failed when the last of the pronghorns died in fall of 1926.[6] Success finally came in 1951 with 15 animals from the Yellowstone NP herd followed by 10 pronghorns from Townsend Flats, between Townsend and Helena, in 1952.

**Bottle-raising pronghorn antelope fawns to prepare for transplanting.**
*(Photograph taken August, 1924 on the Wood Ranch, near Diessner, Nevada.[5])*

In the 1920s, additional transplanting was not conducted until after the P-R Act provided money for wildlife restoration, World War II was over, and new techniques were developed. Faye Couey had brought a pronghorn trap for trial from Wyoming. The trap had several deficiencies that prevented it from being successful. Descriptions indicated that "antelope went under it, over it and through it." Notes from the time said that this trapping effort caused "unusual disturbance" to the pronghorn.

Thoughts, ideas and collective experiences were pooled. Then, Rex Smart, an auto mechanic and general all around mechanically skilled hand of the Montana Fish and Game Department designed and built a sectional trap that could be transported on a truck and easily erected. Covered with fish netting to prevent injury to pronghorns, it was highly successful and used throughout the pronghorn trapping era. The Montana trap and trapping crew visited many other states to trap and help restore their pronghorn herds.

Joe Gaab—

"They had attempted to trap antelope in solid corrals. But that didn't work because antelope would hit the fence and dislocate their necks. So they had to figure out something different and Rex Smart, with the help of the other people around him, built a portable corral that was flexible out of netting. And so the first time that was tried, which was the first time that I had been with them over on Winston Flats, it worked."[7]

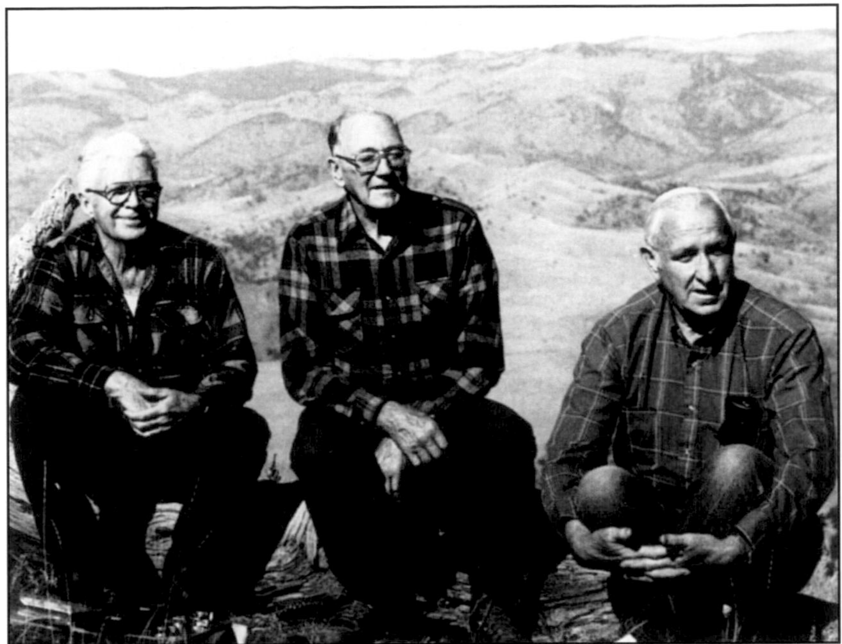

*Bob Cooney, Rex Smart and Jim McLucas. c. 1970.*
*(Courtesy Jim McLucas Photo Collection)*

The portable trap also served as a circular corral or holding pen. Long wings of fencing up to a half mile in length extended out to form a funnel leading to the gate of the trap. A small fixed wing airplane was used to drive pronghorns into the trap. This involved low level and very tricky flying. The first trapping effort using the new trap was on the Winston Flats between

*Scale model of a portable pronghorn antelope trap designed by master mechanic Rex Smart. c. 1950. (Courtesy Jim McLucas Photo Collection)*

*Cliff McBratney, a pilot from Augusta, Montana, hazing pronghorn antelope into a trap on the Townsend Flats near Helena. c. 1947-1953.* *(Courtesy Jim McLucas Photo Collection)*

Helena and Townsend in February of 1946. Cliff McBratney was the pilot chosen for the first efforts using the new trap, flying his Taylorcraft airplane. As Bob Cooney recounts,

> "Come to find out he had been a pilot in the World War .... He (McBratney) said, 'say fellows I'll come down and fly for you and I'll chase those antelope into your trap.' So out here between Helena and Townsend was the first attempt. He said, 'Would you like to take a ride with me?' I said 'Sure.' We came whizzing down here and there were the antelope tearing around. He said, 'now we are going to get pretty close to the ground out here and you've got to get behind those animals. I'm going to do what I call lazy eights behind them and then we'll work them up towards the trap and then I'll get down real low' and he said 'don't be surprised if I hit the ground with the tail wheel. ...' It made quite a racket but we got the antelope in. He was a dandy. Had some big old gloves, mittens on. Those are fun memories."[8]

*"...He (McBratney) said...'I'm going to do what I call lazy eights behind them and we'll work them up towards the trap and then I'll get down real low' and he said 'don't be surprised if I hit the ground with the tail wheel..."* [8]

— Bob Cooney

*Jim McLucas working pronghorn antelope in the trap. c. 1950.* *(Courtesy Jim McLucas Photo Collection)*

*Trapping crew members handling pronghorn antelope in a trap and preparing to put them into a truck for transplanting. c. 1950.* *(Courtesy Jim McLucas Photo Collection)*

Some of the first pronghorns trapped by the Montana Fish and Game Department were taken across the Missouri River northeast of Townsend to start a new population on the slopes of the Big Belt Mountains. Another group was trucked down to the Horseshoe Hills northwest of Bozeman.

Flying was challenging and dangerous. McBratney

struck a fence post with a wing and tore some fabric covering on the airplane. Strangely, mud also pierced the fabric covering several times. Hooves of running pronghorn threw clods of gumbo-mud high into the air where it was struck by the plane, tearing holes in it. Other methods were tried including herding pronghorn into traps with horses and vehicles, but none were successful. Don Brown of the Montana Fish and Game Department and Jim Stradley of the Gallatin Flying Service also flew in pronghorn trapping.

The airplane was such a useful tool for trapping and censusing that Don Brown thought the state should have one, but purchasing one required approval of the state Board of Examiners. Its chairman, Secretary of State Sam Mitchell, finally approved the purchase with the admonition,

> "Well young man, I hope you don't kill yourself."

Don then purchased a Piper Supercub.

About a third of pronghorn transplants bolstered existing populations with the remainder actually establishing new populations.

> "The antelope were fairly scarce and we were able to transplant antelope into various new ranges. Particularly down in that eastern end of Montana. At that time there were practically no antelope down there, but we got them there."[9]
>
> —Bob Cooney

Interviews attested to enthusiastic support for the transplant program among sportsmen. Some ranchers also enthusiastically supported transplants although others were neutral. A few reported damage to grain crops,

*Don Brown with the first state-owned airplane in Montana - 1947.*
*(Courtesy Don Brown Photo Collection)*

*Jim Stradley of the Gallatin Flying Service. c. 1940s. (Courtesy Jim Stradley Family)*

especially on unfenced alfalfa haystacks during the extremely severe winter of 1948-1949.[10] However, ranchers actively participated in the transplant program by furnishing access to herds on their land. Some even furnished trucks and manpower to transport pronghorns. John Cameron, who lived on Hound Creek in Cascade County, was one of these ranchers. He furnished trucks and men to make a round trip of nearly 500 miles to bring 67 pronghorn trapped in Wheatland County to establish a herd south of Great Falls on the northern foothills of the Big Belt Mountains. John shared his wildlife enthusiasm with his family. His son Dave remembers,

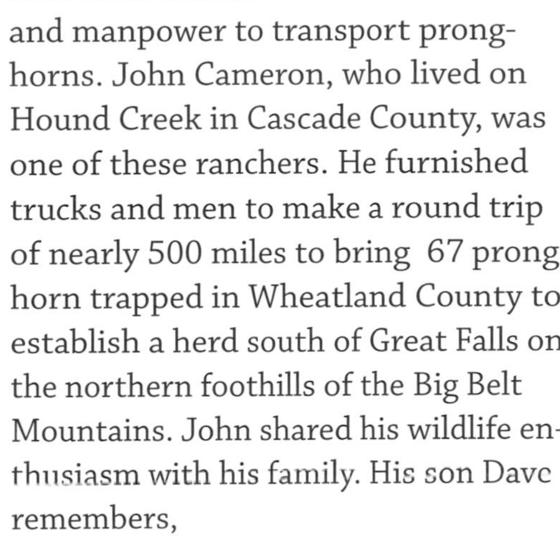

> "My father peeked through the slats on the truck and saw this pile of hair nearly six inches deep and

***"The antelope were fairly scarce and we were able to transplant antelope into various new ranges. Particularly down in that eastern end of Montana. At that time there were practically no antelope down there, but we got them down there."[11]***

**—Bob Cooney**

*Herding pronghorns into a trap using burlap strips. c. 1950.*
*(Courtesy Jim McLucas Photo Collection)*

Another early pronghorn transplant by the Department was into an area in the Bitterroot Valley in 1946. The year after the transplant the landowner plowed up the rangeland. While the third transplant to the National Bison Range succeeded, transplants to the Hot Springs area of the Mission Valley ultimately failed.

The major goal of reestablishing extirpated historic pronghorn herds and supplementing small herds had been achieved in Montana by 1952. After that another 365 were trapped and sent to North Dakota to reestablish herds there. The herd migrating north of Gardiner from Yellowstone NP, furnished 57 of these. An additional 292 from this herd were trapped and transported to Nevada; Kansas received 14; and Utah 131. South Dakota also received 85 pronghorn trapped in 1955 in Carter County which borders their state. As these states built their herds, Jim McLucas was asked to bring his equipment and skills to assist them with their transplanting programs.

he thought, my goodness, we're going to release these animals to a certain death. They jumped out of the truck, bare-sided and all, into the storm, ran up the hillside and started grazing. And it was the best food they had seen for a long time and not one died as far as we could tell over the winter.... So it was through the efforts of my dad, with the cooperation and encouragement of the Fish and Game Department that we had accomplished this successful restoration."[11]

*The major goal of re-establishing extirpated historic pronghorn herds and supplementing small herds had been achieved in Montana by 1952.*

Even though it was winter, they survived to build a flourishing herd despite all the hair lost during the operation.

*Pronghorns in a trap prior to transplanting. c. 1950.*
*(Courtesy Jim McLucas Photo Collection)*

*Loading Montana pronghorn antelope in Seattle, Washington for shipment to Hawaii - 1959.* *(Courtesy Jim McLucas Photo Collection)*

In 1959 some pronghorns went to an unusual destination. Fifty-six pronghorns from the Malta area in northern Montana were sent to Hawaii. Forty-four survived the ocean voyage but 2 more died after arrival. Four were placed in the Honolulu Zoo and 38 released on the island of Lanai. They found the Pacific Ocean water unpalatable and volunteers herded them back to the more suitable upland habitats with fresh water. Some apparently died as a result of encounters with tropical vegetation. The Hawaiian herd dropped in numbers and disappeared probably by the mid 1980s.[12]

***In 1959 some pronghorns went to a more unusual destination. Fifty-five pronghorns from the Malta area in northern Montana were sent to Hawaii.***

In the 1950s, pronghorn, mountain goats and bighorn sheep were trapped for the National Zoological Park in Washington D.C. and transported from Helena to Washington in a Boeing Stratocruiser, the biggest airliner of its day. When President de Gaulle of France visited the United States, he particularly liked pronghorns. President Eisenhower promptly gave him some from the National Zoo. They were flown to Paris for the Paris Zoo. Jim McLucas then had to replace them at the National Zoo. Zoos in Portland, San Diego and Chicago also received some of Montana's pronghorns.[13]

Montana continued to make a few pronghorn transplants within the state and transplanted 359 between 1952 and 1978. As wildlife research programs grew, over a 1,000 pronghorns were trapped, marked and released for study in a number of research projects.

By the end of the transplanting program in 1978, almost 4,000 pronghorns had been transplanted in Montana to

***By the end of the transplanting program in 1978, almost 4,000 pronghorns had been transplanted in Montana to reestablish or augment herds with very low numbers.***

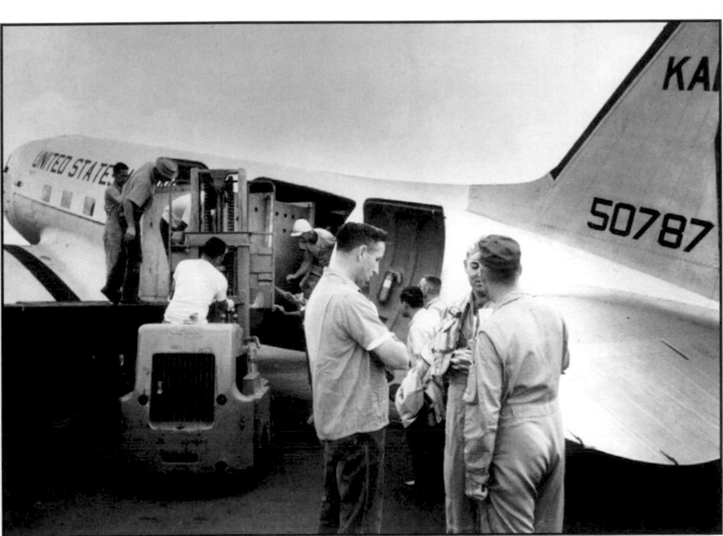


*Pronghorn antelope from Montana being loaded into a Marine Corps plane at Hickman Field, Honolulu, Hawaii for release on the island of Lanai - 1959.* *(Courtesy Jim McLucas Photo Collection)*

reestablish or augment herds with very low numbers. This was 1,000 more pronghorns than existed in the state during the beginning of the 20th century. Another 1,190 were transplanted to other mentioned states to establish herds. At the beginning of the 21th century the pronghorn population in Montana had increased to over 220,000, over 70 times the number present early in the 20th century. This "sportscar of the wild" with all of its remarkable adaptations was once again safe on this portion of its native range.

***In the 1950s pronghorn, mountain goats and bighorn sheep were trapped for the National Zoological Park in Washington D.C. They were transported from Helena to Washington in a Boeing Stratocruiser, the biggest airliner of its day.***

***The pronghorn antelope population in Montana is now doing very well compared to a hundred years ago when there were only 3,000 in the early 1900s to over 220,000 in the year 2008.***
*(Photo courtesy Brent N. Lonner)*

## An annotated listing of Montana pronghorn antelope transplants; 1911-1978.

| Year(s) | Source | Number | Release Area |
|---|---|---|---|
| 1911 | Montana-Yellowstone Nat'l Park | 9(3M,6F) | Wichita National Game Preserve, Oklahoma |
| | Montana-Yellowstone Nat'l Park | 12(4M,8F) | National Bison Range, Lake Co.[1] |
| 1924 | Nevada | 8 | National Bison Range, Lake Co.[2] |
| 1946 | Winston, Broadwater Co. | 22 | East of Canyon Ferry, Broadwater Co.[3] |
| | White Sulphur Springs, Meagher Co. | 69 | Horseshoe Hills, Gallatin Co.[3] |
| | Radersburg, Broadwater Co. | 18 | Stevensville, Ravalli Co.[4] |
| | Radersberg, Broadwater Co. | 31 | Waterloo, Madison Co. |
| 1947 | Musselshell Co. | 68 | Hardin, Big Horn Co. |
| | Musselshell Co. | 19 | Sidney, Richland Co.[5] |
| | Musselshell Co. | 20 | Haxby-Jordan, Garfield Co.[6] |
| | Montana-Yellowstone Nat'l Park | 135 or 172 | Shields River, Park Co.[7] |
| | Montana-Yellowstone Nat'l Park | 48 | Mission Cr., Park Co.[8] |
| | Winston, Broadwater Co. | 49 | Deer Lodge, Powell Co.[3] |
| | Wheatland Co. | 67 | Hound Cr., Cascade Co.[6] |
| | Wheatland Co. | 59 | Big Timber, Sweet Grass Co. |
| | Cascade Co. | 78 | Rochester Basin, Silver Bow Co.[3] |
| | Cascade Co. | 28 | Hound Cr., Cascade Co.[6] |
| | Cascade Co. | 27 | Flat Cr., Lewis and Clark Co. |
| | Cascade Co. | 7 | Ox Bow Ranch, Lewis and Clark Co. |
| | Musselshell Co. | 48 | Pine Ridge, Yellowstone Co.[6] |
| | Source unknown, but in Montana | 80 | Fry Pan Basin – Rattlesnake, Beaverhead Co.[3] |
| 1948 | Cascade Co. | 37 | Fry Pan Basin, Beaverhead Co. |
| | Cascade Co. | 48 | Rattlesnake, Beaverhead Co. |
| | Montana-Yellowstone Nat'l Park | 53 | Rattlesnake, Beaverhead Co. |
| | Shawmut, Wheatland Co. | 146 | Hound Cr., Cascade Co.[6] |
| | Shawmut, Wheatland Co. | 51 | Geyser, Judith Basin Co.[9] |
| | Shawmut, Wheatland Co. | 50 | Plum Cr., Fergus Co.[3] |
| | Musselshell Co. | 41 | Fry Pan Basin, Beaverhead Co. |
| | Musselshell Co. | 49 | Burnetts Ranch, Fergus Co. |
| | Martinsdale, Meagher Co. | 16 | Meagher Ranch, Meagher Co. |
| | Martinsdale, Meagher Co. | 49 | Fry Pan Basin, Beaverhead Co. |
| | Wheatland Co. | 94 | Horse Ranch, Fergus Co. |
| | Carter Co. | 104 | Toluca, Big Horn Co. |
| | Carter Co. | 59 | Sidney, Richland Co. |
| | Carter Co. | 33 | Pilgrim Cr., Powder River Co. |
| | Roundup, Musselshell Co. | 34 | Warm Springs, Deer Lodge Co. |
| | Roundup, Musselshell Co. | 20 | Melstone, Musselshell Co. |
| | Shawmut, Wheatland Co. | 146 | Whitetail Cr., Jefferson Co. |
| | Wheatland Co. | 30 | Roy, Fergus Co.[3] |
| | Wheatland Co. | 25 | Boulder, Jefferson Co.[10] |
| | Wheatland Co. | 32 | Mendenhall Cr., Sweet Grass Co.[7] |
| | Wheatland Co. | 71 | Lewis & Clark Caverns Jefferson Co.[3] |
| | Wheatland Co. | 60 | Waterloo, Jefferson Co.[3] |
| | Wheatland Co. | 85 | Warm Springs, Deer Lodge Co.[11] |

## An annotated listing of Montana pronghorn antelope transplants; 1911-1978, cont.

| Year(s) | Source | Number | Release Area |
|---|---|---|---|
| 1949 | Abbott Ranch, Fergus Co. | 156 | War Horse Lake, Petroleum Co.[6] |
| | Abbott Ranch, Fergus Co. | 36 | Cooney Dam, Carbon Co. |
| | Abbott Ranch, Fergus Co. | 107 | Fromberg, Carbon Co.[3] |
| | Musselshell Co. | 219 | Birch Cr., Chouteau Co. |
| | Musselshell Co. | 74 | 8-mile Coulee, Chouteau Co. |
| | Musselshell Co. | 37 | Ingomar, Rosebud Co. |
| | Golden Valley Co. | 76 | Rosebud Co. |
| | Golden Valley Co. | 32 | Cheadle, Fergus Co. |
| | Golden Valley Co. | 160 | Rosebud Co. |
| | Source unknown | 82 | Fergus-Armells Cr., Fergus Co.[6] |
| 1950 | Stillwater Co. | 60 | Sarpy, Big Horn Co. |
| | Stillwater Co. | 29 | Countryman Cr., Carbon Co. |
| 1951 | Montana-Yellowstone Nat'l Park | 36 | Irving Flats, Lake Co. |
| | Montana-Yellowstone Nat'l Park | 18 | Spring Cr., Madison Co. |
| | Montana-Yellowstone Nat'l Park | 30 | Wigwam Cr. Madison Co. |
| | Montana-Yellowstone Nat'l Park | 30 | St. Joseph Cr., Madison Co. |
| | Montana-Yellowstone Nat'l Park | 30 | Hot Springs, Lake Co.[12] |
| | Montana-Yellowstone Nat'l Park | 15 | National Bison Range, Lake Co.[13] |
| | Roundup, Musselshell Co. | 36 | Medicine Lake, Sheridan Co. |
| | Roundup, Musselshell Co. | 27 | Tiger Butte, Cascade Co. |
| 1952 | Townsend, Broadwater Co. | 10 | National Bison Range, Lake Co. |
| | Townsend, Broadwater Co. | 34 | Gregson Hot Springs, Silver Bow Co. |
| | Townsend, Broadwater Co. | 27 | Indian Cr., Madison Co. |
| | Townsend, Broadwater Co. | 34 | Cedar Cr., Madison Co. |
| 1952-1981 | National Bison Range, Lake Co. | 235 | transplanted to other locations[14] |
| 1953 | Broadwater Co. | 134 | North Dakota |
| 1954 | Montana-Yellowstone Nat'l Park | 57 | North Dakota |
| | Montana-Yellowstone Nat'l Park | 132 | Nevada |
| | Montana-Yellowstone Nat'l Park | 14 | Kansas |
| | Square Butte, Judith Basin Co. | 20 | Sage Cr., Judith Basin Co. |
| 1955 | Carter Co. | 174 | North Dakota |
| | Carter Co. | 85 | South Dakota |
| 1957 | Montana-Yellowstone Nat'l Park | 160 | Nevada |
| 1957 | Montana-Yellowstone Nat'l Park | 4 | France |
| 1959 | Phillips Co. | 56 | Lanai, Hawaii[15] |
| 1950s | Source & Release No. Unknown | | Nat'l Zoological Park, Wash. D.C., Paris France[16] |
| 1965 | Phillips Co. | 65 | Charles M. Russell Game Range, Phillips Co. |
| | Blaine Co. | 60 | Charles M. Russell Game Range, Phillips Co. |
| | Blaine Co. | 50 | Charles M. Russell Game Range, Phillips Co. |

## An annotated listing of Montana pronghorn antelope transplants; 1911-1978, cont.

| Year(s) | Source | Number | Release Area |
|---|---|---|---|
| 1965 cont. | Yellowstone National Park | 131 | Utah |
| 1978 | Northern Valley Co. | 59 | Southern Valley Co. |
| Summary | **Sources of Antelope** | | |
| | **Outside Montana** | **8** | **for transplants into Montana** |
| | **Montana-Yellowstone Nat'l Park** | **407 - 441[7]** | **for transplants within Montana** |
| | **Montana-Yellowstone Nat'l Park** | **507** | **for transplants outside of Montana** |
| | **Montana** | **3,460** | **for transplants within Montana** |
| | **Montana** | **684** | **for transplants outside of Montana** |
| | **Total** | **5,066 - 5,103[7]** | |

Annotations are from: Couey, F.M., D.L. Brown, L.E. Brown and K.E. Riersgard. 1950. Big game transplanting evaluation report eastern Montana. Montana Fish and Game Dept. Helena. 93pp. Augmentation transplants supplement existing populations.

1 Plant to replace extinct population, all pronghorns were killed by predators during the 1921-22 winter.
2 Second plant to replace extinct population. This newly introduced population then went extinct in Oct. 1926. No antelope were on the Bison Range until the Montana Fish and Game Department provided another transplant in 1951.
3 No antelope in area at time of transplant.
4 No antelope in area at time of transplant but transplant failed when landowner plowed up rangeland.
5 Plant to replace population extinct since early 1900s.
6 Augmentation transplant.
7 Quantities in question reflect differences between MFWP and YNPS records.
8 Historic range but population extinct.
9 No antelope in area but the herd on the Sullivan Ranch is a few miles north.
10 No antelope in area at time of transplant but the transplant probably failed due to severe winter weather.
11 No antelope in area at time of transplant, poaching may prevent success.
12 No antelope in area but transplant failed.
13 Plant to restore extinct population.
14 Kraft, E. 2006. Untold tales of bison range trails. Stoneydale Press, Stevensville, MT. 32-33.
15 Cooney, R.F. 1980. Montana Outdoors. July/August. 19. Of the 44 that survived the trip 4 were placed in the Honolulu Zoo and the remainder released.
16 Replacement shipment to National Zoological Park, Washington D.C.
Antelope were also sent to zoos in Chicago, Honolulu, Portland, San Diego, and Texas.

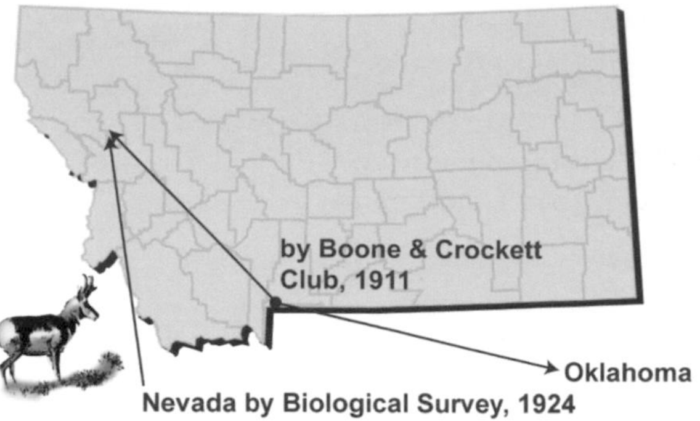


**1911 & 1924 Pronghorn Antelope Transplants**

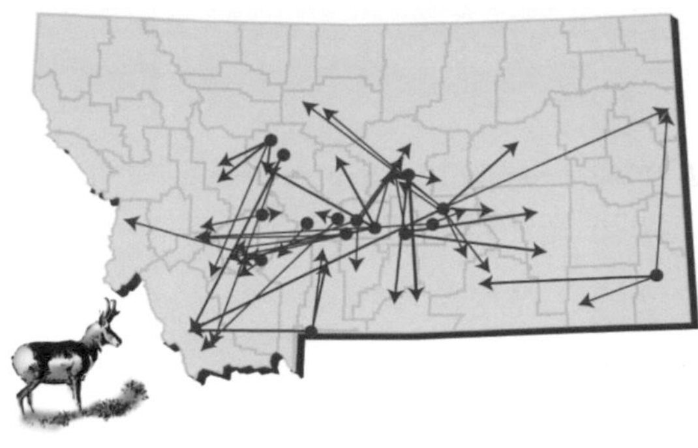

**1946 - 1949 Pronghorn Antelope Transplants**

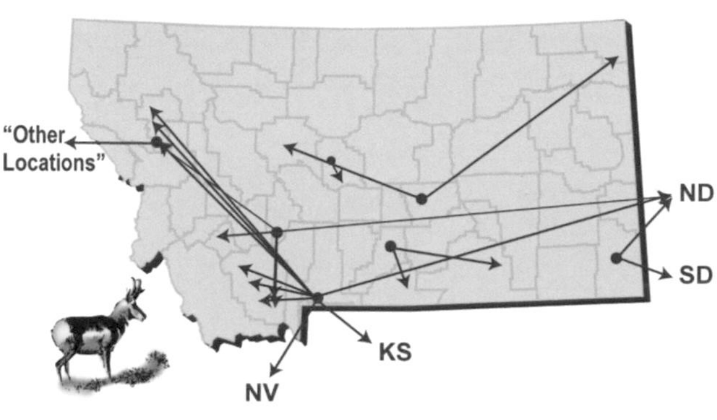


**1950 - 1955 Pronghorn Antelope Transplants**

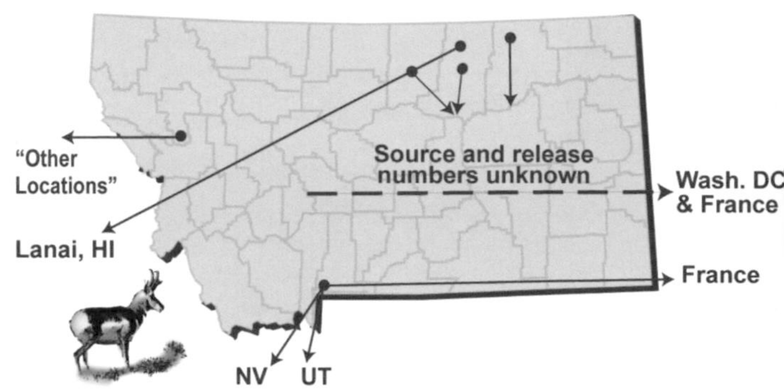


**1956 - 1978 Pronghorn Antelope Transplants**

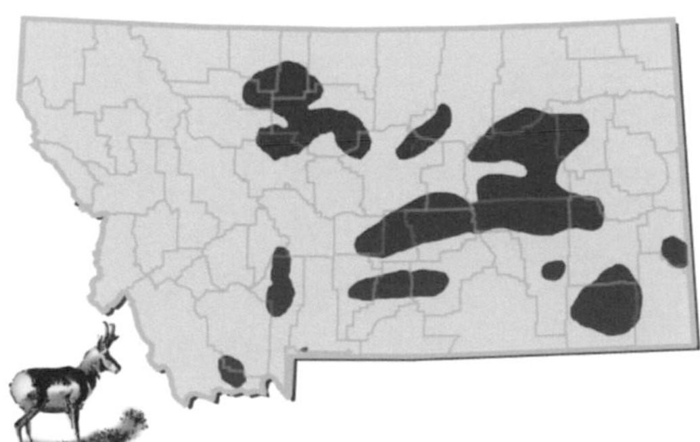

**1923 Pronghorn Antelope Distribution**

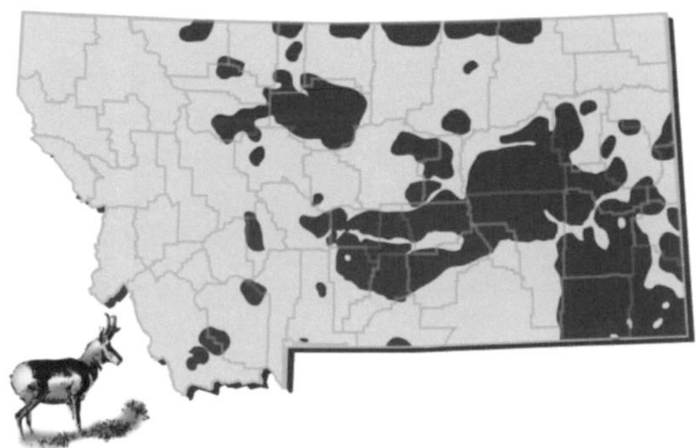

**1942 Pronghorn Antelope Distribution**

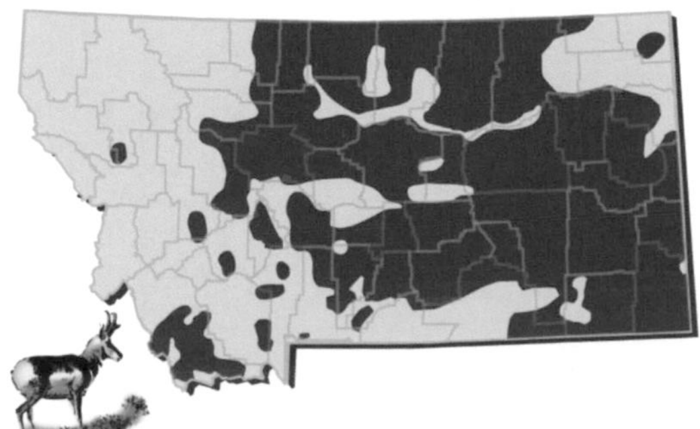

**1970 Pronghorn Antelope Distribution**

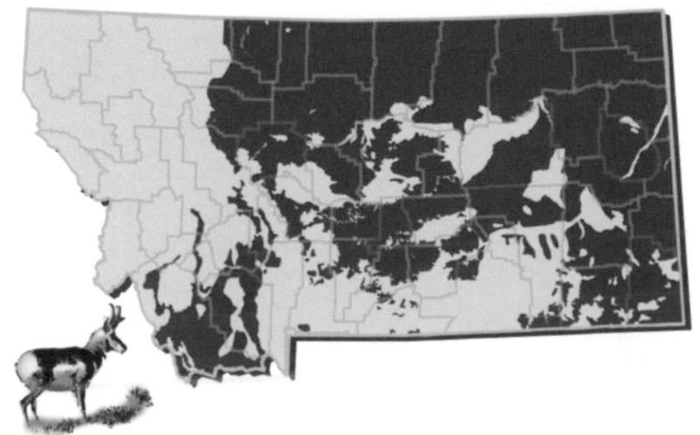

**2008 Pronghorn Antelope Distribution**

# Footnotes

[1] Byers, J. A. 2003. Pronghorn. Chapter 47 in Wild Mammals of North America, G. A. Feldhammer, B.C. Thompson and J. A. Chapman editors. 998-1008.

[2] Byers, J. A. 1997. American pronghorn. University of Chicago Press, Chicago. 300 pp.

[3] Ibid. Byers, J. A. 2003.

[4] Skinner, J. A. 1922. The pronghorn. Journal of Mammalogy 3(2):82-105.

[5] Nelson, E. W. 1925. Status of the pronghorned antelope, 1922-24. U.S. Department of Agriculture Bulletin 136, Government Printing Office, Washington. 69 pp.

[6] Kraft, E. 2006. Untold tales of bison range trails. Stoneydale Press, Stevensville, MT. 32-33.

[7] Gaab, J. 2003. Videotaped interview with Terry Lonner and Tom Manning.

[8] Cooney, R. F. 2003. Videotaped interview with Harold Picton, Terry Lonner and Tom Manning.

[9] Cooney, R. F. 2003. Videotaped interview with Harold Picton, Terry Lonner and Tom Manning.

[10] Couey, F, D. Brown, L. Brown and K. Riersgard. 1950. Big game transplanting evaluation report. Montana Fish and Game Dept. 1-59.

[11] Cameron, D. 2003. Videotaped interview with Terry Lonner and Tom Manning.

[12] http://www.earlham.edu/~biol/hawaii/mammals.htm#pronghorn

Cooney, R .F. 1980. Seventy years of relocating wildlife. Montana Outdoors 11(5):19.

[13] McLucas, J. 1999. Videotaped interview with Harold Picton and Jim Williams.

***Pronghorns being loaded into a 1 1/2 ton truck specially prepared with sand and straw to give footing and comfort to the animals in transit for transplanting. c. 1950.***
***(Courtesy Robert Cooney Photo Collection)***

*Elk on the Sun River Game Range. c. early 1950s.* *(Courtesy Robert Cooney Photo Collection)*

Chapter 10

# Rocky Mountain Elk

A scarcity of Rocky Mountain elk *(Cervus elaphus nelsoni)* in Montana generated enthusiasm for their restoration in 1910. The inherent mystique of elk motivated people to find ways to bring them back. Elk are one of the largest members of the Cervidae or deer family. They are the North American representative of red deer, a group of subspecies that extends across Eurasia to Great Britain.

Elk present in Montana are now the Rocky Mountain subspecies. When the Corps of Discovery entered what is now Montana in 1805 a different subspecies, the Manitoban elk *(Cervus elaphus manitobensis)*, likely occupied valleys of the Missouri and Yellowstone Rivers in eastern Montana. Rocky Mountain elk occupied the western mountains. Manitoban elk are usually darker in color with smaller antlers and a shorter tail than the Rocky Mountain subspecies. Although a Rocky Mountain bull elk weighing over 1,000 lbs. has been recorded, more typical weights are about 770 lbs. for adult bulls and about 450 lbs. for adult cows.

Cows give birth to a single calf in spring, but their well established practice of "baby-sitting" for other mothers gives rise to frequently reported sightings of twins, triplets and even more offspring. The fall rut brings the "bugling," sparring and occasional fighting of bulls. Bulls attempt to

*A cow elk with its newborn calf.* (Photo courtesy Martha A. Lonner)

*Yellowstone Vic Smith and his partner are said to have captured the elk by skiing them down on 10 foot skis in the winter and roping them. They sold 157 of the elk to stock the New Hampshire game preserve of Austin Corbin.*

maintain harems of cows, but females often move as they please in spite of the bulls.

Elk are "mixed feeders," that is they can digest less nutritious plants such as grass as well as richer foods like buds of shrubs. Size enables them to spend time searching out easily digestible broadleaf plants and nutritious new growth and buds to supplement their intake of low quality forage. Typically, elk that live in more open habitats east of the Continental Divide consume grass as the major portion of their winter diet. Elk that live in more forested areas west of the Divide are more likely to rely upon shrubs and conifers in winter.

A misconception is that elk were originally plains animals forced into the mountains by humans. In fact, elk were present historically in the mountains.[1] If this misconception was true, it would be very difficult to explain why elk ignored the superb mountain habitats when they had adaptations to prosper in them.

In the 1890s, over 300 elk were trapped from the Yellowstone NP area, mainly by private individuals, to provide zoos and private wildlife parks with animals.[2] Private trappers were charging $85 for an elk. None of these were transplanted to re-establish wild elk populations in Montana or elsewhere. Yellowstone Vic Smith and his partner are said to have captured elk by skiing them down on 10 foot skis in winter and roping them. They sold 157 elk to stock the New Hampshire game preserve of Austin Corbin. Later the elk startled the horses drawing the carriage of Mr. Corbin. He and his driver were killed in the run-a-way.[3]

The situation of elk in Montana in 1910 was dire. Less than 5,000 elk were estimated scattered over 25,000 square miles in forests and mountains of northwestern Montana. The U.S. Army, in charge of the park from

1886 to 1916 when the National Park Service was established, estimated the Northern Yellowstone Park herd was about 30,000 animals.[4] While these population estimates were based upon animals observed during ground surveys, they were not accurate by modern standards. Some Yellowstone elk did spend winter in Montana in the vicinity of Gardiner. The Gardiner area was much different in "them there days." The Yellowstone NP boundary was at the state line, several miles south of its present location. An industrial mining complex occupied the flats on the west side of Cinnabar Mountain, about five miles north of Gardiner. The town of Aldrich with several coal mines occupied the high valley on the west side of Cinnabar Mountain. The town of Electric, with smoke and fumes spewing from 225 coke ovens occupied the flats at the foot of the mountain until the mines closed in mid 1910. A large spa or "sanatorium" and hotel opened at Corwin Springs in 1909 but caught fire and was badly burned in 1916. Over 1,000 people and their livestock lived in the basin. All of this had considerable impact upon local range vegetation and led the pioneer range and wildlife biologist William Rush to comment,

> "From the time of the settlement of the Yellowstone Valley south of Yankee Jim Canyon in the 1870s up to 1926 all of the present winter elk range was used for stock-raising and the entire area was very heavily grazed by cattle and horses. It was an overgrazed range in 1914 and by 1926 hardly enough forage existed to give hopes of this range ever recovering without extensive artificial reseeding."[6]

Considerable numbers of elk migrated from the Park to spend winter amidst coke ovens, houses, hotels and railroad. Elk in the area appeared to increase after the coal mines closed.

*"From the time of the settlement of the Yellowstone Valley south of Yankee Jim Canyon in the 1870s up to 1926 all of the present winter elk range was used for stock-raising and the entire area was very heavily grazed by cattle and horses. It was an overgrazed range in 1914 and by 1926 hardly enough forage existed to give hopes of this range ever recovering without extensive artificial reseeding."*[6]

— William Rush

*Elk trapped for transplanting at Cinnabar in 1912 near Gardiner, MT.*
*(Courtesy Jim McLucas Photo Collection)*

In 1909 and 1910, members of a sportsmen club in Butte with assistance from Deputy Game Wardens, successfully carried out the first effort to restore wild elk to Montana's unoccupied habitats. They conducted local fund raising campaigns to cover costs of shipping elk on the Northern Pacific Railroad from Gardiner to the Butte area. The cost was $5 per elk or probably about 2 days worth of wages at the time. Because of poor range conditions, elk at Cinnabar

*The first transplant of elk in Montana was shipped by rail from the Cinnabar area near Gardiner to Fleecer Mountain southwest of Butte in 1910. (Courtesy Jim McLucas Photo Collection)*

responded readily to a bait trail of hay into a corral trap. Thirty-one captured elk were loaded into a rail car and 16 hours later were released near Fleecer Mountain southwest of Butte.[7] This reintroduction of elk rapidly caught the fancy of sportsman's clubs in other towns and a transplant program began in earnest in late winter of 1912. Henry Aware commented in spring of 1912,

> "The state Game and Fish Department received numerous applications for other shipments of live elk, but the department, owing to the lateness of the season and taking into consideration the condition of female elk at this season of the year, did not deem it advisable to make further shipments."[8]

In 1912 elk were shipped from the Cinnabar trap site to Hamilton and Deer Lodge, as well as Sanders and Mineral counties on the western boundary of the state in addition to Powell and Jefferson counties. Elk going to more distant counties were in transit for 23 or 24 hours. Railcars were partitioned into three sections; one for cows, one for bulls and the other for yearlings. Rod and gun clubs typically fed and held elk in cattle corrals or at local fair grounds, at their own expense for periods from a few days up to a month. This is what would be called "a soft release" today. Mortality for the first 200 shipped was about eight percent. More experience promoted rapid improvement in techniques, and some of the last car loads had no dead elk, even after spending 24 hours on the road.

As Henry Aware noted,

> "The entire expense of capturing and shipping these animals was borne by the citizens of the respective communities to which the elk were shipped."

*"The entire expense of capturing and shipping these animals was borne by the citizens of the respective communities to which the elk were shipped."*

—Henry Aware

Deputy Game Warden P. W. Nelson commented in the same report,

> "The cost of shipment was $5.00 (per head). The Rod and Gun Clubs have taken it upon themselves to look after the welfare for a few days-possibly a month-at their own expense before turning the elk out upon the range selected for them."[9]

*Elk in holding pen at Mammoth, Yellowstone National Park. c. 1915.*
*(Courtesy Jim McLucas Photo Collection)*

*"...The cost of shipment was $5.00 (per head). The Rod and Gun Clubs have taken it upon themselves to look after their welfare for a few days-possibly a month-at their own expense before turning the elk out upon the range selected for them."* [9]

—Deputy Game Warden P. W. Nelson

Land that now contains Glacier NP was owned by the Blackfoot Indian Tribe before it was purchased by the federal government in 1896. The tribe had suffered through a severe period of starvation during the 1880s and early 1890s after buffalo were eliminated and elk were at best, scarce. This led to the sale that is still controversial. When Glacier NP was established in 1910 it was virtually devoid of elk, like most of the rest of northwestern Montana. Restoration of elk was a high priority for the new park and in 1912, Glacier NP received a shipment of 31 elk from the Yellowstone NP herd.

The National Bison Range at Moiese was established in 1908 and in 1916 received the start of its elk herd with 25 animals from the Gardiner operation. These elk prospered and in 1924, the Montana Fish and Game Commission noted that surplus elk were available for transplanting from the Bison Range.

Initial trapping operations were located outside of Yellowstone NP. Once the program became established, several additional trapping sites were used inside the Park on the Northern Yellowstone Winter Range. Elk were also trapped in 1958, 1959, 1967 and 1972 from the Gallatin elk herd. In 1915, two ranches in Beaverhead County received elk from the Jackson Hole, Wyoming herd.

Earliest elk transplants were to areas in western portions of Montana but in 1917, elk went to Dry Creek in Broadwater County and the Highwood Mountains in central Montana.

*The second transplant of elk in Montana shipped from the Cinnabar area near Gardiner in 1912 to the Hamilton area in the Bitterroot Valley.*
*(Courtesy Jim McLucas Photo Collection)*

*Hauling elk by sleigh at Cinnabar near Gardiner, MT in 1912.*
*(Courtesy Jim McLucas Photo Collection)*

By 1925 deputy game wardens began to receive elk damage reports from ranchers. Of five damage reports received in 1928, three were from new herds begun by transplants and two were from historic herds in the Sun River and Gallatin drainages. The 1917 plant in Broadwater County led to a damage control hunt in 1932.

In the winter of 1927-1928, a truck convoy led by deputy game warden Archie O'Claire spent two weeks breaking through axle deep snow during an epic transplanting effort. His Model-T truck broke trail through the snow. When completed they had successfully transported 27 elk from the National Bison Range at Moiese to a release point in the Fisher River Drainage near Libby.

***Today's burgeoning elk herds in the Missouri River Breaks were started with Yellowstone Park elk in a series of three plants made in 1951.***

*Elk trap and holding corral near Mammoth, Yellowstone National Park. c. 1915.*
*(Courtesy Robert Cooney Photo Collection)*

The Little Belt Mountain's elk herd was started in 1928 with elk from Gardiner as was a herd in the Bears Paw Mountains. The National Bison Range provided elk for transplants to the Red Lodge area and to the northwest corner of the state in Lincoln County. The Yellowstone NP herd furnished elk for the Big Belt Mountains, Judith Mountains and Crow Indian

*Blackfoot-Clearwater elk trap near Ovando, MT. c. 1950s.*
*(Courtesy Robert Cooney Photo Collection)*

Reservation in 1935. In 1942, elk shipped from Yellowstone NP to Custer County in the eastern prairie country of the state began a new herd. Today's burgeoning herds in the Missouri River Breaks were started with Yellowstone elk in a series of three plants made in 1951.

In the 1950s and 1960s efforts were being made to reduce the size of the Northern Yellowstone elk herd. Because few areas were left for establishing new herds, some elk were trapped and hauled distances of a few miles to hundreds of miles and released during the hunting season. Retired Montana Fish and Game Manager and Assistant Chief of the Wildlife Division, Joe Egan, called it a "put and take" situation.[10] General elk trapping and transplanting was discontinued in 1972.

*Game warden O'Claires's Model T breaks trail for an elk transplant caravan in January, 1927. It took 13 days to haul elk from the Moiese Bison Range to the Fisher River near Libby.* (Montana Fish and Game Photo)

Elk transplanting was initiated by Montana citizens and the Montana Fish and Game Department was a means to implement their objectives with the cooperation of landowners, U.S. Army, National Park Service, U.S. Fish and Wildlife Service and U.S. Forest Service. At least 31 more states and 4 countries received thousands of elk from other Yellowstone trapping operations. Washington was the first state when they arranged a shipment of 186 for release into the wild in 1912. Earlier small shipments of elk from Yellowstone NP herds to zoos and zoological parks had been previously made starting in 1892.[11]

Elk populations have continued to naturally colonize new areas including sites well away from mountainous areas. Although resources and technology to accurately determine the number of elk in the state still need improvement, it is apparent that given a chance, biology works.

***General elk trapping and transplanting was discontinued in 1972.***

General impressions derived largely from harvest and aerial surveys by workers over the years give an indication of trends. William Rush estimated that very low numbers of elk present in Montana 1910 had increased to a statewide total of 15,000 by 1932. In 1947, the number was estimated at

*Sportsmen planting elk in the Mill Creek area south of Anaconda, MT on a "plant and take basis".* (Photo and caption from the April, 1954 Anaconda Sportsmen's newsletter, courtesy of Lorry Thomas)

*William Rush, a pioneer range and wildlife biologist, estimated that the very low numbers of elk present in 1910 had increased to a statewide total of 15,000 by 1932. In 1947 the number in Montana was estimated at 38,000. The 1955 population estimate was 52,000 [12], which would increase over the next 50 years to 138,000 to 160,000 or even more today.[13]*

*Dick Klick crossing the north fork of the Sun River with a portable elk trap. c. 1963.*
*(Courtesy Jim McLucas Photo Collection)*

38,000. A 1955 population estimate was 52,000[12], and estimates would increase over the next 50 years from 138,000 to 160,000 and even more today.[13] The $5 investments scraped out of sportsmen's pockets almost 100 years ago have paid major ecological and economic dividends for citizens of the 21st century.

*Jim McLucas (far right) and helpers attempting to contain an elk trying to jump out of an elk trap near Mammoth, Yellowstone National Park. c. 1961.*
*(Courtesy Robert Cooney Photo Collection)*

Retired Montana Fish & Game Manager Charles Eustace:

> "We didn't use to have elk in the Bull Mountains, which lie between Roundup and Billings. Elk showed up there, which I have to assume probably pioneered out of the Belts, from the Belts to the Snowys, and then to the Bull Mountains."[14]

The passion of Montana citizens for reintroduction of elk into "their" areas is perhaps best illustrated by a story that Dave Cameron tells. His father, John Cameron, was a banker and conservation leader in Great Falls. In 1935, an elk plant was set for the northern portion of the Big Belt Mountains near his ranch.

*Herding elk with a helicopter into the Crystal Springs trap in Yellowstone National Park. c. 1963.*
*(Photo National Park Service)*

*"We didn't use to have elk in the Bull Mountains, which lie between Roundup and Billings. Elk showed up there, which I have to assume probably pioneered out of the Belts, from the Belts to the Snowys, and then to the Bull Mountains."*[14]

—Retired Game Manager Charles Eustace

"... My father was involved in the original introduction of elk from Yellowstone Park into this part of the world. He saw the majesty of Rocky Mountain elk and their tenacity. He admired them greatly and when he moved to Cascade he looked at these hills behind us, and thought surely someday we should have elk in the Big Belt Mountains. So it was not surprising that with his interest that the day these elk were transplanted from Yellowstone NP to this region to be sure he was there. The elk had been captured in Yellowstone NP, were put in railroad cattle cars, basically, and had come to Cascade where they were transferred to the stockyard and then into trucks. The whole town of Cascade piled into vehicles and followed these trucks of elk around the corner of that mountain range to witness the release of the elk into the region. At the very moment that they were releasing these elk from the trucks, just around the corner at the mouth of Sheep Creek, my mother went into labor. ... So when the event of the release of the elk was over, my dad was informed that he had

*An elk being released into a holding corral for transplanting. c. 1960s.*
*(Photo Courtesy Harold Picton)*

better get to Great Falls and he claims he made my birth, but my mother is not too sure of that. . .During antelope transplanting later on his ranch he almost missed the birth of another son because of his interest in wildlife restoration. The story got so widespread that women in Great Falls used to joke to each other that if their pregnancy was lasting a little too long all they had to do was get their husbands involved with wildlife restoration and it would surely bring on delivery. . .The elk disappeared and nothing much was heard about them for years. The population didn't really begin to grow significantly until the 50s and 60s and then they spread throughout the area."[15]

Trapping and transplanting efforts often initiated by sportsmen or landowners, along with good law enforcement, research studies and management practices since the early 1900s have led to record numbers of elk throughout Montana at the beginning of the 21st century.

*Efforts initiated in 1910 to restore elk in Montana were very successful and have led to a record number of elk in the state since restoration began almost 100 years ago.* (Photo courtesy Terry N. Lonner)

## An annotated listing of Montana elk transplants; 1890-1997.

| Year(s) | Source | Number | Release Area |
|---|---|---|---|
| 1890-1896 | Upper Madison River | 300 | For private collections.[1] |
| 1910 | Montana-YNP northern herd | 31 | Fleecer Mtn., Silver Bow Co. |
| 1911 | Jackson Hole, Wyoming | 7 | National Bison Range, Lake Co.[2] |
| 1912 | Jackson Hole, Wyoming | 5 | National Bison Range, Lake Co. |
| | Montana-YNP northern herd | 31 | Glacier NP |
| | Montana-YNP northern herd | 105 | Trapped at Gardiner by state and used for Restocking |
| | Montana-YNP northern herd | 80 | Hamilton, Ravalli Co. |
| | Montana-YNP northern herd | 40 | Keystone Cr., Mineral Co. |
| | Montana-YNP northern herd | 171 | Tin Cup-Foster Cr. Deer Lodge Co. |
| | Montana-YNP northern herd | 40 | Woodline - Thompson R., Sanders Co. |
| | Montana-YNP northern herd | 40 | Bull Mtn.. Jefferson Co. |
| | Montana-YNP northern herd | 33 | Little Blackfoot, Powell Co. |
| | See Footnote 3 below | | See Biennial Reports[3] |
| 1913 | Montana-YNP northern herd | 50 | Bull Mtn. Jefferson Co. |
| | Montana-YNP northern herd | 22 | Petty Cr., Missoula Co. |
| 1914 | Montana-YNP northern herd | 30 or 48 | Anaconda, Deer Lodge Co.[4] |

[1] 1890-1896 In the early 1890s Vic Smith (Yellowstone Vic) established an elk ranch just south of the Montana border in the Henry's Lake basin of Idaho. He trapped over 300 elk and shipped them out either by way of Monida or Three Forks. While 157 were shipped to New Hampshire, it is not clear where the remainder went, although eastern locations are the most likely. He and his partner sold them for $85 a head.

[2] Kraft, E. 2006. Untold tales of bison range trails. Stoneydale Press, Stevensville, MT Pp 26-27.

[3] 1912 Biennial report: Henry Avare: Estimated total statewide deer harvest: 15,000. Estimated total elk harvest: 1600 (500 at Gardiner). In spring of 1912, 202 elk were captured and shipped to various points in Montana. 40 elk in each of 4 railcars. (Note: no motor trucks or road system in those days). **First** carload to Hamilton. Held in a park until release. Jumped on to straw and several animals were killed then & also several had died in the car during transport. So then partitioned cars to separate calves (yearlings); cows; bulls. Arrived 3/8/1912; 42 elk: 6 died. 23 hours transit time. **2nd** shipment was 40 sent to Stevensville 3/12/12, 24 hours on road: 4 dead. **3rd** shipment to Woodline in extreme western part of state on 3/22/12, 40 head: 4 dead on road 30 hours. **4th** shipment went to Deer Lodge, Co. after 18 hours on road. 40 elk: 1 dead. **5th** shipment 3/25/12, 40 elk on road 24 hours with no loss. Local Rod & Gun clubs paid $5/elk for shipping. The Rod & Gun fed them for a few days to a month before releasing them.

Have received numerous requests for elk but too late to furnish.

Only 2 portions of state contain numerous elk: Sun River- South Fork of Flathead and the area around Yellowstone NP. The estimates for the Sun River-South Fork of the Flathead area ranged from 300 to 1500 elk.

Elk hunting season was Oct. 1 to Dec. 1 and recommended statewide closed season for 5 years. 57,392 resident hunting licenses and 137 non-resident in 1911.

The 1918 biennial report (D.H. Werform) said the Legislature extended the season in 1915 to Dec. 15 because of the situation around Yellowstone NP. In 1911, 3,500 deer were killed at Whitefish from Nov 15-30 after storms. Vernon Bailey of the U.S. Biological Survey estimated that the Northern YNP herd had been reduced by 30% in 1915. The Bureau chief wrote that the entire Gallatin elk herd might be wiped out in 1916. Vernon Bailey of the U.S. Biological Survey said that the previous elk number estimates of the northern herd were erroneous and double what they should have been.

[4] Quantities in question reflect differences between MF&G and YNPS records.

## An annotated listing of Montana elk transplants; 1890-1997, cont.

| Year(s) | Source | Number | Release Area |
|---|---|---|---|
| 1915 | Jackson Hole, Wyoming | 27 | Vipond Park in Beaverhead Co. |
| | Jackson Hole, Wyoming | 27 | Medicine Lodge in Beaverhead Co. |
| | Jackson Hole, Wyoming | 9 | National Bison Range, Lake Co.[2] |
| | Montana-YNP northern herd | 50 | (27) to Fleecer Mtn., Silver Bow Co. |
| 1916 | Montana-YNP northern herd | 25 | National Bison Range, Lake Co. |
| | Montana-YNP northern herd | 46 | State of Montana, release sites unknown. |
| | Montana-YNP northern herd | 90 | Trapped by state for restocking various areas[5] |
| 1917 | Montana-YNP northern herd | 35 | To Dry Cr. in Broadwater Co.; damage hunt 1932. |
| | Montana-YNP northern herd | 23 | Highwood Mtns. in Chouteau Co. |
| | Montana-YNP northern herd | 6 | Billings, Yellowstone Co. |
| | Montana-YNP northern herd | 22 | Petty Cr. in Missoula Co. |
| | Montana-YNP northern herd | 25 | Bald Hill in Mineral Co. |
| 1923 | Montana-YNP northern herd | 40 | Garnett Range in Granite Co. |
| 1925 | Elk damage reported on farm in Powell Co. | | |
| 1927 | Montana-YNP northern herd | 27 | Wolf Creek near Libby in Lincoln Co. |
| | Elk damage reported in Broadwater Co. | | |
| 1928 | National Bison Range, Lake Co. | 29 | Wolf Creek near Libby in Lincoln Co. |
| | National Bison Range, Lake Co. | 89 | DuRand Ranch, Meagher Co.[2] |
| | National Bison Range, Lake Co. | 388 | Massachusets[2] |
| | Montana-YNP northern herd | 86 | Judith River, Judith Basin Co., |
| | Montana-YNP northern herd | 32 | Havre (Bears Paw Mtns., Hill Co.) |
| | Elk damage complaint from Highwood Mts, Cascade Co. | | |
| | Elk damage complaint from Pleasant Valley, Flathead Co. | | |
| | Elk damage complaint from Ovando, Powell Co. | | |
| | Elk damage complaint from Sun River, Lewis & Clark Co. | | |
| | Elk damage complaint from Gallatin Gateway, Gallatin Co. | | |
| 1929 | National Bison Range, Lake Co. | 49 | Red Lodge, Carbon Co. |
| | National Bison Range, Lake Co. | 105 | Lincoln Co. |
| | Elk damage complaints from elk planted in Bears Paw Mtns., Blaine Co. | | |
| | Elk damage complaints from Highwood Mts., Cascade Co. | | |
| 1930 | Elk damage complaints at Martinsdale, Meagher Co., Corwin Springs, Park Co. and Ford Cr. at Augusta, Lewis & Clark Co., Ovando, Powell, Co. | | |
| 1932 | Elk damage complaints near Martinsdale, Meagher Co. and in Carbon Co. | | |
| | Elk damage season in Deep Cr., Big Belt Mts., Broadwater Co. to alleviate damage from 1917 plant. | | |
| | Elk damage near Big Sandy in Hill Co. (Bears Paw Mtns.) | | |
| | Elk damage complaint from Pleasant Valley, Lincoln Co. | | |

[5] These elk were apparently released onto the Bison Range at Moiese, Lake County in 1916, In 1924 the MF&G Commission noted that surplus elk were available from the bison range.

## An annotated listing of Montana elk transplants; 1890-1997, cont.

| Year(s) | Source | Number | Release Area |
|---|---|---|---|
| 1933 | Elk damage by transplanted elk at Missoula.<br>Elk damage in Carbon Co.<br>Elk damage in Jefferson Co. | | |
| 1934 | Montana-YNP northern herd | 9 | Dillon (Hazelbaker), Beaverhead Co. |
| 1935 | Montana-YNP northern herd | 4 | Beartooth Fox Farms, Red Lodge, Carbon Co. |
| | Montana-YNP northern herd | 150 | Crow Indian Reservation, Big Horn Co. |
| | Montana-YNP northern herd | 70 | Great Falls Wildlife Assoc., Big Belt Mtns., Sheep Cr., Cascade Co. |
| | Montana-YNP northern herd | 24 | Judith Mountains, Fergus Co. |
| | Montana-YNP northern herd | 24 | Lewis & Clark Rod & Gun Club, Lewis & Clark Co., Big Belt Mtns. |
| 1936 | Montana-YNP northern herd | 384 | Crow Indian Reservation in Big Horn Co., Special elk season near Utica, Judith River, Little Belt Mtns., Judith Basin Co. |
| 1937 | Montana-YNP northern herd | 77 | Anaconda Sports Club, Deer Lodge Co. |
| | Montana-YNP northern herd | 14 | W.L. Hughes, Wise River, Beaverhead Co. |
| | Montana-YNP northern herd | 12 | Lima in Beaverhead Co. |
| | Montana-YNP northern herd | 82 | Blacktail Cr. in Beaverhead Co |
| | Montana-YNP northern herd | 19 | Unaccounted for |
| | Montana-YNP northern herd | 43 | Pardee- Four Mile in Mineral Co. |
| | National Bison Range, Lake Co. | 46 | Cutoff Creek in Mineral Co. |
| | Montana-YNP northern herd | 77 | Warm Springs in Deer Lodge Co. |
| 1939 | Montana-YNP northern herd | 57 | Anaconda Sports Club, Georgetown-Deer Lodge Co. |
| | Montana-YNP northern herd | 152 | Rocky Mountain Sports Assoc., Silver Bow Co. |
| | Montana-YNP northern herd | 17 | Brown's Gulch, Silver Bow Co. |
| | Montana-YNP northern herd | 11 | Basin Cr., Silver Bow Co. |
| | Montana-YNP northern herd | 33 | Davis Ranch, Beaverhead Co. |
| | Montana-YNP northern herd | 15 | Holter Ranch, Beaverhead Co. |
| | Montana-YNP northern herd | 7 | Pipestone Canyon, Jefferson Co. |
| | Montana-YNP northern herd | 36 | Elkhorn Mtns., Jefferson Co. |
| 1939 | Montana-YNP northern herd | 9 | Oxbow Ranch, Wolf Creek, Cascade Co. |
| 1940 | Montana-YNP northern herd | 16 | Rocky Mountain Sports Assoc, Butte; Brown's Gulch, Silver Bow Co. |
| 1941 | Montana-YNP northern herd | 11 | Rocky Mountain Sports Assoc., Butte; Basin Cr., Jefferson Co. |
| 1942 | Montana-YNP northern herd | 36 | Davis Ranch, Beaverhead Co. |
| | Montana-YNP northern herd | 24 | Silver Bow Co. |
| | Montana-YNP northern herd | 25 | Knowlton Sportsmen, Custer Co. |
| 1944 | Montana-YNP northern herd | 8 | W. L. Hughes, Wise River, Beaverhead Co. |
| 1948 | Montana-YNP northern herd | 12 | W.E. Brogan, Corwin Springs, Park Co. |

## An annotated listing of Montana elk transplants; 1890-1997, cont.

| Year(s) | Source | Number | Release Area |
|---|---|---|---|
| 1950 | Montana-YNP northern herd | 25 | Pine Ridge, Yellowstone Co. |
| | Montana-YNP northern herd | 47 | Horseshoe Hills, Gallatin Co. |
| | Montana-YNP northern herd | 212 | Garnet Range near Drummond, Powell Co. |
| | Montana-YNP northern herd | 36 | Superior area of Mineral Co. |
| 1951 | Montana-YNP northern herd | 53 | Blacktail Cr., Beaverhead Co. |
| | Montana-YNP northern herd | 65 | Deer Lodge area, Powell Co. |
| | Montana-YNP northern herd | 29 | McCartney Mtn. near Melrose, Madison Co. |
| | Montana-YNP northern herd | 44 | C&K Cr., Fort Peck Game Range (C.M. Russell), Phillips Co. |
| | Montana-YNP northern herd | 46 | Fort Peck Game Range (C.M. Russell), & Pines area, Phillips and Valley Counties |
| | Montana-YNP northern herd | 31 | Fort Peck Game Range (C.M. Russell), Roy area, Fergus Co. |
| | Montana-YNP northern herd | 26 | Vermillion River, Sanders Co. |
| | Montana-YNP northern herd | 69 | released by MF&G at Phelps Cr. near Gardiner for hunting. |
| | Montana-YNP northern herd | 3 | See Em Alive Zoo, Red Lodge, Carbon Co. |
| 1952 | National Bison Range, Lake Co | 26 | East Fisher River, Lincoln Co. |
| | Montana-YNP northern herd | 2 | Wonderland Zoo, Billings, Yellowstone Co |
| | Montana-YNP northern herd | 30 | Rocky Hills near Dillon, Beaverhead Co. |
| | Montana-YNP northern herd | 45 | Cougar Cr., Missoula Co. and head of Rocky Cr., Granite Co. |
| | Montana-YNP northern herd | 30 | Wolf Ranch near Hardin, Big Horn Co. |
| | Montana-YNP northern herd | 51 | Fort Peck Game Range (C.M. Russell NWR), Phillips Co. |
| | Montana-YNP northern herd | 53 | Beartooth Mtns. (?W.F. Rock Cr.), Red Lodge, Carbon Co. |
| | Montana-YNP northern herd | 30 | Mill Cr. near Anaconda, Deer Lodge Co. |
| | Montana-YNP northern herd | 28 | McCartney Mtn. near Melrose, Madison Co. |
| | Montana-YNP northern herd | 49 | Vermillion River, Sanders Co. |
| | Montana-YNP northern herd | 629 | Released at Phelps Cr., Park Co., for hunters. |
| 1953 | Montana-YNP northern herd | 50 | Birch Cr., Pioneer Mtns. near Dillon, Beaverhead Co. |
| | Montana-YNP northern herd | 50 | Hells Canyon, Rochester Basin in Highland Mtns., Madison Co. |
| | Montana-YNP northern herd | 115 | Madison Co. |
| | Montana-YNP northern herd | 50 | Near Red Lodge in Carbon Co. |
| 1954 | Montana-YNP northern herd | 44 | Blackfoot Clearwater Game Range, Ovando, Missoula Co. |
| | Montana-YNP northern herd | 26 | National Bison Range, Lake Co. |
| | Montana-YNP northern herd | 30 | Near Red Lodge in Carbon Co. |
| | Montana-YNP northern herd | 641 | Elk releases for hunting in Trail Cr., Park Co. |
| | Montana-YNP northern herd | 74 | Released at Eagle Creek, Park Co., for hunters. |
| 1955 | Montana-YNP northern herd | 50 | Rock Cr. near Red Lodge, Carbon Co. |
| | Montana-YNP northern herd | 84 | Hells Canyon in Highland Mtns., Madison Co. |
| | Montana-YNP northern herd | 31 | Maxville in Boulder area, Granite Co. |
| | Montana-YNP northern herd | 29 | Missouri Flats in Madison Co. |
| | Montana-YNP northern herd | 47 | Blackfoot-Clearwater Game Range, Missoula and Powell Co. |
| | Montana-YNP northern herd | 29 | Modesty Cr. in Warm Springs Area, Deer Lodge Co. |
| | Woodward Ranch, Beaverhead Co. | 31 | Blackfoot-Clearwater Game Range, Missoula and Powell Co. |
| | Montana-YNP northern herd | 8 | Released at Eagle Creek, Park Co., for hunters. |

## An annotated listing of Montana elk transplants; 1890-1997, cont.

| Year(s) | Source | Number | Release Area |
|---|---|---|---|
| 1956 | Montana-YNP northern herd | 16 | National Bison Range, Lake Co. |
| | Montana-YNP northern herd | 74 | Blackfoot-Clearwater Game Range, Missoula and Powell Co. |
| | Montana-YNP northern herd | 95 | Red Lodge, Carbon Co. |
| 1957 | Montana-YNP northern herd | 17 | Blackfoot-Clearwater Game Range, Missoula Powell Co. |
| | Montana-YNP northern herd | 34 | Rochester Basin, Highland Mtns., Madison Co. |
| | Montana-YNP northern herd | 13 | Rochester Basin, Highland Mtns., Madison Co. |
| 1958 | Gallatin-YNP herd | 28 | Ratio Mtns., Jefferson Co. |
| | Gallatin-YNP herd | 11 | Red Lodge, Carbon Co. |
| | Gallatin-YNP herd | 52 | Hells Canyon, Highland Mtns., Madison Co. |
| | Gallatin-YNP herd | 5 | Anaconda Zoo, Deer Lodge Co. |
| | Gallatin-YNP herd | 51 | Foster Cr. near Anaconda, Deer Lodge Co. |
| | Gallatin-YNP herd | 50 | Red Lodge, Carbon Co. |
| | Gallatin-YNP herd | 77 | Hells Canyon, Highland Mts., Madison Co. |
| | Gallatin-YNP herd | 30 | Bear Cr., Madison Co. |
| | Gallatin-YNP herd | 41 | Walkerville-Butte, Silver Bow Co. |
| 1959 | Gallatin-unaccounted for | 20 | MF&G (total number difference)[6] |
| 1960 | Montana-YNP northern herd | 28 | Swamp Cr., near Thompson Falls, Sanders Co. |
| | Montana-YNP northern herd | 30 | Olson-Foster Cr., Deer Lodge Co. |
| | Montana-YNP northern herd | 40 | Walkerville, Silver Bow Co. |
| | Montana-YNP northern herd | 12 | Cherry Cr. Highland Mtns., Madison Co. |
| | Montana-YNP northern herd | 15 | Strawberry Cr., Park Co. |
| | YNP unaccounted for | 10 | Difference in State & Yellowstone NP numbers[6] |
| 1961 | Montana-YNP northern herd | 45 | Walkerville, Silver Bow Co. |
| | Montana-YNP northern herd | 46 | Highland Mts., Madison Co. |
| | M. Fork of Flathead R. Flathead Co. | 3 | Pinkham Cr., Lincoln Co. |
| 1962 | M. Fork of Flathead R. Flathead Co. | 4 | Doris Cr., Flathead, Co. |
| | Montana-YNP northern herd | 45 | Walkerville, Silver Bow Co. |
| | Montana-YNP northern herd | 45 | Highland Mts., Madison Co. |
| | Montana-YNP northern herd | 10 | Strawberry Cr., Park Co. |
| | Montana-YNP northern herd | 30 | Olsen Cr., Deer Lodge Co. |
| | Montana-YNP northern herd | 17 | Eight Mile Creek, Madison Co. |
| | Montana-YNP northern herd | 60 | Elkhorn-Hound Cr., Lewis and Clark Co. |
| 1963 | M. Fork of Flathead R. Flathead Co. | 14 | Doris Cr., Flathead, Co. |
| | Montana-YNP northern herd | 378 | Wyoming. |
| | Montana-YNP northern herd | 30 | S. Dakota Indian Reservations |
| | Montana-YNP northern herd | 103 | Scientific Collections by Mt. F & G |
| | Montana-YNP northern herd | 30 | West of Deer Lodge, Powell Co. |
| | Montana-YNP northern herd | 45 | Walkerville, Silver Bow Co. |
| | Montana-YNP northern herd | 30 | Bear Cr.(Madison River), Madison Co. |
| | Montana-YNP northern herd | 90 | Hubbart-Blacktail, Flathead Co. |
| | Montana-YNP northern herd | 29 | Blackleaf-Lussendon, Teton Co. |
| | Montana-YNP northern herd | 29 | Brock-Warm Springs, Powell Co. |
| | Montana-YNP northern herd | 30 | Clancy, Jefferson Co. |
| | Montana-YNP northern herd | 10 | Private McDowell & Associates, Beaverhead Co. |

[6] Quantities in question reflect differences between MF&G and YNP records.

## An annotated listing of Montana elk transplants; 1890-1997, cont.

| Year(s) | Source | Number | Release Area |
|---|---|---|---|
| 1964 | Montana-YNP northern herd | 100 | Walkerville, Silver Bow Co. |
| | Montana-YNP northern herd | 32 | Swamp Cr., Sanders Co. |
| | Montana-YNP northern herd | 72 | Blackfoot-Clearwater Game Range, Missoula & Powell Co. |
| | Montana-YNP northern herd | 48 | Elkhorn-Hound Cr., Lewis & Clark Co. |
| | Montana-YNP northern herd | 33 | Blackleaf-Lussendon, Teton Co. |
| | Montana-YNP northern herd | 31 | Clancy, Jefferson Co. |
| | Montana-YNP northern herd | 6 | Private, McDowell and associates, Beaverhead Co. |
| | Montana-YNP northern herd | 30 | Stryker-Stillwater, Flathead Co. |
| | Montana-YNP northern herd | 35 | Pinkham-Eureka, Lincoln Co. |
| | Montana-YNP northern herd | 101 | South Boulder River, Tobacco Root Mtns., Madison Co. |
| | Montana-YNP northern herd total | 518 | indicates a discrepancy of 30 animals from MF&G totals.[7] |
| 1965 | Montana-YNP northern herd | 30 | Olson-Foster Cr., Deer Lodge Co. |
| | Montana-YNP northern herd | 75 | Walkerville, Silver Bow Co. |
| | Montana-YNP northern herd | 101 | Hubbart-Blacktail, Flathead Co. |
| | Montana-YNP northern herd | 23 | Clancy, Jefferson Co. |
| | Montana-YNP northern herd | 10 | Ross Fork, Lincoln Co. |
| 1966 | Montana-YNP northern herd | 47 | Walkerville, Silver Bow, Co. |
| | Montana-YNP northern herd | 30 | Brock-Warm Springs, Powell Co. |
| | Montana-YNP northern herd | 35 | Big Creek, Lincoln Co. |
| | Montana-YNP northern herd | 31 | Kennedy Gulch, Lincoln Co. |
| | Montana-YNP northern herd | 3 | Don Larson, Boulder, Jefferson Co. |
| | Montana-YNP northern herd | 4 | Nels Sevalstead, Wise River, Beaverhead Co. |
| | Montana-YNP northern herd total | 162 | indicates a discepancy of 12 from MF&G total of 150. |
| 1967 | Montana-YNP northern herd (Crystal Cr.trap) | 33 | Blackfoot-Clearwater Game Range, Missoula & Powell Co. |
| | Big Hole (Christenson Ranch), Beaverhead Co. | 38 | Fleecer Game Range, Silver Bow Co. |
| | Big Hole (Christenson Ranch), Beaverhead Co. | 18 | Fleecer Game Range, Silver Bow Co. |
| | Big Hole (Christenson Ranch), Beaverhead Co. | 17 | Brown's Gulch, Silver Bow Co. |
| | Big Hole (Christenson Ranch), Beaverhead Co. | 10 | Brown's Gulch, Silver Bow Co |
| | Gallatin-YNP herd | 13 | Garrity Mountain, Powell Co. |
| | Gallatin-YNP herd | 15 | Garrity Mountain, Powell Co. |
| | Montana-YNP northern herd | 81 | Crow Indian Reservation, Big Horn Co. |
| | Montana-YNP northern herd | 31 | Crow Indian Reservation, Big Horn Co.[8] |
| 1968 | M. Fork of Flathead R., Flathead Co. | 3 | Pinkham Cr., Lincoln Co. |
| | M. Fork of Flathead R., Flathead Co. | 14 | Pinkham Cr., Lincoln Co. |
| | Montana-YNP northern herd | 50 | South Boulder River, Tobacco Roots Mtns., Jefferson Co. |
| | Montana-YNP northern herd | 48 | Brown's Gulch, Silver Bow Co. |
| 1972 | Big Hole (Christenson Ranch), Beaverhead Co. | 32 | Callahan Cr., Lincoln Co. |
| | Gallatin-YNP herd | 44 | Garrity Mountain, Powell Co. |
| | Gallatin-YNP herd | 42 | Warm Springs Cr., Powell Co. |
| 1976 | National Bison Range, Lake Co. | 19 | Stryker Ridge, Lincoln Co. |

[7] The difference in 30 animals probably is due to elk collected for research studies and museums during 1964.

[8] These 31 were destroyed by Bureau of Indian Affairs because they had been exposed to scabies, thus, including the 81 above, the total removed from YNP was 112.

## An annotated record of Montana elk transplants; 1890-1997, cont.

| Year(s) | Source | Number | Release Area |
|---|---|---|---|
| **1981** | National Bison Range, Lake Co. | 42 | Deerhorn Creek, Sanders Co. |
| **1981-82** | Wallace Ranch, Ravalli Co. | 144 | released in west central Montana. |
| | Wallace Ranch, Ravalli Co. | 135 | released in west central Montana.. |
| **1983** | National Bison Range, Lake Co. | 38 | Yaak (17 mile Creek), Lincoln Co. |
| | National Bison Range, Lake Co. | 19 | Vinal Cr., Lincoln Co. |
| 1984 | National Bison Range, Lake Co. | 15 | Flathead Indian Reservation, Lake Co. |
| 1986 | National Bison Range, Lake Co. | 3 | Whitetail Face, Yaak, Lincoln Co. |
| | National Bison Range, Lake Co. | 26 | Pete Cr., Lincoln Co. |
| 1987 | National Bison Range, Lake Co. | 34 | Murphy Lake, Lincoln Co. |
| 1988 | National Bison Range, Lake Co. | 31 | Murphy Lake, Lincoln Co. |
| 1990 | National Bison Range, Lake Co. | 29 | Ashley Lake, Flathead Co. |
| 1992 | National Bison Range, Lake Co. | 31 | Ashley Lake, Flathead Co. |
| 1994 | National Bison Range, Lake Co. | 17 | Pleasant Valley, Lincoln Co. and Bear Springs Cr., Sanders Co. |
| 1997 | National Bison Range, Lake Co. | 14 | Thompson River, Lincoln Co. |
| **Summary** | **Sources of Elk** | | |
| | **Montana-Yellowstone NP Northern Herd** | **7,267** | **for transplants, zoos & scientific collections** |
| | **Gallatin Herd of Yellowstone NP** | **343** | **for transplants and zoos** |
| | **Jackson Hole Elk Herd** | **75** | **for transplants** |
| | **National Bison Range** | **1,116** | **for transplants** |
| | **M. Fork of Flatheard River** | **38** | **for transplants** |
| | **Private ranches** | **302** | **for transplants** |
| | **Total** | **9,141** | |
| | **Northern Herd of Yellowstone Park** | **1,923** | **Releases for hunting** |
| | **Upper Madison River, Henry's Lake Herd** | **300** | **Removed for shipment** |

Estimated total number of elk moved in these efforts: 11,364

The sources used in the preparation of this table include: Unpublished Montana Fish and Game Dept. reports and files; Kraft, E. 2006. Untold tales of bison range trails, Stoneydale Press, Stevensville, MT.; Smith, V. 1997. The champion buffalo hunter. Two Dot Press, Helena, MT; Thomas, J. W. and D. E. Toweill. 1982. Elk of North America. Stackpole Books, Harrisburg, PA. (This includes a summary of records from Yellowstone National Park.)

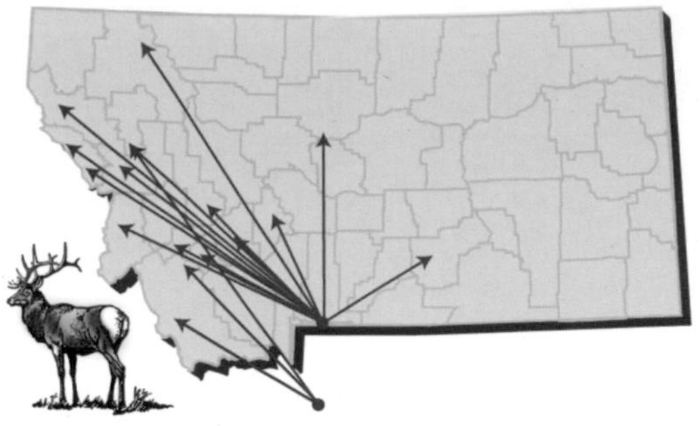

1910 - 1919 Elk Transplants

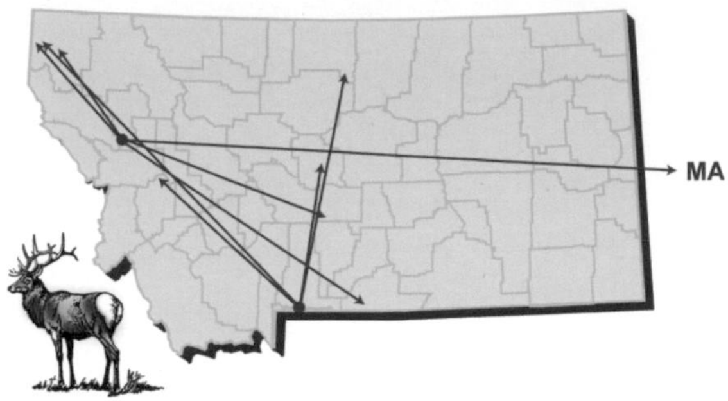


1920 - 1929 Elk Transplants

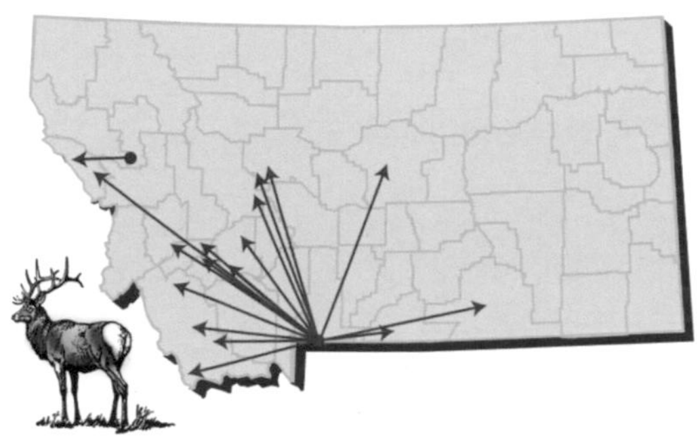

1930 - 1939 Elk Transplants

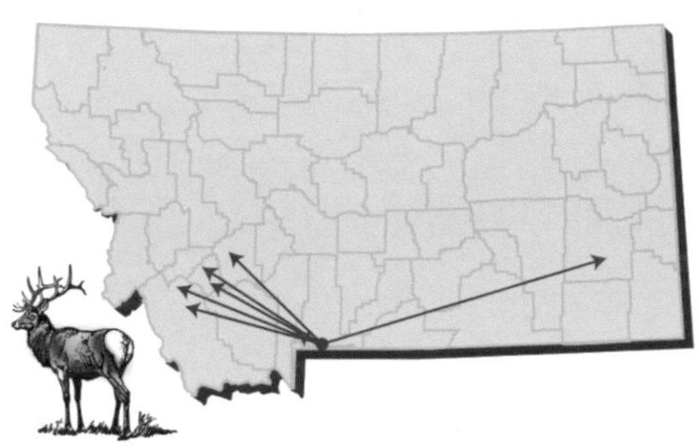

1940 - 1949 Elk Transplants

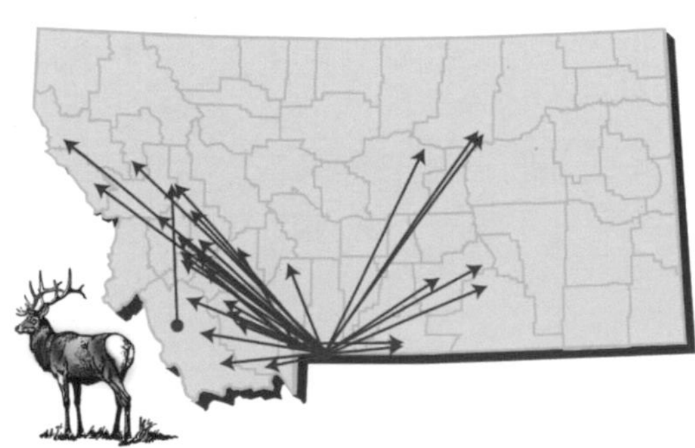

1950 - 1959 Elk Transplants

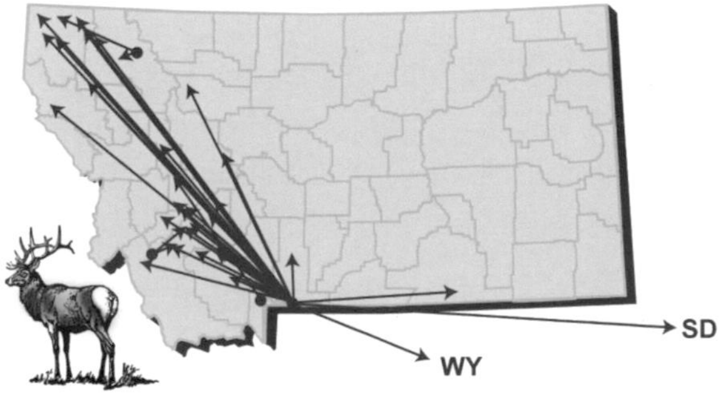


1960 - 1969 Elk Transplants

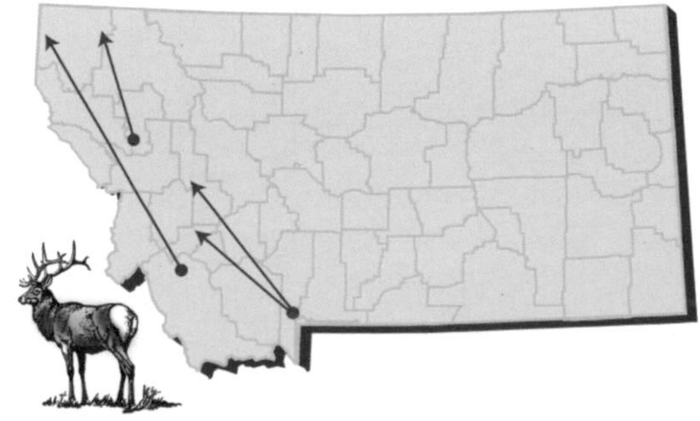

1970 - 1979 Elk Transplants

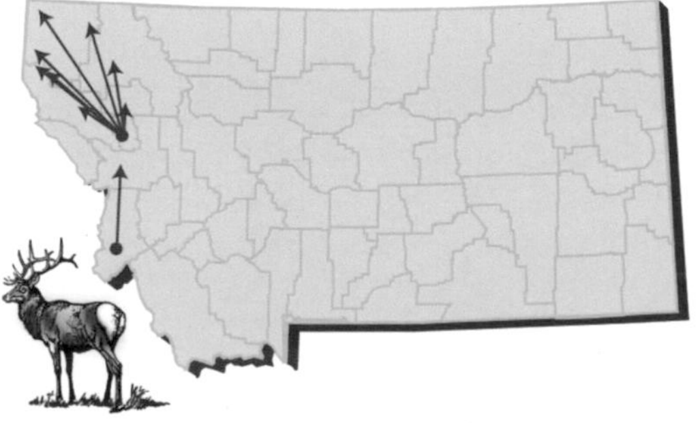

1980 - 1999 Elk Transplants

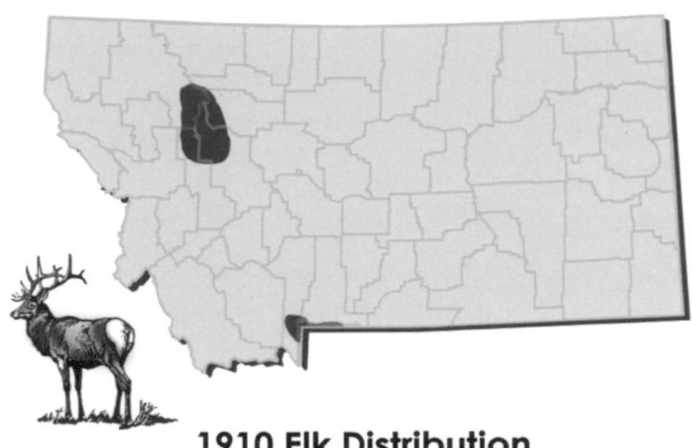

**1910 Elk Distribution**

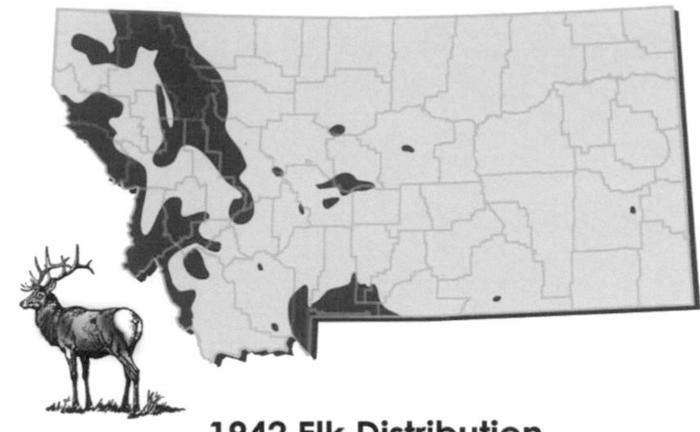

**1942 Elk Distribution**

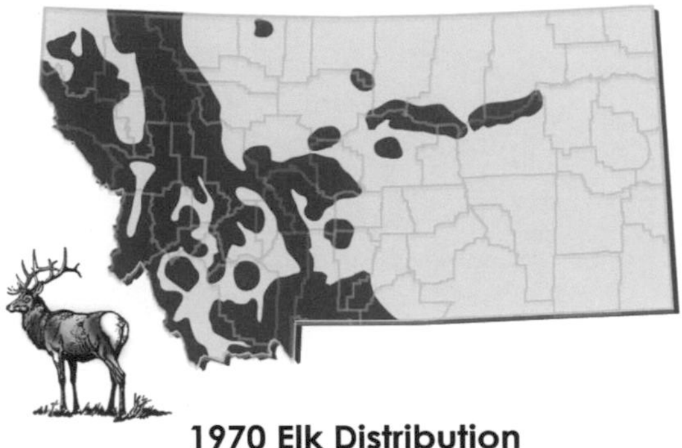

**1970 Elk Distribution**

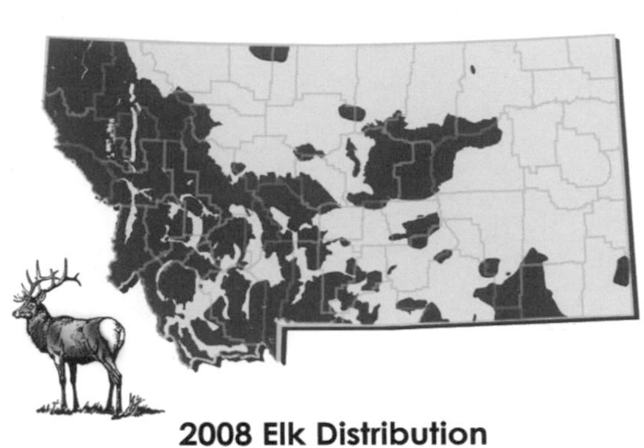

**2008 Elk Distribution**

*Hard-rubber-tire 4x4 truck with chains and three crates of elk to load on the train at Gardiner, MT. c. 1924. (Courtesy Jim McLucas Photo Collection)*

# Footnotes

[1] Russell, O. 1965. Journal of a Trapper: 1834-1843. Editor: A. I. Haines. University of Nebraska Press. 191 pp.

Peek, J. 2003. Wapiti. Chapter 42 in Wild Mammals of North America. Edited by: G. A. Feldhammer, B. C. Thompson and J. A. Chapman. Johns Hopkins University Press. 877-888.

[2] Smith, V. G. 1997. The champion buffalo hunter: The frontier memoirs of Yellowstone Vic Smith. Editor: J. Prodgers. Two Dot Press, Helena, MT. 257 pp.

Robbins, R. L., D. E. Redfern and C. P. Stone. 1982. Refuges and elk management, Chapter 12 in Elk of North America. Stackpole Books. 479-507.

[3] Ibid. Smith, V. G. 1997.

[4] Houston, D. B. 1982. The northern Yellowstone elk herd: Ecology and management. Macmillan Publishing Co., New York. 219-237.

[5] Whithorn, D. 2001. Paradise valley on the Yellowstone. Arcadia Publishing, Chicago, IL. 128 pp.

[6] Rush, W. M. 1932. Northern Yellowstone elk study. Montana Fish and Game Commission, Helena. 131 pp.

[7] Craig, V. and J. McLucas. 1962. Montana elk herds through the years. Montana Wildlife, January. 15-21.

[8] Aware, H. 1912. 1911-1912 Biennial report of the State Game and Fish Warden, Montana. Helena. 43 pp.

[9] Ibid.

[10] Egan, J. 1999. Videotaped interview with Harold Picton.

[11] Robbins, R. L., D. E. Redfern and C. P. Stone. 1982. Refuges and elk management, Chapter 12 in Elk of North America. Stackpole Books, Harrisburg, PA. 479-507.

[12] Biennial reports: 1931-1932; 1946-1948; and 1954-1956. Montana Fish and Game Commission, Helena.

[13] Montana Statewide Elk Management Plan. 2004. Montana Fish, Wildlife and Parks, Wildlife Division, Helena. 397 pp.

[14] Eustace, C. 2004. Videotaped interview with Terry Lonner and Tom Manning.

[15] Cameron, D. 2003. Videotaped interview with Terry Lonner and Tom Manning.

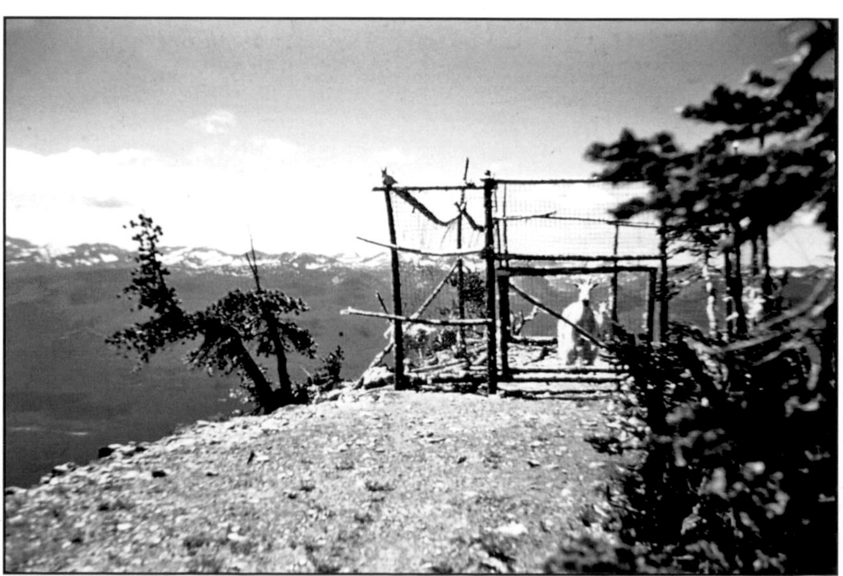

***Mountain goats in a trap on top of the Swan Mountain Range. c. 1948.***
***(Courtesy Robert Cooney Photo Collection)***

Chapter 11

# Mountain Goat

Mountain goats *(Oreamnos americana)* are found only in North America and were native to only four states (Alaska, Idaho, Montana and Washington) and four Canadian provinces (Alberta, British Columbia, Northwest Territories and Yukon). Colorado, Oregon, Nevada, South Dakota, Utah and Wyoming all have introduced populations.

Mammalogists classify them as members of Bovidae or the cattle, sheep and goat family. Mountain goats are not actually a "true" goat but are in a category referred to as Rupicaprini or "rock goats" which includes the European chamois *(Rupicapra rupicapra)*. DNA work suggests a distant relationship to bighorn sheep (*Ovis canadensis*) and other members of the genus *Ovis* rather than goats.[1]

Mountain goats are unique in several ways. Their habitat is usually mountainous and remote, which ensured their existence was seldom threatened by man. Cliffs are an important component of mountain goat habitat. The steeper the terrain the more goats seem to like it. The nature of their habitat restricts them to small home ranges. They are very selective in their feeding taking only the more

*Mountain goat distribution suggests they were native to major mountain ranges in western Montana. They were absent from isolated mountain ranges of Montana where habitat was suitable. In these isolated mountain ranges there was the habitat to enlarge sport hunting and for esthetic enjoyment of this big game animal.*

—Montana Fish and Game Commission.[3]

nutritious parts of grasses, broadleaf plants and shrubs. Feeding is usually restricted to areas above and below cliffs, avalanche chutes, as well as cliff faces.

Nannies give birth to their first kids at about three years of age. Single kids are probably the rule but twins are common when food has been abundant for nannies. Steep cliffs not only provide security from predators, but caves on cliff faces also furnish shelter from storms and summer heat. Breath-taking maneuvers of mountain

s, including their kids, on cliff faces have long made them favorites of wildlife viewers. Studies have found that accidental falls and avalanches do produce some mortality. There are an estimated 75,000 to 110,000 mountain goats in North America of which 2,300 to 3,100 occur in Montana. British Columbia and Alaska are thought to have the largest populations.[2]

The original distribution of this species in Montana included only the far western portion. They were absent from isolated mountain ranges of the state where habitat was suitable. For reasons that are not clear to biologists, there were at least 12 mountain ranges in central and southwestern Montana that historically did not have mountain goats. The fossil record of goats is poor so we do not know if goat absence in these ranges represents lack of colonization or more recent extinctions. In these isolated mountain ranges there was suitable habitat to enlarge sport hunting and for esthetic enjoyment of this big game animal.[3]

In spring of 1940, Mr. Barney Brannin, a rancher with holdings in the Sweetgrass Creek drainage north of Big Timber, contacted Mr. Cooney suggesting that mountain goats be transplanted to the Crazy Mountains of south central Montana. The project was appealing and efforts were begun. District Ranger Rubottom of the U.S. Forest Service immediately supported the project. By mid –July Mr. Brannin had completed a holding pen for transplanted goats in the Crazy Mountains. In the meantime, Bob Cooney was working with deputy game wardens

*Mountain goats in the Deep Creek trap west of Choteau, Montana to be transplanted to the Crazy Mountains in south central Montana. c. 1941.* (Courtesy Robert Cooney Photo Collection)

and U.S. Forest Service personnel to find the best place to trap mountain goats. A site in the Pintler Mountain Range, west of Phillipsburg, was considered, because a local woodsman, "Moose" Johnson, had already built the first goat trap on a salt lick at a site in the Pintlers. He had trapped a few mountain goats and managed to transport some out of the Pintlers to Butte. They were displayed in the zoo[4] at the Columbia Gardens theme park in Butte.[5] However, because of remoteness and problems with the safe transport of goats it was eventually eliminated. By August 1940 another site high above Deep Creek on the Rocky Mountain Front west of Choteau was selected for the first official effort by the Montana Fish and Game Department to capture goats for transplanting.[6] The first goat capture efforts attempted by the Department was done by using large hand nets.

*The first known account of mountain goats trapped and transplanted in Montana was done from the Anaconda-Pintler Mountains to the Columbia Gardens Theme Park east of Butte by "Moose" Johnson. c. 1940.*

*(Courtesy World Museum of Mining Photo Archives, Butte, MT)*

This method failed and the decision was then made to use bait traps.[7]

Bob Cooney reported,

> "The site was on a windblown ridge, 6 miles from the end of an old logging road. Stockmen placed salt there for many years. The goats had taken advantage of this and each spring would drift

> ***. . . a local woodsman, "Moose" Johnson, built the first goat trap on a salt lick at a site in the Pintler Mountain Range. He had trapped a few mountain goats and managed to transport some out of the Pintlers to Butte.[4]***
>
> –Jim McLucas

*A mountain goat trap constructed on a high mountain ridge 6 miles from the end of a logging road above Deep Creek west of Choteau, Montana. c. 1941.*

*(Courtesy Robert Cooney Photo Collection)*

in from nearby mountain peaks. On our first visit in early March of 1941, we found 32 goats busy at the site. No time was lost in building a pen. We managed to get woven wire up there by means of an improvised two-wheeled cart made from the back bunks of a wagon. The team had all they could do to pick their way up a steep winding skid trail to the top of the ridge."[8]

*An improvised two-wheeled cart and a team of horses used to haul trap making material to the Deep Creek mountain goat trap site west of Choteau, MT. This horse cart was also used to haul crates of goats to the nearest road for transfer to a truck. c. 1942.* *(Courtesy Jim McLucas Photo Collection)*

"We improvised a trip gate that could be dropped by pulling a wire, which extended about a quarter of a mile up the ridge. The trap was completed on March 30. A block of salt was placed in the pen. Our first catch of four goats was made two weeks after the pen was set. A week later we caught 8 more. They were taken off the mountain in individual crates perched rather precariously on the two-wheeled cart."

Poles to construct the trap were cut from the nearest stand of timber. The operation had to cross the ranch of J. Salmond to get to the base of the mountain. He rented a team of horses for $3/day for the project and also hired on as part of the trapping and transporting crew composed of himself and R. Gibler, C. Arps, and H. Smith. Each member of the crew was paid $4/day. They were supervised by Bob Cooney and Faye Couey.

*Mountain goats were hauled from the Deep Creek trap west of Choteau, Montana to a pickup truck for transporting to various locations in the state. c. 1942.* *(Courtesy Jim McLucas Photo Collection)*

Cooney's report continues,

> "The goats were transported approximately 300 miles by pickup to the Crazy Mountain range in central Montana and released. Last spring in the same trap we captured 12 more. Due to heavy snowdrifts in the area, it was impossible to reach the trap with the two-wheeled cart as had been done the previous year. Anticipating this, crates were built that could be packed on horses. These were found to be quite satisfactory for the six mile trip, and it is felt that it would be possible to pack goats considerably farther in this manner. These goats were placed in the Beartooth range, the highest mountains in the state, located just north of Yellowstone Park."[9]

*Hilary Gollehon assisted with transporting mountain goats by horse from the Deep Creek trap west of Choteau, Montana when snows were too deep for wheeled vehicles to get to the trap. The goat heads were tied off to the side so they wouldn't "hook" the horses hind quarters. c. early 1940s.* (Courtesy Jim McLucas Photo Collection)

Trapped mountain goats were lassoed in the trap and loaded in crates. No one was gored by the sharp "stiletto" goat horns in these early

*The first Montana Fish & Game Department mountain goat transplanting effort involved trapping goats in the mountains west of Choteau. The captured goats were crated and trucked over 300 miles to the Crazy Mountains in south central Montana. The last leg of their journey was by horse drawn two-wheeled trailers. Robert Cooney is in the middle of the photo sitting on top of a crate. c. 1942.* (Courtesy Jim McLucas Photo Collection)

***Trapped mountain goats were lassoed in the trap and loaded in crates. No one was gored by the sharp "stiletto" goat horns in these early operations.***

operations. Goats captured in 1942 were released from switchbacks of the Beartooth Highway, south of Red Lodge, after a trip of about 450 miles.

Mountain goat transplanting continued during the war years with transplants in 1943 and 1945. The Deep Creek trap continued to be used and furnished all 77 goats transplanted from 1941 to 1948. A shipment of 9 goats also was sent to Colorado in 1948. The mountain goat population on the National Bison Range was started with only 4 goats (one male and three females) trapped from this site in 1964 by Jim McLucas.[10]

***The mountain goat transplanting program was expanded after the end of World War II.***

The mountain goat transplanting program was expanded after the end of World War II. Lloyd McDowell erected second and third traps at sites on banks of the South Fork of the Flathead River in the Bob Marshall Primitive Area.[11] This roadless area imposed new logistical challenges, particularly for transport of the goats. These traps were used from 1948 through 1953. Don Williams, Bert Angstman, Jim McLucas, Dwight Stockstad and other crew members would load the crated goats into rubber rafts and float them over the rapids to the wilderness airstrip at Black Bear. There, with their legs trussed, they were loaded into an airplane to be flown to a waiting truck at an airfield outside of the primitive area. A four seat Stinson Station Wagon was one of the first planes used.

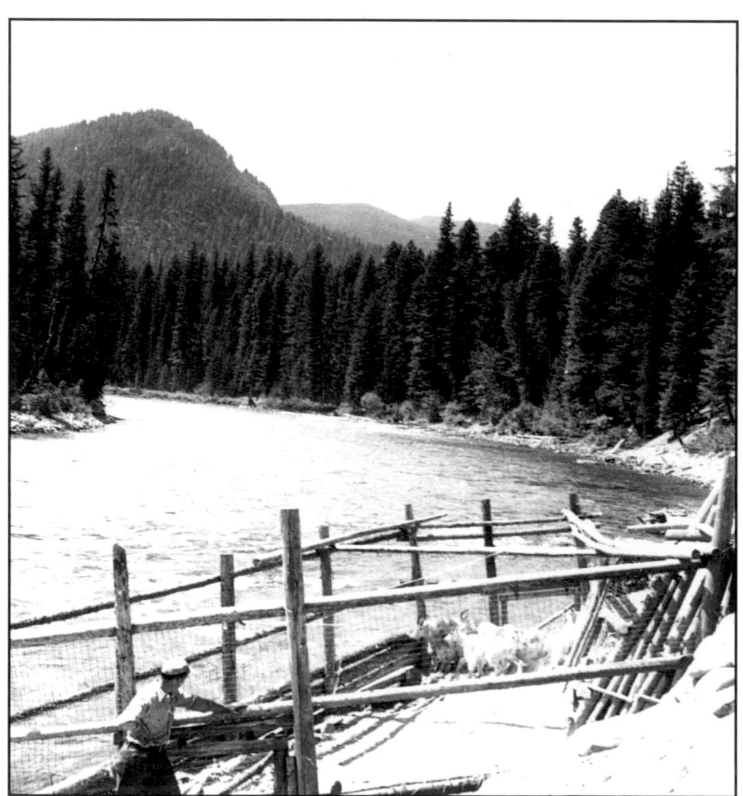

*A unique mountain goat trap located on the south fork of the Flathead river in the Bob Marshall wilderness. This trap was located on the river's edge near a natural salt lick. c. 1948.* *(Courtesy Jim McLucas Photo Collection)*

*Mountain goats were loaded into a Stinson Station Wagon airplane at the Black Bear Airstrip for transplanting after being transported by raft down the S. Fork of the Flathead River. c. 1950.* *(Courtesy Lloyd McDowell Photo Collection)*

Lloyd McDowell's understated account reads, "The back seat and right front seat were removed and three goats placed on the floor. They were blindfolded and had their feet tied; a safety strap was run through their horns to hold them down. This method was fairly successful, but it is believed that if they are given a sedative it will improve the safety factor by keeping them quiet especially during takeoffs."[12] The larger Travelair and workhorse Ford Tri-motor aircraft were also used when available. The technique of protecting handlers against goring by placing a loop of three-quarters inch garden hose over the horns was developed during this operation.

> "...we camped at Little Salmon Park so I went up to check the goat trap one morning.... So I'm walking up this trail and here's big old grizzly tracks going up the trail. So I'm pretty cautious, the game trail had turned into where the trap was.... So I'm looking real careful and I said, "he's still in there." I worked up a little closer, and saw he'd killed a raghorn bull elk in the trap, and ate most of him. Later, I was worried about the grizzly being around, so that was the end of trapping goats with the grizzly smell there. I drug what was remaining (of the elk carcass) and threw him over the bank and got the hell out of there."
>
> —Jim McLucas.[13]

Floating goats down the South Fork of the Flathead had its own elements of adventure. Goat trapping was done in cool weather of spring and when the river was swollen with runoff. This made a fast float of about an hour down to the boat landing site at Black Bear airstrip. Rapids, whirlpools and logs always kept the level of adrenaline raised in the men. Getting the raft into the landing at Black Bear was another thing. Below Black Bear bridge the river flows into an increasingly inaccessible

***Floating the goats down the South Fork of the Flathead had its own elements of adventure... After several miles frequent rapids in this stretch of river culminates in the narrow cleft of Meadow Creek Gorge with its shear walls, dangerous turbulence and almost impassable class 5 rapids. To prevent being swept into the gorge, the crew rigged a horizontal rope below the horse bridge at Black Bear so they could grab it as they came near the gorge and pull themselves to shore.***

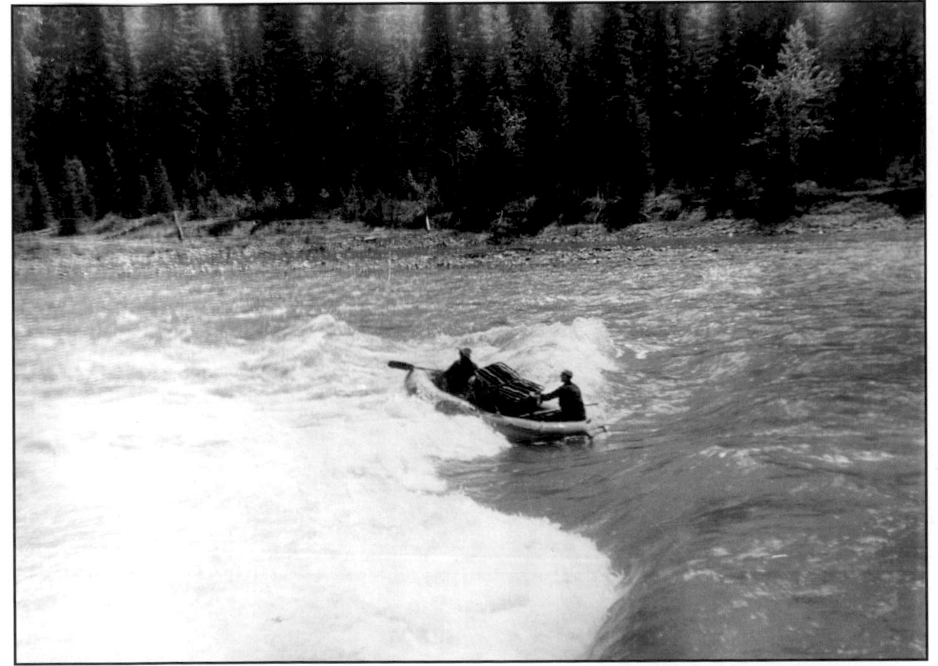

*A rubber raft was used to float mountain goats 9 miles down the S. Fork of the Flathead River to the Black Bear Airstrip. Lloyd McDowell and Dwight Stockstad are in the raft. c. 1950. (Courtesy Jim McLucas Photo Collection)*

*Jim McLucas and a few other individuals were gored by goats necessitating trips to emergency rooms to repair puncture wounds in their legs.*

canyon. Moderate class 2 and 3 rapids are a short distance below the bridge. After several miles, frequent rapids in this stretch of river culminates in the narrow cleft of Meadow Creek Gorge with its shear walls, dangerous turbulence and almost impassable class 5 rapids. To prevent being swept into the gorge, the crew rigged a horizontal rope below the horse bridge at Black Bear so they could grab it as they came near the gorge and pull themselves to shore.

Another trap site was used at a man made salt lick at Van Mountain fire lookout in the Swan Range. Goats trapped at this site were transported 7 miles on packhorses to the Condon Range Station in the Swan Valley. A trap at a fire lookout in the Mission Range yielded no goats. Beginning in 1953, the Canyon Creek site in the Pioneer Mountains of Beaverhead County became a prolific supplier of goats until 1962. New trapping sites on the National Bison Range and Gates of the Mountains Wilderness proved to be highly successful and replaced the Pioneer Mountains site.

Sodium penta-barbital was used as a sedative during aerial transports from 1948 to 1953. Deaths of three goats from a group of 25 captured in July convinced the crew that transplanting should only be attempted in cool weather. In general, goats were not difficult to handle and mortality was low.

Jim McLucas and a few other individuals were gored by goats necessitating trips to emergency rooms to repair puncture wounds in their legs.

After World War II, a Jeep provided access to the Deep Creek trap, which was used until 1957. A broken brake line gave some exciting moments on the steep and rugged mountain side until McLucas was able to steer the Jeep into a grove of aspens to bring it to a stop. There were other occasions when the trapping crew ended up inside the trap with the goats

*Dr. Gus Swanson injecting sodium penta-barbital to calm a mountain goat before floating it down the S. Fork of the Flathead River on a rubber raft; transferring it to an airplane at Black Bear airstrip and flying it to a landing site to transfer it to a truck for its final trip to a release site. Dr. Don C. Quimby is holding the goats horns. c. 1950.* *(Courtesy Robert Cooney Photo Collection)*

*The jeep at the Deep Creek mountain goat trap west of Choteau, MT that was used to access the trap weather permitting. c. 1947. (Courtesy Robert Cooney Photo Collection)*

outside the trap. Most of the time Jim trapped goats with the assistance of others, but once in a while he did it alone.

> "The last time I trapped goats here (Deep Creek)...I needed two male goats for the Elkhorn Mountains and I came up here and set the trap and the next morning I had two billies in here. The first billy I got out right at the gate. I could back my pickup to the gate and got him and got the hose on his horns. I'd have to hold back the swinging gate with my head to keep it closed and then leave it open to get him in (the pickup), The first one wasn't too bad, I got him into the crate on the back of the trap, closed the door and then I came out to get the second one. I got him out and was just getting the hose on his horns when he bolted and took me down over the edge. I was laying there puffing and the goat wasn't even breathing hard. Finally I thought, he don't have any hose on his horns and I don't dare turn him loose, he's liable to hook me. So I lay there awhile catching my breath and I got him on his feet and he ran up the hill right towards the trap and right towards the gate and I got him down again, rested awhile, put the hose on his horns. I went to put him in the truck...and had to hold the gate closed with my head to keep the other one from getting out. I got ready and got a hold of him everywhere I could and went to push him in. The goat in the truck kept banging him right back out and I had to roll him in head first and push him into the truck. They started fighting so I quickly got into the truck and started down the road which is pretty rough. That settled them down"
>
> —Jim McLucas.[13]

***"...then I came out to get the second one. I got him out and was just getting the hose on his horns when he bolted and took me down over the edge. I was laying there puffing and the goat wasn't even breathing hard. Finally I thought, he don't have any hose on his horns and I don't dare turn him loose, he's liable to hook me..."***

**—Jim McLucas.[13]**

*Trapped mountain goats were often lassoed in the trap and then loaded into crates. c. 1942. (Courtesy Jim McLucas Photo Collection)*

*National recognition was given to the pioneering Montana mountain goat transplanting program when it received the Nash-Kelvinator (American Motors) Conservation Award. A unique mountain goat trapping effort conducted in 1984 also received national attention when it was shown on the popular television program "Wild Kingdom."*

Both Colorado and Wyoming received mountain goats from this transplanting program. The National Zoological Park in Washington D. C. also received goats from Montana. National recognition was given to the pioneering Montana mountain goat transplanting program when it received the Nash-Kelvinator (American Motors) Conservation Award.[14]

A unique mountain goat trapping effort conducted in 1984 also received national attention when it was shown on the popular television program "Wild Kingdom." This project was carried out on the National Bison Range. A helicopter was used to net-gun goats. This was probably the first time the method had been used on goats. It involved firing a net over a goat from a low flying helicopter. Bart O'Gara from the Cooperative Wildlife Research Unit at the University of Montana served as gunner and Doug Goetz of the Montana Fish and Game Dept. was the pilot.

Another trapping effort on the Bison Range used a helicopter to drive goats into a net in 1987. This was probably the first time drive netting was used to catch mountain goats. Students from the University of Montana under the supervision of Bart O'Gara participated in the project. The goats were transplanted into the Rattlesnake Wilderness northeast of Missoula.[15]

*"Robert F. Cooney of Helena, state game manager of the Montana Fish & Game Department, was one of ten national professional conservationists chosen to receive the American Motors Conservation Award in 1958".[14]*

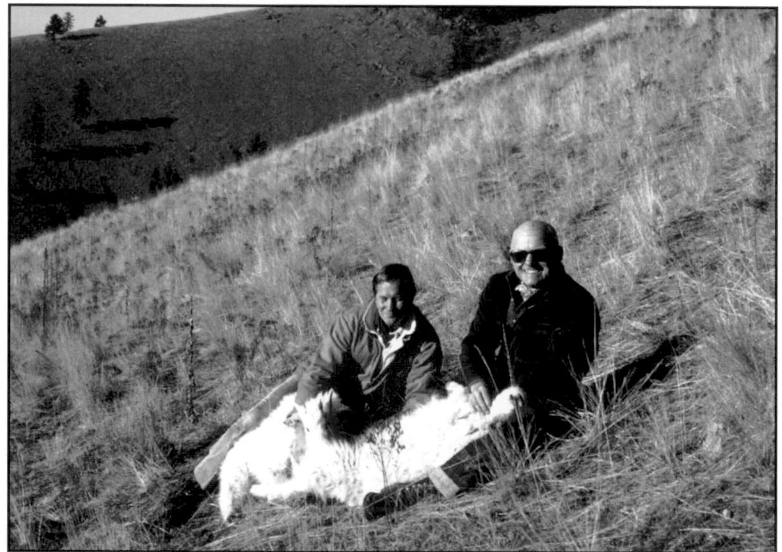

*Jim Fowler of Wild Kingdom and Dr. Bart O'Gara with two mountain goat kids captured by net-gunning on the National Bison Range - 1984.*
*(Montana Fish, Wildlife and Parks Photo by John Firebaugh)*

The mountain goat transplanting program expanded hunting opportunities and provided highly popular viewing opportunities. Some individuals also had hopes that mountain goats would cross with Angora goats and add some of the characteristics of their fine coats to the domestic variety. Of course they are not related and the commercial hopes were for naught.

Mountain goats that were planted in the Absaroka Range and the Madison Range have colonized the Gallatin Range. They have extended their range into the northern part of Yellowstone NP where they are considered an exotic/non-native species, although they are popular with wildlife watchers.

Mountain goats were transplanted from Olympic National Park in Washington in 1985 to Cougar

Peak in the Cabinet Mountains in an effort to increase genetic diversity of Montana mountain goat populations. Another shipment of goats from Olympic NP was used in an attempt to establish a herd on Red Mountain in northern Lewis and Clark County in 1989.

*Helicopter in Olympic National Park slinging a mountain goat for transplanting to Montana - 1989.*
*(Montana Fish, Wildlife and Parks photo courtesy Bob Henderson)*

*The goats were captured in Washington and Bob hauled them east across the plains of Washington and mountains of Idaho. Bob stopped frequently to raid ice machines along the way to keep the goats cool.*

The National Park Service was attempting to reduce the troublesome mountain goat population in Olympic NP in Washington in 1989. Bob Henderson, the Montana wildlife biologist for the district including Red Mountain, decided to accept the offer of goats from the Park. Goats were captured in Washington and Bob hauled them east across the plains of Washington and mountains of Idaho and had to stop frequently to raid ice machines along the way to keep the goats cool. The goats were transported to new homes on Red Mountain in Lewis and Clark County. Apparently they were not particularly attracted to their new locale. They dispersed from the site in multiple directions. One headed south about 80 miles to the general vicinity of Butte. Another moved to the southeast across prairie as well as mountains to the Birdtail area west of Cascade. Dispersal and disappearance of the Olympic NP goats left Red Mountain as a site for another attempt at reintroduction into historic habitat.[16]

The next transplants to Red Mountain were from the Crazy Mountains in 2002 and Square Butte in the eastern portion of the Highwood Mountains in 2005. A helicopter was used to capture goats by net-gunning and then transfer them to a truck. At the other end of the truck ride a helicopter lifted the goats from the end of the road to their new home on Red Mountain.

A transplant of goats from the Deep Creek trap site west of Choteau to Square Butte occurred in 1943. Sixty-five years later in 2008 the reverse

*Helicopter lowering a mountain goat to a staging area on Hurricane Ridge in Olympic National Park for transplanting to Montana - 1989.*
*(Montana Fish, Wildlife and Parks photo courtesy Bob Henderson)*

*Mountain goat from Olympic National Park being released on Red Mountain in Lewis & Clark County - 1989. (Montana Fish, Wildlife and Parks photo courtesy Bob Henderson)*

*Mountain Goats from the Crazy Mountains being released on Red Mountain, Lewis & Clark County - 2005. (Montana Fish, Wildlife and Parks photo courtesy Tom Lemke)*

occurred. A transplant of goats from Round Butte in the eastern portion of the Highwood Mountains went to Ear Mountain just north of the Deep Creek trap site.

When animals are transplanted and new populations started, genetic diversity of the new population is limited to genes present in the few animals that founded the population. This "bottle necking" can have major negative effects as generations pass, which is a serious problem for most species discussed in this book. As populations of these other species expanded they came into contact with resident populations or received multiple transplants from other sources which increased genetic diversity.

The situation with mountain goats is different. A number of introduced

*A net-gunned mountain goat from Round Butte (in the background) in the eastern part of the Highwood Mountains for transplanting to the Ear Mountain Wildlife Management Area in Teton County - 2008. (Montana Fish, Wildlife and Parks photo courtesy Brent N. Lonner)*

populations exist on mountain ranges isolated from historical native populations. Inbreeding resulting from such genetic isolation usually results in a slow failure of the isolated populations, but in a few cases could theoretically produce better adapted animals and even the origin of new subspecies or species over a long period of time. Some mountain goat herds have been isolated for over 20 generations.

Random introductions of new transplants to introduce genetic diversity bring the risk of carrying new viral and other diseases into long isolated populations. Genetic techniques of the 21st century bring a potential of low cost genetic monitoring. The Crazy, Tobacco Root, and Snowy Mountain herds are examples of populations started from only a single genetic source. The Beartooth, Cabinet and Madison Mountains each received transplants from three genetic sources. The original Deep Creek trapping site in the Sun River area proved to be highly productive contributing 135 goats over a 16 year period.

***The original Deep Creek trapping site in the Sun River area proved to be highly productive contributing 135 goats over a 16 year period.***

*Several mountain ranges east of the Continental Divide were not historically inhabited by mountain goats until successful trapping and transplanting efforts of this high mountain animal occurred between 1941-2008).* (Photo courtesy Della R. Lonner)

## An annotated listing of Montana mountain goat transplants; 1941 - 2008.

| Year(s) | Source | Number | Receiving Area |
|---|---|---|---|
| 1941 | Deep Cr., Teton Co. | 10 | Crazy Mtns., Sweet Grass Co. |
| | Deep Cr., Teton Co. | 4 | Benchmark, Lewis & Clark Co. |
| 1942 | Deep Cr., Teton Co. | 14 | Rock Cr., Beartooth Mtns., Carbon Co. |
| 1943 | Deep Cr., Teton Co. | 11 | Crazy Mtns., Sweet Grass Co. |
| | Deep Cr., Teton Co. | 4 | Square Butte, Highwood Mtns, Chouteau Co. |
| 1945 | Deep Cr., Teton Co. | 10 | Stillwater Canyon, Beartooth Mtns., Stillwater Co. |
| 1946 | Deep Cr., Teton Co. | 9 | Beartooth Mtns., Stillwater Co. |
| 1947 | Deep Cr., Teton Co. | 6 | West Fork Gallatin River, Gallatin Co. |
| 1948 | Canyon Cr., Pioneer Mtns., Beaverhead Co. | 9 | Colorado |
| | South Fork of the Flathead R., Flathead Co. | 5 | Stillwater Canyon, Beartooth Mtns., Stillwater Co. |
| 1949 | Deep Cr., Teton Co. | 3 | Stillwater Canyon, Beartooth Mtns., Stillwater Co. |
| | South Fork of the Flathead R., Flathead Co. | 2 | Gates of the Mountains, Lewis & Clark Co. |
| | South Fork of the Flathead R, Flathead Co. | 5 | Stillwater Canyon, Beartooth Mtns., Stillwater Co. |
| | Van Lookout, Lake Co. | 1 | Stillwater Canyon, Beartooth Mtns., Stillwater Co. |
| 1950s | Canyon Cr., Pioneer Mtns., Beaverhead Co. | 1 to 4 | National Zoological Park, Washington DC [1] |
| 1950 | Deep Cr., Teton Co. | 40 | Madison Dam, Spanish Peaks, Madison Co. |
| | Deep Cr., Teton Co. | 3 | Colorado Springs area, Colorado |
| 1951 | Deep Cr. Teton Co. | 4 | Gates of the Mountains, Lewis & Clark, Co. |
| | South Fork of the Flathead R., Flathead Co. | 29 | Gates of the Mountains, Lewis & Clark, Co. |
| | Van Lookout, Lake Co. | 12 | Madison Dam, Spanish Peaks, Madison Co. |
| 1952 | South Fork of the Flathead R., Flathead Co. | 18 | East Rosebud R., Beartooth Mtns., Carbon Co. |
| | Canyon Cr., Pioneer Mtns., Beaverhead Co. | 2 | East Rosebud R., Beartooth Mtns., Carbon Co. |
| 1953 | Canyon Cr., Pioneer Mtns., Beaverhead Co. | 11 | Snowy Mtns., Fergus Co. |
| | South Fork of the Flathead R., Flathead Co. | 7 | East Rosebud R., Beartooth Mtns., Carbon Co. |
| 1954 | Canyon Cr., Pioneer Mtns., Beaverhead Co. | 11 | Snowy Mtns., Fergus Co. |
| 1955 | Canyon Cr., Pioneer Mtns., Beaverhead Co. | 15 | South Boulder R., Jefferson Co. |
| 1956 | Deep Cr., Teton Co. | 15 | Elkhorn Mtns., Jefferson Co. |
| | Canyon Cr., Pioneer Mtns., Beaverhead Co. | 12 | Mill Cr., Tobacco Root Mtns., Madison Co. |
| | Canyon Cr., Pioneer Mtns., Beaverhead Co. | 8 | Pine Cr., Absaroka Mtns., Park Co. |
| | Canyon Cr., Pioneer Mtns., Beaverhead Co. | 10 | Wyoming, Sybill Research Unit |
| 1957 | Deep Cr., Teton Co. | 2 | Elkhorn Mtns., Jefferson Co. |
| | Canyon Cr., Pioneer Mtns., Beaverhead Co. | 10 | Pine Cr., Absaroka Mtns., Park Co. |

## An annotated listing of Montana mountain goat transplants; 1941 - 2008, cont.

| Year(s) | Source | Number | Receiving Area |
|---|---|---|---|
| 1958 | Canyon Cr., Pioneer Mtns., Beaverhead Co. | 2 | Elkhorn Mtns., Jefferson Co. |
| | Canyon Cr., Pioneer Mtns., Beaverhead Co. | 4 | Pine Cr., Absaroka Mtns., Park Co. |
| 959 | Canyon Cr., Pioneer Mtns., Beaverhead Co. | 27 | Wolf Cr., Madison Co. |
| 962 | Canyon Cr., Pioneer Mtns., Beaverhead Co. | 7 | Highland Mtns., Silver Bow Co. |
| 964 | Source unknown | 4 | National Bison Range, Lake Co.[2] |
| 969 | Gates of the Mountains, Lewis & Clark Co. | 13 | Bridger Mtns., Gallatin Co. |
| 970 | Gates of the Mountains, Lewis & Clark Co. | 13 | Mt. Edith, Big Belt Mtns., Broadwater Co. |
| 1971 | Gates of the Mountains, Lewis & Clark Co. | 7 | Square Butte, Highwood Mtns.,Chouteau Co. |
| | Gates of the Mountains, Lewis & Clark Co. | 6 | Mt. Edith, Big Belt Mtns., Broadwater Co. |
| 97 | Gates of the Mountains, Lewis & Clark Co. | 12 | Snowcrest Mtns., Madison Co. |
| 980 | Olympic National Park, Washington | 7 | Drift Cr., Lincoln Co. |
| 985 | Olympic National Park, Washington | 12 | Cougar Peak, Cabinet Mtns., Sanders Co. |
| 1987 | National Bison Range, Lake Co. | 12 | West Fork Thompson R., Cabinet Mtns., Sanders Co. |
| | National Bison Range, Lake Co. | 12 | Rattlesnake Cr., Missoula Co. |
| 989 | Olympic National Park, Washington | 13 | Red Mountain, Lewis and Clark Co. |
| 1990 | National Bison Range, Lake Co. | 2 | Wyoming |
| | National Bison Range, Lake Co. | 2 | West Fork Thompson R., Cabinet Mtns., Sanders Co. |
| | National Bison Range, Lake Co. | 6 | Copper Cr., Lewis and Clark Co. |
| 002 | Crazy Mountains, Park Co. | 13 | Red Mountain, Lewis and Clark Co. |
| 005 | Square Butte, Chouteau Co. | 5 | Red Mountain, Lewis and Clark Co. |
| 008 | Round Butte, Chouteau Co. | 10 | Ear Mountain Wildlife Management Area, Teton Co. |
| **Summary** | **Sources of Goats** | | |
| | **Montana** | **435** | **for transplants within Montana** |
| | **Montana** | **25 - 28** [1] | **for transplants outside of Montana** |
| | **Outside of Montana** | **32** | **for transplants into Montana** |
| | **Total** | **492 - 495** [1] | **135 from Deep Cr. over a 16 year period** |

Genetic sources: The Beartooth Mountains' goat population is from 3 different source populations
The Cabinet Mountains' goat population is probably from 3 different source populations.
The Madison Range goat population is probably from 3 different source populations.

[1] Quantities in question reflect differences in Montana Fish, Wildlife and Parks records.
[2] Plant was used to start a population. Kraft, E. 2006. Untold tales of bison range trails. Stoneydale Press, Stevensville, MT. p 36.

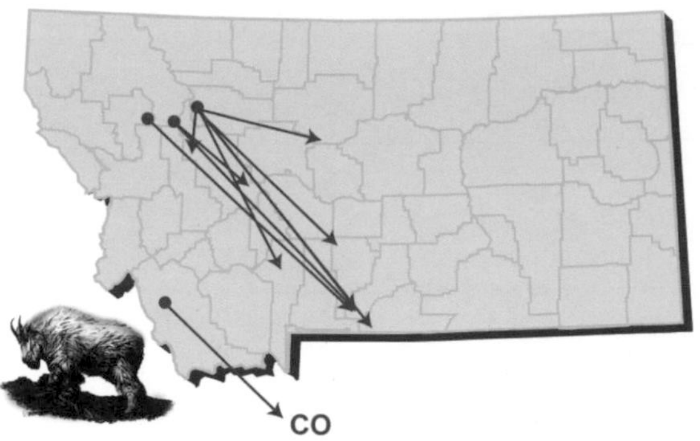


1941 - 1949 Mountain Goat Transplants

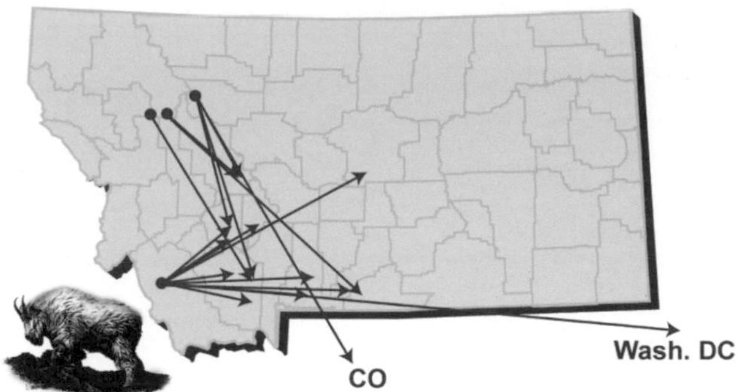


1950 - 1959 Mountain Goat Transplants

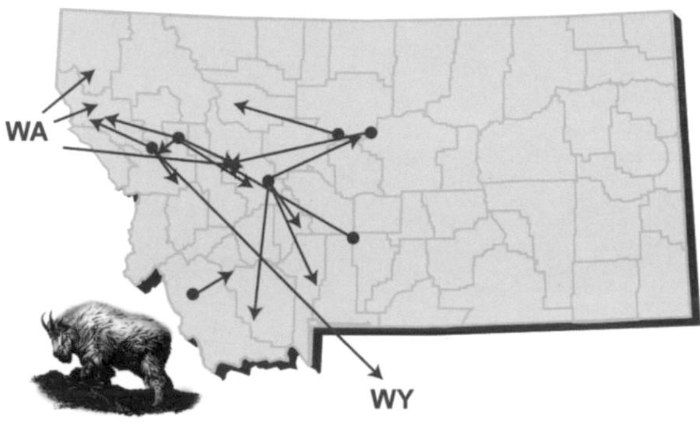


1960 - 2008 Mountain Goat Transplants

1942 Mountain Goat Distribution

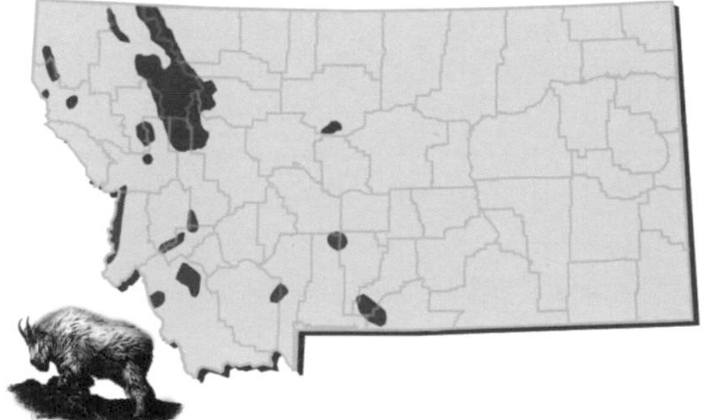

1947 Mountain Goat Distribution

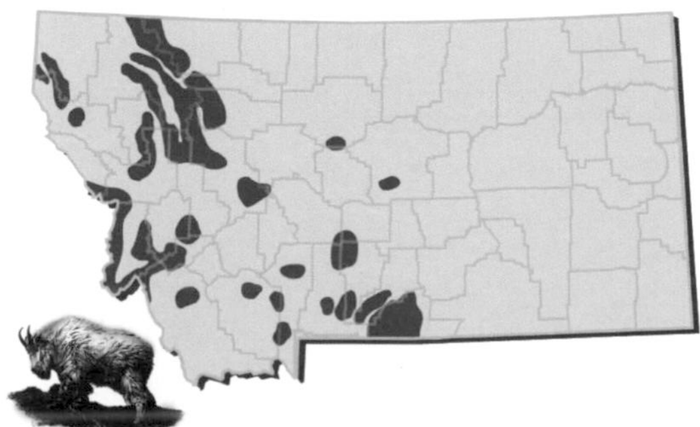

1970 Mountain Goat Distribution

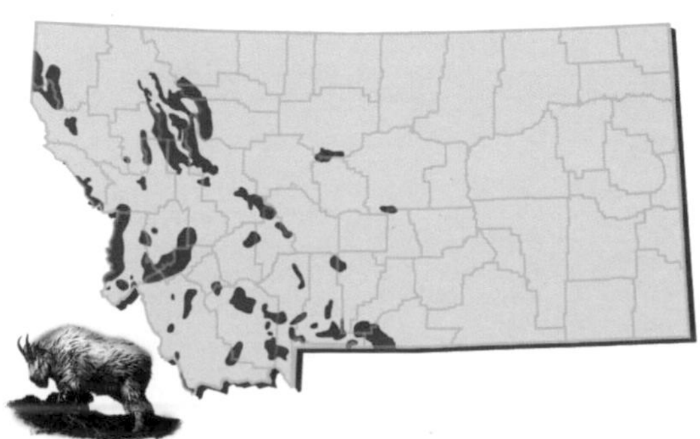

2008 Mountain Goat Distribution

# Footnotes

[1] Cote', S. D. and M. Festo-Bianchet. 2003. Mountain goat. Chapter 49 in Wild Mammals of North America, Editors: G. A. Feldhammer, B. C. Thompson and J. A. Chapman. Johns Hopkins University Press 1061-1075.

[2] Ibid.

[3] Montana Fish and Game Dept. typewritten memo. c. 1940s. "It should be in mind that wildlife management programs are paid for by hunting licenses and the money does not come from general tax revenues. Mountain goat transplants became major tourist attractions in the most accessible areas such as the Gates of the Mountains."

[4] McLucas, J. 1999. Videotaped interview with Harold Picton and Jim Williams.

[5] Kearney, P. 1994. Butte's pride: The Columbia Gardens. Skyhigh Publications. 130 pp.

[6] Letters, Montana Fish, Wildlife and Parks Dept., Helena. B. Brannin to Bob Cooney 7/10/1940; B. Brannin to I. V. Anderson (USFS) 7/11/1940; C. A. Joy (USFS) to B. Brannin 7/15/1940; E. E. Redman (USFS) to C. A. Joy 7/10/1940; I. V. Anderson (USFS) memorandum of cooperation with the state of Montana, goat transplanting 8/30/1940; R. Cooney to B. Brannin 7/20/1940.

[7] Gaab, J. 1955. Those Crazy Mountain goats. Montana Wildlife. 5(1):15-17.

[8] Cooney, R. F. 1942. Trapping and transplanting mountain goats. Typewritten memorandum to Montana Fish and Game Commission. Montana Fish and Game Dept., Helena. 5 pp. Note: A skid trail is the trail left by dragging or "skidding" logs.

[9] Cooney, R. F. 1942. Trapping and transplanting Mountain goats. Typewritten memorandum to the Montana Fish and Game Commission.. Montana Fish, Wildlife and Parks Dept., Helena. 5 pp.

[10] West, Bill (Manager of the National Bison Range). 2008. Personal communication with Terry Lonner.

[11] Primitive areas were the forerunners of wilderness areas. The rules for their management differed slightly from those of the modern Wilderness Areas. A few airstrips were maintained for fire fighting purposes and aircraft were permitted to land in them for other special purposes. Wheeled vehicles and motorized appliances are prohibited in Wilderness areas.

[12] McDowell, L. 1949. Wildlife restocking report. Montana Fish and Game Dept., Helena. 14 pp. Part of what was left out of this understated account is perhaps told in an uncorroborated account: One of the goats managed to get a hoof free and kicked a hole through the fabric side of the airplane on takeoff. The pilot was irate and brought out the "hundred mile an hour tape" to patch the hole temporarily.

[13] Ibid. McLucas, J. 1999.

[14] Craig, Vernon, editor. 1958. Montana Wildlife, August 1958. 32.

[15] Henderson, R. 2006. Personal communication with Harold Picton.

West, B. 2008. Personal communication with Terry Lonner.

[16] Ibid. Henderson, R. 2006.

*Loading bighorn sheep into a truck for transit and transplanting. c. 1960.*
*(Courtesy Jim McLucas Photo Collection)*

*Herding bighorn sheep with a helicopter toward a trap on Wildhorse Island. c. 1979.*
*(Photo courtesy Glenn Erickson)*

# Chapter 12

# Rocky Mountain Bighorn Sheep

Bighorn sheep (*Ovis spp.*) is another species unique to North America. Enormous horns of rams sometimes approach 10 percent of their body weight. While both sexes have horns, those of bighorn rams are proportionately larger than those of any other sheep species in the world. These horns are not shed annually and grow throughout a sheep's lifetime.

Rocky Mountain bighorn, (*Ovis canadensis canadensis*), is the subspecies found in Montana. Historically, "Audubon" sheep occupied breaks or badland areas along the Missouri and Yellowstone Rivers. The "breaks" or Audubon sheep became extinct when the last was killed by a hunter in 1916.[1] Audubon sheep may not have been regarded a distinct subspecies. DNA from a very limited number of historic specimens suggests that there is not enough difference from Rocky Mountain bighorn populations to justify subspecies status.[2] The historic name is useful for identification of bighorns that occupied unique badland habitat. At the other end of the scale, the Sun River population seems to have more genetic diversity than other sheep herds and therefore may be considered more of a subspecies than Audubon sheep.[3]

Bighorns utilize broken country with rock outcrops. Low cliffs with neighboring, but relatively level areas

***Horns of bighorn sheep rams are proportionately larger than those of any other species in the world.***

*The "breaks" or Audubon sheep became extinct when the last one was killed by a hunter in 1916.[1]*

*An Audubon sheep mount displayed as part of the wild animal collection in the Valley Pioneer Museum in Glasgow, MT. c. 1980. (Montana Fish, Wildlife and Parks photo by Mike Aderhold)*

*During the breeding season in December rams often compete with one another by meeting head on in a full charge and the shock of these collisions is borne by the sophisticated shock absorbing structure of both horns and skull.*

with good visibility over surrounding terrain seem particularly suitable. These serve as bedding areas as well as a source of food. They eat grasses as well as the higher food quality broad leaf plants and shrubs.

Bighorn sheep become sexually mature at about 18 months of age but are not yet socially mature. Ewes typically become pregnant for the first time at 2 to 3 years old. Males are usually not large enough to rank well in the breeding hierarchy until they are 6 to 8 years old. Ewes give birth to a single lamb born in late May after a gestation period of about 175 days.[4] The horns of males are instruments of sexual competition. During the breeding season in December rams often compete with one another by meeting head on in a full charge and the shock of these collisions is borne by the sophisticated shock absorbing structure of both horns and skull. Horn size of rams is a reflection of both age and habitat quality of their home range.[5] Rams and ewe-lamb groups have separate home ranges through most of the year. They come together on home ranges of ewes in late fall and early winter for the rut.

Mountain sheep are gregarious and live on patches of habitat. If they migrate from winter to summer ranges the migration route may follow convoluted pathways. Bighorns are often referred to as being highly traditional, because lambs learn migration routes from older rams and ewes. These migration pathways are very difficult to reestablish if mortality inhibits the passage of the knowledge of

***Bighorn sheep at the head of Gibson Reservoir, Sun River - 1975.*** *(Montana Fish and Game Department photo by Robert Cooney)*

them. It may take transplanted sheep a long time to develop optimal use of new habitat, but it does occur.

Disease is a major problem for bighorn sheep management. Epidemics inflicted by many different disease organisms, may rage through populations killing up to 80 percent. Scabies, a skin parasite and bacterial diseases such as pink-eye and anthrax are some of the many diseases that have affected Montana bighorns. Certain organisms, such as *Pasteurella hemolytica* are carried by domestic sheep without harm but can be passed on to bighorn sheep, causing a virulent and fatal pneumonia. Most bighorn populations are infected with lungworm *(Protostrongylus spp.)*, a parasite that lives in a tiny snail for part of its life cycle. Lungworm does not necessarily cause problems for adult sheep but promotes pneumonia if they contract other diseases. Lungworm can kill lambs if infected at an early age.[6] Disease relationships between wild and domestic sheep probably mean that the domestic sheep population of over five million early in the 20th century had to decline to a major degree before it became biologically feasible to attempt restoration of bighorn populations. Such a decline in domestic sheep had occurred in Montana by the 1950s.

Originally, scattered populations of bighorn sheep were found throughout the state, frequently occupying sizable rock outcrops across the prairie as well as mountains and badlands along rivers. Archeological studies have found sheep hunting sites thousands of years old. Bighorns were a preferred food item by Indians and settlers. Small scattered populations quickly disappeared under the onslaught of settlers. The Shoshone Indian Tribe inhabiting the area that is now Yellowstone NP called themselves Sheepeaters because they relied upon bighorns as a major food source. All fish and game agencies of the western states regarded bighorn sheep as "endangered" by 1941,[7]

***Originally, scattered populations of bighorn sheep were found throughout the state, frequently occupying sizable rock outcrops across the prairie as well as mountains and badlands along rivers.***

although the federal Endangered Species Act was not passed for decades to come.

Transplanting bighorn sheep in Montana began in 1922 when a group of sheep were moved from Banff, Alberta Canada and released on the National Bison Range. The Bison Range sheep population grew, leading to a transplant from the Bison Range to Hart Mountain Wildlife Refuge in Oregon in 1939.[8] In a private effort in 1939, the owner of Wildhorse Island on Flathead Lake obtained a ram and a ewe from the extreme southern end of the Mission-Salish Mountain area on the Flathead Indian Reservation and moved them to the island. There were horses and mule deer on the island at the time. The sheep survived and increased to six by 1947.[9]

*In a private effort in 1939 the owner of Wildhorse Island on Flathead Lake obtained a ram and a ewe from the extreme southern end of the Mission-Salish Mountain area on the Flathead Indian Reservation and moved them to the island.*

Efforts by the state of Montana to transplant bighorns began in 1942 with 11 sheep from the Sun River area to the Gates of the Mountains near Helena in Lewis and Clark County. A similar transplant of three was made in 1944. Faye Couey was conducting a research study of the estimated 280 Sun River sheep at the time.[10] He found poor range conditions with a high incidence of lungworm and concluded the best way to help bighorns was to transplant some from this area to new ranges. The poor situation for Sun River sheep did not change until after purchase of the Sun River Wildlife Management Area in 1947 and a substantial reduction of elk numbers during 1957-1959.[11]

Five bighorn sheep traps were built in the 1940s. The primary area used for transplanting were two traps in the Sun River. The goat trap in neighboring Deep Creek also had sheep visiting it which furnished another source for transplanting. One was located along the Kootenai River in the Ural-Tweed area on a site now flooded by Libby Dam on the Kootenai River. Two rams from this area were transplanted to the West Fork of the Gallatin River. A trap in the West Fork of the Gallatin River drainage furnished a ram that was released in the Sun River area. Salt was used to draw sheep into traps. They were then lassoed, placed in crates and transported. Sometimes transportation was by packhorse and then by truck. Sheep caught at the Scattering Springs trap in the upper Sun River canyon were transported the

*Bighorn sheep in and around the Scattering Springs trap in the upper Sun River Canyon - 1975. (Montana Fish and Game Department photo by Robert Cooney)*

length of Gibson Reservoir in a boat and then loaded into trucks.

The reason for exchanging rams between herds was to counteract popular opinion that sheep populations were doing poorly because of inbreeding. The concept could not be directly tested because DNA technology was not yet available. Faye Couey offered his view which was derived from field research that ended individual ram transplants:

*Bighorn Sheep trapped near Gibson Reservoir, Sun River and Sun River Canyon were transported by boat to a road where they were loaded into trucks for transplanting. c. 1970s.* *(Courtesy Jim McLucas Photo Collection)*

***Faye Couey concluded that parasites, disease and range conditions were the major influences depressing bighorn sheep populations, not inbreeding.***

> "The thought is rather prevalent that our bighorn herds have been isolated in small groups so long that they have become inbred, run-down, decreased in size, become impotent, barren, and less disease resistant. Little evidence to support this has been found in this investigation other than the bighorns are subject to parasites and disease. Rams have been seen wandering great distances from known bands of sheep. This wandering habit should insure a mixture of breeding stock in most bands."[12]

*Flathead sportsmen help Montana Fish and Game Department employees with driving Bighorn sheep (along with a few deer) into the wings and down the lane of a portable big game trap on Wildhorse Island - 1954.* *(Courtesy Jim McLucas Photo Collection)*

DNA analyses conducted in the 1990s indicated Couey was correct.[13]

In 1947, seven sheep from the Sun River were released on Wildhorse Island to supplement the six that were there. By 1962, the original 80 horses that were on the island had declined to two. Mule deer, estimated at 600 had declined to 200 while the bighorn population had increased to 132.[14] Beginning in 1954, the island served as a new source of bighorns for transplanting.

Several ideas had been proposed to benefit the Montana bighorn

*In 1954 when Bighorn Sheep were trapped on Wildhorse Island, they were put into a sled and pulled to the shore for a boat to take them off the island.* *(Courtesy Jim McLucas Photo Collection)*

*Bighorn sheep in a typical corral trap used for trapping and transplanting. c. 1950s. (Courtesy Jim McLucas Photo Collection)*

***"...a cross between a Mouflon and a Desert Bighorn was kept at the Fairgrounds in Helena by the Montana Fish & Game Department. He broke the wires of the pen he was in and got out. So I hear he's over at the Helena airport looking in the window at people, so I catches up with him and he's headed down north Montana street through the cemetery..."***

—Jim McLucas

sheep program. One was to have a mountain sheep ranch on Castle Reef on the north side of the Sun River. A confined group of sheep would be raised where competitors and predators could be controlled. As the herd grew, surplus sheep would be used for transplanting. Although the site was not used, the idea led to use of Wildhorse Island as a transplanting source.

A second idea came from a chance visit during World War II. Ken Thompson had been called from his biological duties to serve in the U.S. Navy during World War II. On shore leave he visited the San Diego Zoo where he saw an exhibit on European Mouflon Sheep (*Ovis musimon*) and learned that they were resistant to lungworm. Returning to Montana after the war, he proposed that Mouflon and bighorn sheep be interbred to produce a strain resistant to lungworm. The Montana Fish and Game Department acquired a Mouflon and housed it with a Desert Bighorn (*Ovis canadensis nelsoni*) acquired from out-ot-state in a facility at Helena. The sheep were housed in a racehorse stall at the fairgrounds. There were 2 by 4's on the walls and the sheep would use them for exercise, running up and along the walls and then into the outside pen. Jim McLucas;

> "This cross between a Mouflon and a Desert Bighorn was kept at the Fairgrounds in Helena by the Montana Fish & Game Department. He broke the wires of the pen he was in and got out. So I hear he's over at the Helena airport looking in the window at the people, so I catches up with him and he's headed down north Montana through the cemetery and comes out of the cemetery into Lamb's ranch. There's two old work horses standing there. They see this strange looking thing and they jump the fence and are running up through the cemetery. I followed him down the lane and he ran in the garage. I rushed in with the pickup and closed the doors. He kind of tried to jump through the window and I finally caught him and brought him back to the fairgrounds. He got loose again, but all I'd have to do was get some grain and holler for him and he'd come. He roamed the fairgrounds and that area. He never left the fairgrounds. I guess that one trip out was enough for him."[15]

The crossbreeding experiment was ended and no sheep from it were released into the wild.

Of the ideas proposed to benefit established sheep herds, most effective have been those to improve range and habitat conditions. Sheep trapped for transplanting have been typically treated to rid them of lungworm as appropriate drugs have become available. Sheep populations may later pick up infections from natural sources so the treatments can't be regarded as permanent for new populations.

One long-term goal was to get a population of bighorn sheep reestablished in the Missouri Breaks. Because all Montana populations had lungworm, an effort was made to obtain sheep from other states. In the 1940s and 50s, the Tarryall sheep herd in Colorado was believed to be free of lungworm. A barter of mountain goats for bighorns was arranged. Mountain goats were trapped and sent to Colorado. In return, 16 bighorns were transported to the Billy Creek area in the eastern portion of the Missouri River Breaks northwest of Jordan in 1947. Ironically, this is where the last Audubon Sheep was killed in 1916.

The Colorado sheep were held in a 320 acre fenced pasture at Billy Creek in the Garfield County portion of the Charles M. Russell National Wildlife Refuge for 3 years. When their numbers increased, they were released in 1950 and 1952. The population continued to increase after the fence was removed. An incomplete survey in 1955 by the U.S. Fish and Wildlife Service and Montana Fish and Game Department found 78 sheep. The survey was incomplete because a cloudburst left the expedition "gumboed" in the notorious mud of the breaks. Mud balls on their feet restricted mobility of both horses and men. A dry spell and stimulus provided by vanishing food finally allowed the expedition to escape across water filled gullies. The discovery that grasshoppers ate holes in sweaty clothes also contributed to the education of the senior author. Later, a hunting season for a few mature rams was initiated.[16] By 1965, the population was extinct for unknown reasons, but disease was not thought to be a factor.

*Billy Creek area in the Missouri River Breaks in central Montana where bighorn sheep from Colorado were transplanted in 1947, held in a 320 acre fenced pasture and then released in 1950 and 1952 on the Charles M. Russell National Wildlife Refuge. c. 1954. (Photo courtesy Harold Picton)*

A second attempt to repopulate the Missouri Breaks with bighorn sheep was made by a cooperative effort by federal and state agencies and resulted in construction of a fenced pasture on Two-Calf Creek north of Lewistown in the western portion of the Breaks.

*Bighorn sheep being released to help restore populations on historical ranges in Montana and the West. c. 1970s. (Courtesy Jim McLucas Photo Collection)*

*Another method of trapping sheep was "drive-netting". Once in the net they could be handled and moved. c. 1987. (Photo courtesy Glenn Erickson)*

*Efforts to restore bighorns to native ranges continues. Re-introductions require a great deal of cooperation and trust among private land owners, sportsmen, federal agencies such as the U.S. Forest Service, the Bureau of Land Management, U.S. Fish and Wildlife Service, Montana Fish, Wildlife and Parks and Indian tribes.*

Stocking began in 1958 with 9 sheep from the Sun River. This was followed by 24 sheep from the National Bison Range in 1959 and 1960. An additional dozen Sun River bighorns were added in 1962. Predators and competing species such as deer were removed from the pasture. As sometimes occurs in sheep transplants, the population increased rapidly. The dense population then suffered a die-off and by 1970 only a few sheep survived. These few survivors ranged in the Breaks outside of the pasture. Another effort to populate the Breaks with sheep was made in 1980. Twenty-eight sheep from the Sun River were released in the Armell's –Two-Calf Creek area of Fergus County on the south side of the Missouri River. An additional 28 Sun River sheep were released at the same time north of the river in southern Phillips County. The current robust population in the Breaks is the result of colonization from these transplants. This population has succeeded to the extent that it has provided a number of rams for hunters as well as a large number of sheep to start other populations including some in other states.

Attempts to restore bighorn sheep to native habitat in other parts of eastern Montana were made in 1976. A plant of 25 Sun River sheep was released in the Blue Hills near Miles City. This population persists today.

Efforts to restore bighorns continues. Re-introductions require a great deal of cooperation and trust among private land owners, sportsmen, federal agencies such as the U.S. Forest Service, Bureau of Land Management, U.S. Fish and Wildlife Service, Montana Fish, Wildlife and Parks and Indian tribes. For example, in 2008 bighorn sheep were transplanted from the Flathead Indian Reservation in western Montana to the Rocky Boy's Indian Reservation in north central Montana. Netgunning from a helicopter is now the preferred method of capture.

The popularity of bighorn sheep trapping and transplanting was featured on Mutual of Omaha's Wild

*Bighorn sheep caught by netgunning from a helicopter for transplanting - 2008. (Montana Fish, Wildlife and Parks photo courtesy Brent N. Lonner)*

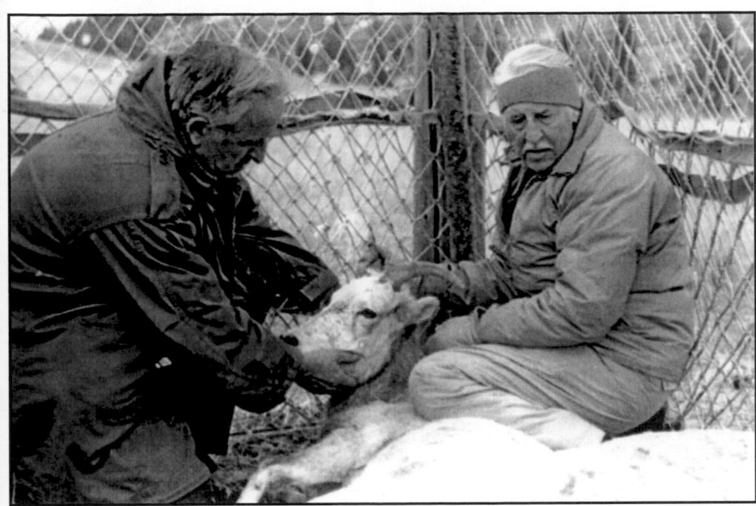

*Jim McLucas of the Montana Fish and Game Dept. and Marlin Perkins with Mutual of Omaha's Wild Kingdom handle a bighorn sheep ewe during a trapping and filming session on Wildhorse Island - 1975. (Photo Courtesy Jim McLucas Collection)*

Kingdom in 1975. This documentary was done on Wildhorse Island with Jim McLucas in charge and Marlin Perkins, host of the TV program. Jim McLucas also furnished technical assistance to the province of British Columbia to help them capture and transplant California bighorns (*Ovis canadensis californiana*).

In the last few decades of the 20th century much of the management and re-introduction efforts have been funded by The Foundation for North American Wild Sheep (FNAWS), through a cooperative agreement with Montana Fish, Wildlife and Parks. Less money is available for management of low density species such as sheep, goats and moose because of the small number of hunting licenses that can be sold. FNAWS has reached agreements with a number of states including Montana which allows them to auction a single sheep hunting permit for that state at their annual convention. While the holder of this special permit is allowed to pick whatever hunting area they wish, they must follow all other laws and regulations. There is no refund if a bighorn ram is not taken.

Bighorn rams are a charismatic species and bidding can be intense. As a premier bighorn state, the Montana permit has gone for as high as $310,000 although the average is considerably lower. These auctions have furnished considerable amounts of money for Montana's bighorn sheep management programs.

The bighorn sheep transplanting program has been successful in re-establishing several dozen self sustaining populations in the state. Very little mortality resulted from the actual transplanting process. However, the success rate in re-establishing populations is lower than for other species. Diseases remain a major unsolved problem for bighorn populations.

Bighorn sheep face other natural hazards. Jim Williams, a Montana State University graduate student, was

***In the last few decades of the 20th century much of the bighorn sheep management and re-introduction efforts have been funded by the private Foundation for North American Wild Sheep through a cooperative agreement. Less money is available for the management of low density species such as sheep, goats, and moose because of the small number of hunting licenses that can be sold for such species.***

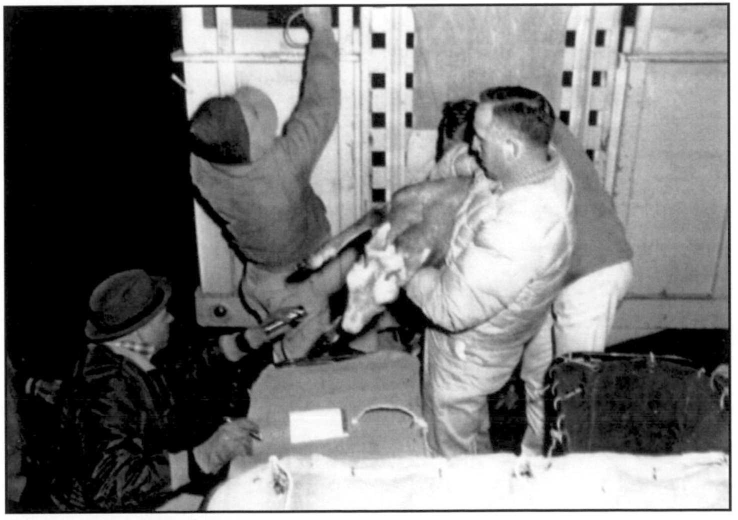

*Montana Fish and Game trapper Jim McLucas assisting with the trapping and transplanting of California bighorns from British Columbia to Idaho - 1963. (Courtesy Jim McLucas Photo Collection)*

*The bighorn sheep transplanting program in Montana has been successful in re-establishing several dozen self sustaining populations in the state.*

researching mountain lions in the Sun River area when he found a one-eyed mountain lion that seemed to be specializing in killing bighorns. Some of his kills had horns that would have made any trophy hunter cry with envy. The lion used a steep gorge where a migratory route brought dinner to him. He apparently had led a tough life because he also had a permanent kink in his tail.

By the 1990s bighorn restoration was successful enough that Montana could assist other states in recovering their sheep populations. Bighorns were transplanted to Nebraska, North Dakota, Idaho, Oregon, Utah, Washington and Wyoming. Five of the six populations contributing bighorns to these efforts were populations that had been started during transplant efforts in Montana. The benefits of the Montana program begun in the 1940s have been spread across the west.

*Bighorn sheep have been successfully transplanted to many areas with suitable habitat in Montana and beyond. A major source for transplanting is from one of the largest concentrations of bighorns in North America on the East Front west of Great Falls.* (Montana Fish, Wildlife and Parks photo by Brent N. Lonner)

## An annotated listing of Montana bighorn sheep transplants; 1922-2008.

| Year(s) | Source | Number | Release Location |
|---|---|---|---|
| 1922 | Banff, Alberta, Canada | 12 | National Bison Range, Lake Co. |
| 1939 | National Bison Range, Lake Co. | 23 | Hart Mountain Refuge, Oregon[1] |
| | National Bison Range, Lake Co. | 2 | Washington State University, Pullman (for research) |
| | Mission Mtns., Missoula Co. | 2 | Wild Horse Island, Lake Co. |
| 1942 | Sun River, Teton Co. | 11 | Gates of the Mountains, Lewis & Clark Co. |
| 1943 | Sun River, Teton Co. | 3 | Gates of the Mountains, Lewis & Clark Co. |
| 1944 | West Gallatin, Gallatin Co. | 1 | Sun River, Teton Co. |
| | Ural-Tweed, Lincoln Co. | 1 | West Gallatin River, Gallatin Co. |
| 1947 | Sun River, Teton Co. | 2 | West Gallatin River, Gallatin Co. |
| | Sun River, Teton Co. | 7 | Wild Horse Island, Lake Co. |
| | Colorado, Tarryall herd, Park Co. | 16 | Billy Cr., Missouri River Breaks, Garfield Co. |
| 1954 | Sun River, Teton Co. | 6 | 16 Mile Canyon, Gallatin Co. |
| | Wildhorse Island, Lake Co. | 12 | Kootenai Falls, Lincoln Co. |
| 1955 | Wild Horse Island, Lake Co. | 9 | 16 Mile Canyon, Gallatin Co. |
| | Wild Horse Island, Lake Co. | 5 | Bull Mtn., Jefferson Co. |
| | Wild Horse Island, Lake Co. | 3 | Bull Mtn., Jefferson Co. |
| | Wild Horse Island, Lake Co. | 3 | Kootenai Falls, Lincoln Co. |
| | Sun River, Teton Co. | 5 | Bull Mtn., Jefferson Co. |
| 1956 | Sun River, Teton Co. | 13 | Sheep Cr., Cascade Co. |
| | Wild Horse Island, Lake Co. | 7 | Blue Hills, Custer Co. |
| | Sun River, Teton Co. | 5 | Blue Hills, Custer Co. |
| | No source available | 1 to 4 | National Zoological Park, Washington, D.C. |
| 1957 | Sun River, Teton Co. | 7 | Bull Mtn., Jefferson Co. |
| | Wild Horse Island, Lake Co. | 6 | Bull Mtn., Jefferson Co. |
| 1958 | Wild Horse Island, Lake Co. | 5 | Sheep Cr., Cascade Co. |
| | Sun River, Teton Co. | 9 | Two-Calf Cr., Missouri River Breaks, Fergus Co. |
| | Wild Horse Island, Lake Co. | 13 | Blue Hills, Custer Co. |
| | Sun River, Teton Co. | 3 | Blue Hills, Custer Co. |
| 1959 | Sun River, Teton Co. | 13 | Eddy Cr., Sanders Co. |
| | Wild Horse Island, Lake Co. | 6 | Thompson River, Sanders Co. |
| | National Bison Range, Lake Co. | 13 | Two Calf Cr., Missouri River Breaks, Fergus Co. |
| 1960 | National Bison Range, Lake Co. | 34 | Stickney Cr, Big Belt Mtns., Lewis & Clark Co. |
| | National Bison Range, Lake Co. | 11 | Two-Calf Cr., Missouri River Breaks, Fergus Co. |
| | Sun River, Teton Co. | 8 | Hannon Gulch, Sun River, Teton Co. |
| | Sun River, Teton Co. | 3 | Sheep Cr., Big Belt Mtns., Cascade Co. |
| 1961 | Sun River Teton Co. | 1 | Two Calf Cr., Missouri River Breaks, Fergus Co. |
| | Sun River, Teton Co. | 11 | Two Calf Cr., Missouri River Breaks, Fergus Co. |

## An annotated listing of Montana bighorn sheep transplants; 1922-2008.

| Year(s) | Source | Number | Release Location |
|---|---|---|---|
| 1922 | Banff, Alberta, Canada | 12 | National Bison Range, Lake Co. |
| 1939 | National Bison Range, Lake Co. | 23 | Hart Mountain Refuge, Oregon[1] |
| | National Bison Range, Lake Co. | 2 | Washington State University, Pullman (for research) |
| | Mission Mtns., Missoula Co. | 2 | Wild Horse Island, Lake Co. |
| 1942 | Sun River, Teton Co. | 11 | Gates of the Mountains, Lewis & Clark Co. |
| 1943 | Sun River, Teton Co. | 3 | Gates of the Mountains, Lewis & Clark Co. |
| 1944 | West Gallatin, Gallatin Co. | 1 | Sun River, Teton Co. |
| | Ural-Tweed, Lincoln Co. | 1 | West Gallatin River, Gallatin Co. |
| 1947 | Sun River, Teton Co. | 2 | West Gallatin River, Gallatin Co. |
| | Sun River, Teton Co. | 7 | Wild Horse Island, Lake Co. |
| | Colorado, Tarryall herd, Park Co. | 16 | Billy Cr., Missouri River Breaks, Garfield Co. |
| 1954 | Sun River, Teton Co. | 6 | 16 Mile Canyon, Gallatin Co. |
| | Wildhorse Island, Lake Co. | 12 | Kootenai Falls, Lincoln Co. |
| 1955 | Wild Horse Island, Lake Co. | 9 | 16 Mile Canyon, Gallatin Co. |
| | Wild Horse Island, Lake Co. | 5 | Bull Mtn., Jefferson Co. |
| | Wild Horse Island, Lake Co. | 3 | Bull Mtn., Jefferson Co. |
| | Wild Horse Island, Lake Co. | 3 | Kootenai Falls, Lincoln Co. |
| | Sun River, Teton Co. | 5 | Bull Mtn., Jefferson Co. |
| 1956 | Sun River, Teton Co. | 13 | Sheep Cr., Cascade Co. |
| | Wild Horse Island, Lake Co. | 7 | Blue Hills, Custer Co. |
| | Sun River, Teton Co. | 5 | Blue Hills, Custer Co. |
| | No source available | 1 to 4 | National Zoological Park, Washington, D.C. |
| 1957 | Sun River, Teton Co. | 7 | Bull Mtn., Jefferson Co. |
| | Wild Horse Island, Lake Co. | 6 | Bull Mtn., Jefferson Co. |
| 1958 | Wild Horse Island, Lake Co. | 5 | Sheep Cr., Cascade Co. |
| | Sun River, Teton Co. | 9 | Two-Calf Cr., Missouri River Breaks, Fergus Co. |
| | Wild Horse Island, Lake Co. | 13 | Blue Hills, Custer Co. |
| | Sun River, Teton Co. | 3 | Blue Hills, Custer Co. |
| 1959 | Sun River, Teton Co. | 13 | Eddy Cr., Sanders Co. |
| | Wild Horse Island, Lake Co. | 6 | Thompson River, Sanders Co. |
| | National Bison Range, Lake Co. | 13 | Two Calf Cr., Missouri River Breaks, Fergus Co. |
| 1960 | National Bison Range, Lake Co. | 34 | Stickney Cr, Big Belt Mtns., Lewis & Clark Co. |
| | National Bison Range, Lake Co. | 11 | Two-Calf Cr., Missouri River Breaks, Fergus Co. |
| | Sun River, Teton Co. | 8 | Hannon Gulch, Sun River, Teton Co. |
| | Sun River, Teton Co. | 3 | Sheep Cr., Big Belt Mtns., Cascade Co. |
| 1961 | Sun River Teton Co. | 1 | Two Calf Cr., Missouri River Breaks, Fergus Co. |
| | Sun River, Teton Co. | 11 | Two Calf Cr., Missouri River Breaks, Fergus Co. |

## Errata for Page 164

**The contents of page 163 were inadvertently repeated on page 164. The correct contents for page 164 are on the reverse side of this page.**

*Bighorn sheep lamb caught during a trapping and transplanting operation on Wildhorse Island. c. 1955 (Courtesy Jim McLucas Photo Collection)*

*Bighorn sheep ram captured on Wildhorse Island for transplanting; hog-tied and transported to the lake shore in a stone boat. Chain in photo was not to hold the ram, but to keep the planks on the boat from falling off. c. 1955 (Courtesy Robert Cooney Photo Collection)*

*Bighorn sheep near the head of the Sun River with Arsenic Peak in the background. c. 2008 (Photo courtesy Terry N. Lonner)*

## An annotated listing of Montana bighorn sheep transplants; 1922-2008, cont.

| Year(s) | Source | Number | Release Location |
|---|---|---|---|
| 1962 | Sun River, Teton Co. | 18 | Sheep Cr., Little Belt Mtns., Meagher Co. |
| 1963 | National Bison Range, Lake Co. | 6 (rams) | Ural-Tweed, Lincoln Co. |
| | National Bison Range, Lake Co. | 6 (rams) | West Gallatin River, Gallatin Co. |
| | National Bison Range, Lake Co. | 14 | Doris Mtn., Flathead Co. |
| 1964 | Sun River, Teton Co. | 25 | Willow Cr., Tobacco Root Mtns., Madison Co. |
| 1967 | Sun River, Teton Co. | 22 | Highland Mtns., Silver Bow Co. |
| | Sun River, Lewis & Clark Co. | 26 | Olson & Foster Cr., Deer Lodge Co. |
| 1968 | Sun River, Teton Co. | 32 | Prickley Pear Cr., Lewis and Clark Co. |
| | Sun River, Teton Co. | 2 | Stillwater River, Beartooth Mtns., Stillwater Co. |
| | Sun River, Teton Co. | 16 | Petty Cr., Missoula Co. |
| | National Bison Range, Lake Co. | 15 | Teakettle Mtn., Flathead Co. |
| 1969 | Sun River, Teton Co. | 18 | Highland Mtns., Silver Bow Co. |
| | Sun River, Teton Co. | 24 | Berray Mtn., Cabinet Mts, Sanders Co. |
| | Sun River, Teton Co. | 31 | Highland Mtns., Silver Bow Co. |
| 1970 | Sun River, Teton Co. | 2 | Stillwater River, Beartooth Mtns., Stillwater Co. |
| 1971 | Sun River, Teton Co. | 35 | Pryor Mtns., Carbon Co. |
| | Ford Cr., Lewis & Clark Co. | 5 | Beartooth Game Range, Big Belt Mtns. Lewis & Clark Co. |
| | Sun River, Teton Co. | 36 | Beartooth Game Range, Big Belt Mtns. Lewis & Clark Co. |
| | Ford Cr., Lewis & Clark Co. | 8 | Beartooth Game Range, Big Belt Mtns. Lewis & Clark Co. |
| | Sun River, Teton Co. | 3 | State Veterinary Laboratory, Gallatin Co. (for research) |
| 1972 | Sun River, Teton Co. | 19 | East Fork Bitterroot River, Ravalli Co. |
| | Sun River, Teton Co. | 16 | East Fork Bitterroot River, Ravalli Co. |
| | Ford Cr., Lewis & Clark Co. | 21 | East Fork Bitterroot River, Ravalli Co. |
| 1973 | Sun River, Teton Co. | 5 | Beartooth Game Range, Big Belt Mtns. Lewis & Clark Co. |
| | Sun River, Teton Co. | 6 | State Veterinary Laboratory, Gallatin Co. (for research) |
| 1974 | Sun River, Teton Co. | 28 | Pryor Mtns., Carbon Co. |
| | Sun River, Teton Co. | 21 | Little Rocky Mtns., Phillips Co. |
| | Sun River, Teton Co | 19 | Pryor Mtns., Carbon Co. |
| 1975 | Sun River, Teton Co. | 31 | Rock Cr., Granite Co. |
| | Ford Cr., Lewis & Clark Co. | 32 | Berray Mtn., Sanders Co. |
| | Sun River, Lewis & Clark Co. | 12 | Beartooth Game Range, Big Belt Mtns., Lewis & Clark Co. |
| | Sun River, Lewis & Clark Co. | 47 | Beartooth Game Range, Big Belt Mtns., Lewis & Clark Co. |
| | Wild Horse Island, Lake Co. | 3 | Berray Mtn., Sanders Co. |
| | National Bison Range Lake Co. | 56 | Cabinet Mtns., Lincoln Co. |
| 1976 | Sun River, Teton Co. | 25 | Blue Hills, Custer Co. |
| | Sun River, Teton Co. | 37 | Sheep Cr., Pondera Co. |

## An annotated listing of Montana bighorn sheep transplants; 1922-2008, cont.

| Year(s) | Source | Number | Release Location |
|---|---|---|---|
| 1979 | Wild Horse Island, Lake Co. | 41 | 14 Mile Cr., Sanders Co. |
| | Wild Horse Island, Lake Co. | 25 | Rock Cr., Granite Co. |
| | Wild Horse Island, Lake Co. | 18 | Washington State University, Pullman |
| | Wild Horse Island, Lake Co. | 14 | Flathead Indian Reservation, Little Money Cr., Sanders Co. |
| | Wild Horse Island, Lake Co. | 11 | Flathead Indian Reservation, Sanders Co. |
| 1980 | Sun River, Teton Co. | 28 | Missouri River Breaks, Fergus Co. |
| | Sun River, Teton Co. | 28 | Missouri River Breaks, Phillips Co. |
| 1981 | Wild Horse Island, Lake Co. | 5 | 14-Mile Cr., Sanders Co. |
| 1982 | Sun River, Teton Co. | 13 | Washington State University, Pullman, WA (for research) |
| 1984 | Rock Creek, Granite Co. | 1 | Release location unknown |
| | National Bison Range, Lake Co. | 3 | Stillwater River, Beartooth Mtns., Stillwater Co. |
| 1985 | National Bison Range, Lake Co. | 4 | Petty Cr. Missoula Co. |
| | Thompson Falls, Sanders Co. | 2 | Lost Cr., Deer Lodge Co. |
| | Thompson Falls, Sanders Co. | 7 | Mill Cr. Absaroka Mtns., Park Co. |
| | Lost Creek, Deer Lodge Co. | 20 | Boulder River, Absaroka Mtns., Park Co. |
| | Lost Creek, Deer Lodge Co. | 39 | Tendoy Mtns., Beaverhead Co. |
| | Cinnabar Mtn., Park Co. | 13 | Mill Cr., Absaroka Mtns., Park Co. |
| | Thompson Falls, Sanders Co. | 2 | National Bison Range, Lake Co. |
| 1986 | Thompson Falls, Sanders Co. | 14 | Tendoy Mtns., Beaverhead Co. |
| 1987 | Lost Cr., Deer Lodge Co. | 28 | Ranch Cr., Granite Co. |
| | Lost Cr., Deer Lodge Co. | 9 | Boulder River, Absaroka Mtns., Park Co |
| | Upper Rock Cr., Granite Co. | 10 | Boulder River, Absaroka Mtns., Park Co. |
| | Ural-Tweed, Lincoln Co. | 2 | Wild Horse Island, Lake Co. |
| | Thompson Falls, Sanders Co. | 5 | Boulder River, Absaroka Mtns, Park Co. |
| | Upper Rock Creek, Granite Co. | 27 | Bonner, Missoula Co. |
| 1988 | Thompson Falls, Sanders Co. | 19 | Squaw Cr., Madison Co. |
| 1989 | Lost Creek, Deer Lodge Co. | 36 | Boulder River, Absaroka Mtns., Park Co. |
| | Thompson Falls, Sanders Co. | 5 | Quake Lake, Hilgard Peaks, Madison Co |
| | Lost Creek, Deer Lodge Co. | 18 | Taylor & Hilgard Peaks, Gallatin Co. |
| | Sun River, Teton Co. | 8 | Joseph, Washington |
| 1990 | Sun River, Teton Co. | 36 | Painted Rocks, Bitterroot Mtns., Ravalli Co. |
| | Sun River, Teton Co. | 31 | Bonner, Missoula Co. |
| 1991 | Lost Creek, Deer Lodge Co. | 32 | Blackleaf Canyon, Teton Co. |
| | Lost Creek, Deer Lodge Co. | 24 | West Fork Bitterroot River, Bitterroot Mtns., Ravalli Co. |
| 1992 | Highland Mtns., Silver Bow Co. | 35 | Sleeping Giant, Big Belt Mtns., Lewis & Clark Co. |

## An annotated listing of Montana bighorn sheep transplants; 1922-2008, cont.

| Year(s) | Source | Number | Release Location |
|---|---|---|---|
| 1993 | Wild Horse Island, Lake Co. | 32 | Sleeping Giant, Big Belt Mtns., Lewis & Clark Co. |
| | Wild Horse Island, Lake Co. | 15 | Walling Reef, Teton Co. |
| | Wild Horse Island, Lake Co. | 26 | Little Mile Cr., Gallatin Co. |
| | Wild Horse Island, Lake Co. | 8 | Washington State University, Pullman (for research) |
| | Thompson Falls, Sanders Co. | 3 | National Bison Range, Lake Co. |
| 1994 | Wild Horse Island, Lake Co. | 32 | Sleeping Giant, Big Belt Mtns., Lewis & Clark Co. |
| | Wild Horse Island, Lake Co. | 15 | Walling Reef, Teton Co. |
| | Wild Horse Island, Lake Co. | 26 | Taylor Hilgard Mtns., Madison Co. |
| | Wild Horse Island, Lake Co. | 8 | Washington State University, Pullman (for research) |
| | Wild Horse Island, Lake Co. | 47 | Oregon (2 sites) |
| 1995 | Perma, Sanders Co. | 19 | Beartooth WMA[2], Lewis & Clark & Cascade Cos.<br>Big Belt Mtns., Cascade Co. |
| | Perma, Sanders Co. | 26 | Boulder River, Sweet Grass Co. |
| 1996 | Rock Cr., Granite Co. | 20 | Beartooth WMA, Lewis & Clark & Cascade Cos<br>Big Belt Mtns., Lewis & Clark Co. |
| | Rock Cr., Granite Co. | 25 | Elkhorn Mtns., Jefferson Co. |
| 1997 | Bonner, Missoula Co. | 30 | Elkhorn Mtns., Jefferson Co. |
| | Rock Cr., Granite Co. | 20 | Tendoy, Mtns., Beaverhead Co. |
| | Rock Cr., Granite Co. | 30 | Boulder River, Sweet Grass Co |
| 1998 | Bitterroot Mtns., Ravalli Co. | 22 | Deep Cr., Teton Co. |
| 2000 | Missouri River Breaks, Phillips Co. | 20 | Elkhorn Mtns., Jefferson Co. |
| | Thompson Falls, Sanders Co. | 16 | Kootenai Falls, Lincoln Co. |
| | Sun River, Teton Co. | 27 | Sapphire, Mtns., Ravalli Co. |
| 2001 | Sun River, Teton Co. | 32 | Highland Mtns,, Silver Bow Co. |
| 2002 | Missouri River Breaks, Phillips Co. | 20 | Idaho/Oregon Hells Canyon |
| | Sula, Ravalli Co. | 23 | Utah |
| | Sula, Ravalli Co. | 14 | Tendoy Mtns., Beaverhead Co. |
| | Sun River, Lewis & Clark Co. | 30 | Highland Mtns, Silver Bow Co. |
| 2003 | Missouri River Breaks, Blaine Co. | 30 | Greenhorn Mtns., Madison Co. |
| | Bonner, Missoula Co. | 2 | Kootenai Falls, Lincoln Co. |
| 2004 | Sun River, Lewis and Clark Co. | 24 | Kootenai Falls, Lincoln Co. |
| | Sun River, Teton Co. | 40 | Greenhorn Mtns., Madison Co. |
| | Sun River, Lewis and Clark Co. | 10 | Bitterroot Mtns., Ravalli Co. |
| | Bitterroot, Ravalli Co. | 12 | Sheep infected with Brucella ovis, Colorado[3] (for research) |
| | Thompson Falls, Sanders Co. | 35 | Utah, Flaming Gorge |
| 2006 | Missouri River Breaks, Phillips Co. | 19 | North Dakota, Little Missouri River |
| | Missouri River Breaks, Phillips Co. | 20 | Wyoming, Big Horn Mountains |
| | Ten Lakes, Lincoln Co. | 2 | Ural-Tweed, Lincoln Co. |

## An annotated listing of Montana bighorn sheep transplants; 1922-2008, cont.

| Year(s) | Source | Number | Release Location |
|---|---|---|---|
| 2007 | Sun River, Teton Co. | 32 | Nebraska |
| | Sun River, Lewis and Clark Co. | 30 | Utah |
| | Missouri River Breaks, Phillips Co. | 20 | North Dakota |
| | Missouri Breaks, Chouteau Co. | 20 | Nebraska |
| | Ruby Mountains, Madison Co. | 18 | Highland Mtns, Silver Bow Co. |
| | Plains, Sanders Co. | 42 | Wyoming (Laramie Peak) |
| | Bonner, Missoula Co. | 27 | Utah |
| | Rock Cr., Granite Co. | 15 | Utah |
| | E. Fk. Bitteroot River, Ravalli Co. | 25 | Utah |
| 2008 | McCarty Hill/Ford Cr., Lewis & Clark Co. | 18 | Soap Gulch, Highland Mtns.,Silver Bow Co. |
| | Willow Cr./Ford Cr., Lewis & Clark Co. | 13 | Soap Gulch, Highland Mtns., Silver Bow Co. |
| | Sun Canyon/Castle Reef, Teton Co. | 24 | Camp Cr., Highland Mtns., Silver Bow Co. |
| | Mortimer & Big George Gulch, Teton Co. | 10 | Camp Cr., Highland Mtns., Silver Bow Co. |
| | Wildhorse Island, Lake Co. | 38 | Kootenai Falls WMA, Lincoln Co. |
| | Flathead Indian Reservation, Lake Co. | 24 | Rocky Boys Indian Reservation, Hill & Chouteau Cos. |
| Summary | **Sheep Transplants:** | | |
| | **Total Sheep Trapped within Montana** | **2,258** | **for transplants within Montana** |
| | **Total Sheep Trapped within Montana** | **406** | **for transplants outside of Montana** |
| | **Total Sheep Trapped outside of Montana** | **28** | **for transplants to Montana** |
| | **Total Sheep Trapped (management)** | **2,692** | **transplanted for restoration or augmentation** |
| | **Total Sheep Trapped (special)** | **74** | **for research studies & Zoos** |

[1] Kraft, E. 2006. Untold tales of bison range trails. Stoneydale Press, Stevensville, MT. Pp 24-25
[2] Wildlife Management Area
[3] Sent to Colorado as part of a bighorn stress/disease study.

Note: The National Bison Range has exchanged rams with other "parks, private refuges and agencies" over the years. Kraft, E. 2006. Untold tales of bison range trails. Stoneydale Press, Stevensville, MT. Pp 34-35.

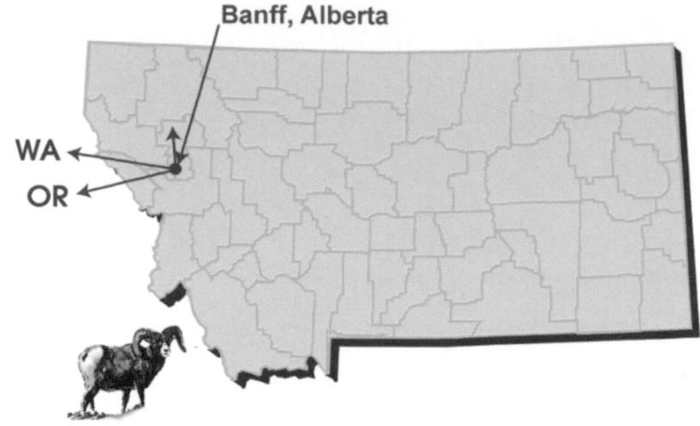


1922 - 1939 Bighorn Sheep Transplants

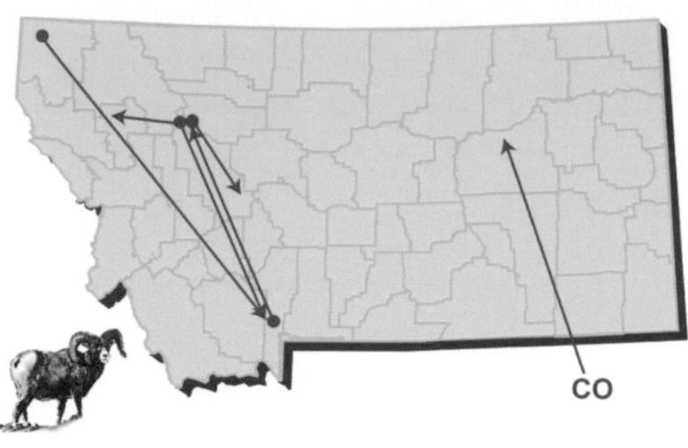


1940 - 1949 Bighorn Sheep Transplants

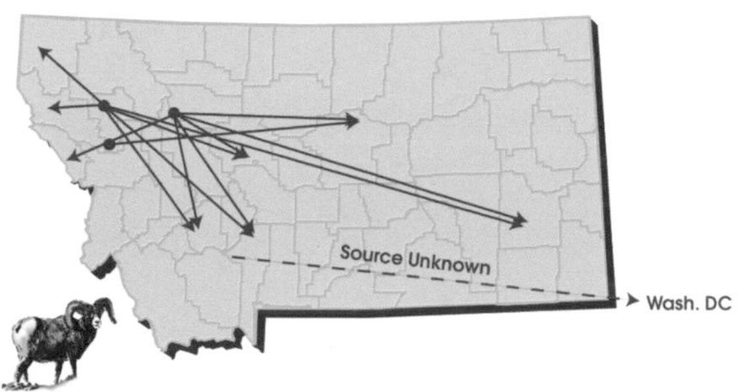


1950 - 1959 Bighorn Sheep Transplants

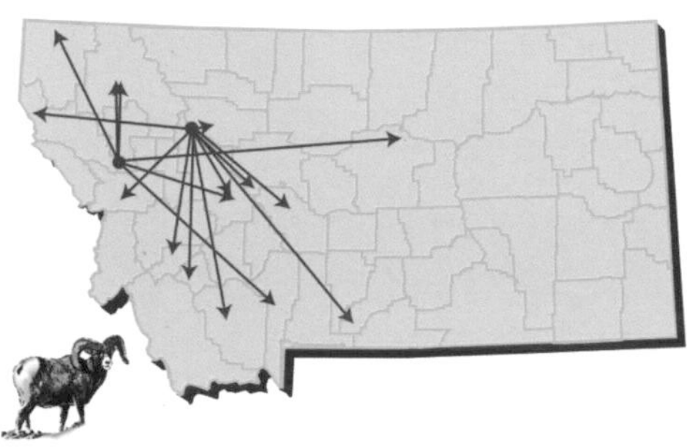

1960 - 1969 Bighorn Sheep Transplants

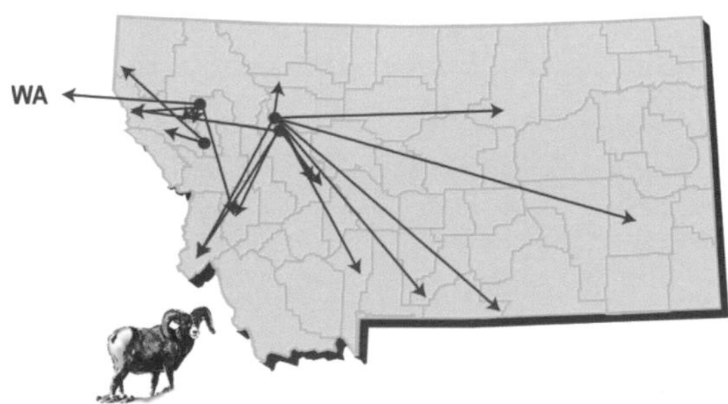


1970 - 1979 Bighorn Sheep Transplants

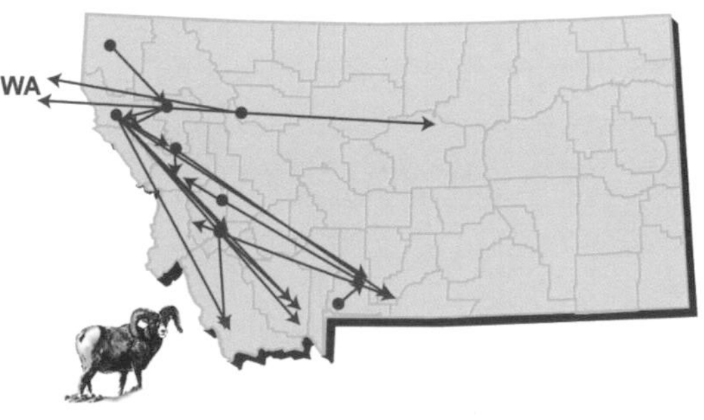


1980 - 1989 Bighorn Sheep Transplants

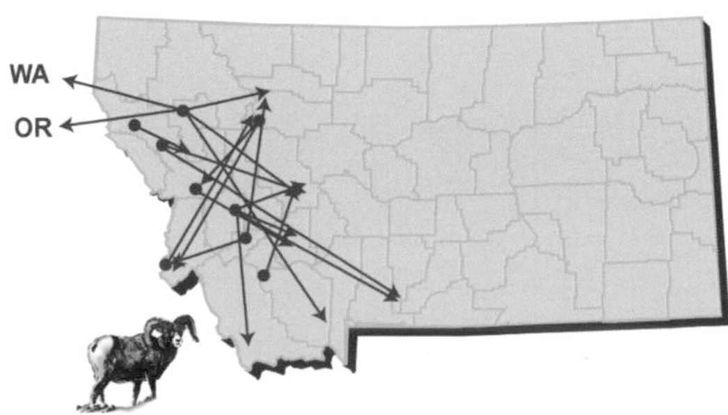


1990 - 1999 Bighorn Sheep Transplants

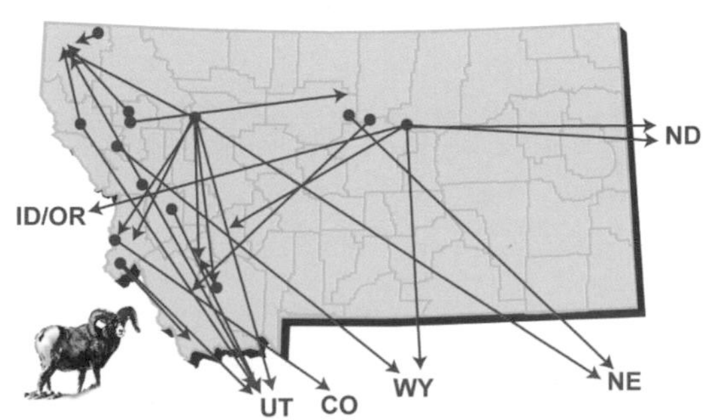


2000 - 2008 Bighorn Sheep Transplants

1860 Audubon Sheep Distribution

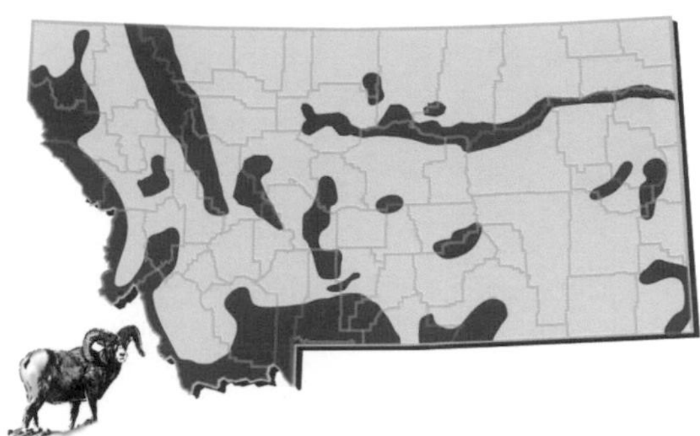

1890 Both Subspecies Distribution

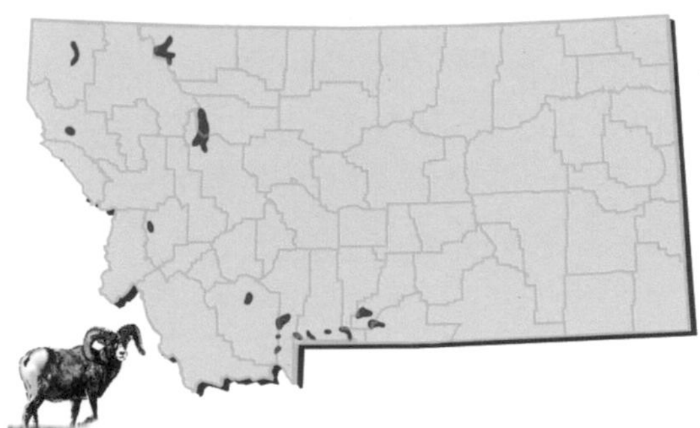

1942 Bighorn Sheep Distribution

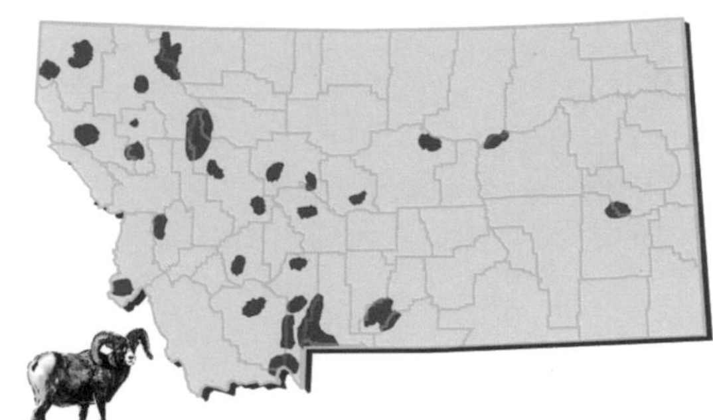

1970 Bighorn Sheep Distribution

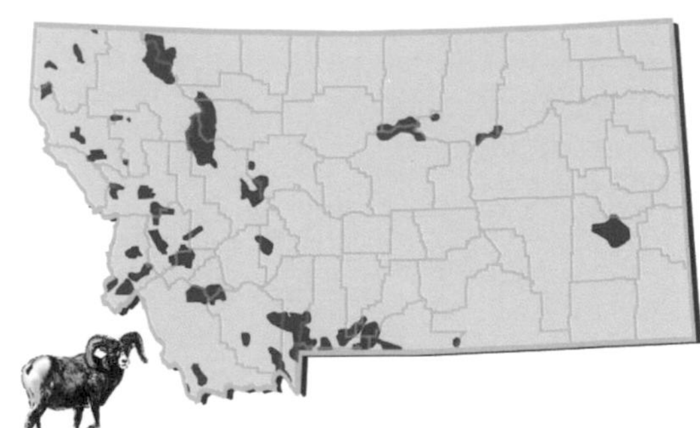

2008 Bighorn Sheep Distribution

# Footnotes

[1] Couey, F. and A. Schallenberger. 1971. Bighorn sheep. Chapter 10 in Game Management in Montana. Montana Fish and Game Dept., Helena. 97-105.

[2] Wehausen, J. and R. Raney. 2000. Cranial morphometric and evolutionary relationships in the northern range of *Ovis canadensis*. Journal of Mammalogy 85:145-161.

[3] Luikart, G. and F. W. Allendorf. 1996. Mitochondrial-DNA variation and genetic -population structure in Rocky Mountain bighorn sheep (*Ovis canadensis canadensis*). Journal of Mammalogy 77:109-123.

Fitzsimmons, N. N., S. W. Buskirk and M. H. Smith. 1995. Population history, genetic variability, and horn growth in bighorn sheep. Conservation Biology 9:3 14-323.

[4] Krausman, P. R. and R. T. Bowyer. 2003. Mountain sheep. Chapter 51 in Wild Mammals of North America. Johns Hopkins University Press, Baltimore. 1095-1115.

[5] Valdez, R. and P. R. Krausman. 1999. Mountain sheep of North America. University of Arizona Press. 153 pp.

[6] Ibid.

[7] Ibid. Couey, F. and A. Schallenberger. 1971.

[8] Kraft, E. 2006. Untold tales of bison range trails. Stoneydale Press, Stevensville, MT. 34-35.

[9] Woodgerd, W. 1964. Population dynamics of bighorn sheep on Wildhorse Island. Journal of Wildlife Management. 28:381-391.

[10] Couey, F. M. 1950. Rocky Mountain Bighorn sheep of Montana. Montana Fish and Game Commission, Helena. 90 pp.

[11] Picton, H. D. and I. E. Picton. 1975. Saga of the Sun. Montana Fish and Game Dept., Helena. 55 pp.

[12] Couey, F. M. 1950. Rocky Mountain Bighorn sheep of Montana. Montana Fish and Game Dept., Helena. 71.

[13] Ibid. Luikart, G. and F. W. Allendorf. 1996.

Ibid. Fitzsimmons, N. N., S. W. Buskirk and M.H. Smith. 1995.

[14] Ibid. Woodgerd, W. 1964.

[15] McLucas, J. 1999. Videotaped interview with Harold Picton and Jim Williams.

[16] Couey, F. 1956. Montana's big game transplanting program. Montana Wildlife 6(1):22-24.

Couey, F. 1953. Are the bighorns doomed? Montana Wildlife 3(1):16-18.

# Chapter 13

# Grizzly and Black Bears

## GRIZZLY BEARS

(*Ursus arctos horribilis*)

The Grizzly bear is a subspecies of brown bear. Brown bears may be confused with the brown color phase of black bears, but are a different species. Brown bears are found across Europe and Asia as well as northwestern North America. The grizzly bear occupies inland regions of western Canada and the United States. While smaller than the large salmon-feeding brown bears of the west coast, grizzlies have the reputation of being particularly aggressive. Females usually become sexually mature between 4 and 7 years old before mating for the first time in May-June. They give birth to an average of two cubs with an approximate interval between litters of 3 years.

Grizzlies first became known to science through writings of Captain Lewis with the Corps of Discovery. The Mandan Indians also included descriptions of these bears in their education of the captains.

*"The white bear have become so troublesome to us that I do not think it prudent to send one man alone on an errand of any kind, particularly where he has to pass through the brush."*

**—Captain Lewis, June 28, 1805**

April 29, 1805 brought them their first encounter with grizzlies in Montana (near the current town of Wolf Point not too far from the North Dakota border).

"...about 8 A.M. we fell in with two brown or (yellow)(white) bear; both of which we wounded; one of them made his escape, the other after firing on him pursued me seventy or eighty yards, but fortunately had been so badly

*Hunting of the Grizzly Bear by Karl Bodmer*
*(Courtesy Rare Books Division, Special Collections, J. Willard Marriott Library, University of Utah)*

form of buffalo carcasses. The largest skull of inland grizzlies on the Boone and Crockett list is from the Missouri Breaks near Jordan in Garfield County. The skull was collected in April, 1890, and shows no signs of weathering.[3] It and several other skulls in similar condition suggest that grizzly bears persisted in the eastern breaks and prairie country at least into the 1890s.

By the 1930s, occupied grizzly bear habitat in the lower 48 states had been reduced to the Yellowstone Park area, the vicinity of Glacier NP, Middle Fork of the Flathead drainage (now the Great Bear Wilderness) and the Bob Marshall Wilderness. In 1936 William Rush, of the U.S. Biological Survey, suggested creation of a grizzly bear refuge in the South Fork of the Flathead drainage and Mission Mountains.

There seemed to be considerable grizzly bear activity in the Bob Marshall Wilderness during the 1930s and 1940s. It was during that period, a grizzly entered through the door of a Forest Service Guard Station at Holbrook in the South Fork of the

***The largest skull of the inland grizzlies on the Boone and Crockett list is from the Missouri Breaks in the area of Jordan in Garfield County. . . It was collected in April, 1890.[3]***

wounded that he was unable to pursue so closely as to prevent my charging my gun; we again repeated our fire and killed him. ...the Indians may well fear this animal equipped as they generally are with their bows and arrows or indifferent fuzees, but in the hands of skillful riflemen they are by no means as formidable or dangerous as they have been represented."[1]

By June 28th his attitude had changed,

"The white bear have become so troublesome to us that I do not think it prudent to send one man alone on an errand of any kind, particularly where he has to pass through the brush."[2]

Grizzly bears of the eastern plains had abundant food available to them in the

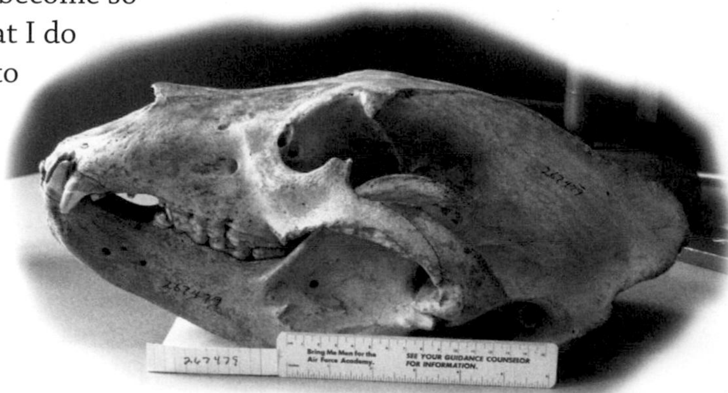

***Grizzly bear skull found in the Missouri River Breaks area in 1888.***
***(Photo courtesy Harold Picton from the Smithsonian Collection)***

***Grizzly bear sow with a yearling cub.*** *(Photo Courtesy Martha A. Lonner)*

Flathead drainage. Unfortunately the bear left through the wall of the wood frame cabin.

In the summer of 1942, a grizzly bear gained considerable notoriety in the area north of Yellowstone NP. Domestic sheep were grazed in the Absaroka wilderness and U.S. Forest Service cabins and others were being raided by a bear that had lost a toe. It lost the toe trying to enter a cabin where two long logger's cross cut saws had been nailed across the door in an effort to keep bears out. It had then torn a hole in the roof to get in and left by tearing out a window. Another cabin had a root cellar with a trap door in the cabin floor. It entered the root cellar through the trap door but pushed the entire floor up when it left. It carried a lot of canned goods and a sack of flour up a draw and buried them about 100 yards from the cabin. Although the sack of flour was leaking some from a puncture it was intact when dug up. The hunting season began in September and fieldman Lloyd McDowell was leading a pack string back to their camp in Hellroaring Creek. He and fieldman Marshall Moy were conducting a moose survey in the area. In personal notes of the story McDowell states,

> "A huge silver tip bear stopped about 75 feet in front of me. The bear seemed ready to charge as I hit the ground taking my 270 rifle from the gun scabbard."[4]

***. . . U.S. Forest Service cabins and others were being raided by a bear that had lost a toe. It lost a toe when trying to enter a cabin where two long logger's cross cut saws had been nailed across the door in an effort to keep bears out.***

***Grizzly bear breaking into a cabin. c. 1990.***
*(Photo courtesy Kevin Frey)*

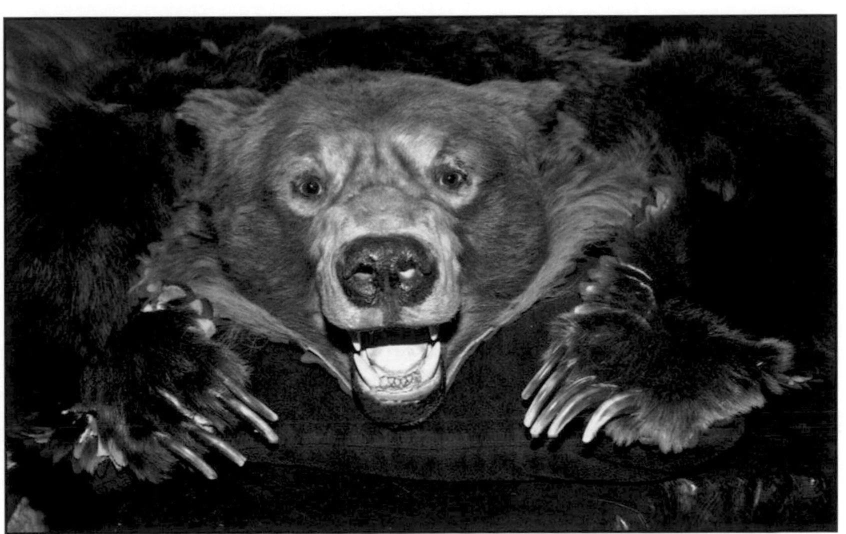

***Grizzly bear taken by Lloyd McDowell used by Hector LaCasse to design the Montana Fish & Game Department's Logo in 1942.*** *(Photo courtesy Martha Lonner with permission from Marilyn McDowell Stonehocker - Lloyd's daughter)*

*Lloyd McDowell in his Fish & Game Office with the Grizzly bear taken by him in 1942 that was used for designing the Montana Fish & Game Department's logo.* *(Photo courtesy Marilyn McDowell Stonehocker)*

*Original Montana Fish and Game logo drawing by Hector LaCasse. c. 1942. (Courtesy Marilyn McDowell Stonehocker)*

***The Montana Fish & Game Warden patch. c. 1950s.***

*Montana Fish, Wildlife and Parks Logo as of 2008.*

***The Montana Fish, Wildlife and Parks patch in 2008.***

***A Legally tagged hide of the mature 8 to 11 year old bear was converted into a rug. Hector LaCasse made a meticulously accurate sketch of the head with its slightly deformed lower jaw.[4] This drawing became the logo of the Montana Fish and Game Department and remains so today.***

McDowell fired breaking the bear's shoulder. The bear charged but rolled off the trail into heavy brush. Lloyd followed and eventually fired 3 additional shots to dispatch the bear. His partner, left tending the nervous horses on the trail, was uncertain who would emerge from the brush in the quiet that ensued after the thrashing and roaring stopped. The horses were not enthusiastic about carrying the bear to camp. The gentlest horse in the pack string had to be restrained by a pole to stiffen its lead rope as it tried to run up on the other horses to get away from the grizzly on its back. Once back at camp, Lloyd had to take a thorough bath in the icy waters of Hellroaring Creek to clean off the bear smell before the horses would let him approach. The hide of the legally tagged mature 8 to 11 year old bear was converted into a rug.

Hector LaCasse, another fieldman with the Montana Fish and Game Department, made a meticulously accurate sketch of the head with its slightly deformed lower jaw.[4] This drawing became the logo of the Montana Fish and Game Department and remains so today. It commemorates the early workers and their efforts to conserve Montana's wildlife resources. In 1982, 50,000 Montana school children voted to make the grizzly bear the official state mammal. The Legislature and the Governor followed their wishes. Elk came in second in the voting.

Montana began grizzly bear studies in 1941 with surveys by Bob Cooney and Ray Gibler in the large wilderness complex south of Glacier NP. On August 27, 1941 they were surveying the area near Badger Pass south of Glacier NP. Sign of considerable activity of both black and grizzly bears was evident as documented in Cooney's fieldnotes;

Griz Br - Dropping
Badger Pass - 2 1/4"
50% - White ~~Pine~~ Barked Pine
25% - Huckleberry
20% Grasses -

Food & Feeding Habits
Today we noticed ~~that~~ two grizzly bear droppings showing an important use of White Barked Pine seeds. One was made up entirely of this food & the other half. There is little doubt but that grizzly bear are searching for these nuts in squirrel caches at this time at high elevations where

An excerpt from Bob Cooney's field notes on his observations of grizzly bear food habits. c. 1941. (Courtesy Robert Cooney)

*Grizzly bears at a feeding station probably near Canyon, Yellowstone National Park. (From Montana Fish and Game files, date and photographer unknown)*

*Whitebark Pine tree with cones of pine nuts are an important source of food for grizzly bears where they are present. (Photo Courtesy Harold Picton)*

"Grizzly bear dropping - Badger Pass: 50% whitebark pine nuts, 25% Huckleberry, 25% Grasses... Today we noticed two grizzly bear droppings showing an important use of whitebark pine seeds. One was made up entirely of this food and the other half. There is little doubt but that grizzly bear are searching for these nuts in squirrel caches at this time at high elevations where whitebark pine is found. These nuts would be strong in fats and oils so that at this time when bear are trying to put on as much fat as possible preparing for hibernation. Huckleberry fruit is still the most important food. Some little use of grass yet but this has fallen off a great deal since the fruit crops became ripe."[5]

Since these surveys, an introduced disease, blister rust, has killed the majority of whitebark pine trees in Glacier NP and adjacent areas to the south eliminating pine nuts as a significant food source in the area.

Food habits of grizzlies varies across their range in Montana. Studies using ratios of chemical isotopes indicate grizzly bears in the Cabinet-Yaak and Glacier NP areas have a diet of about 21 percent animal matter (including insects) and 79 percent plant material. Grizzlies in the Yellowstone

***Montana began grizzly bear studies in 1941 with surveys by Bob Cooney and Ray Gibler in the large wilderness complex south of Glacier NP.***

***Pine nuts are no longer an important bear food in the Glacier NP area because of the human introduced blister rust disease which has killed most of the whitebark pine trees.***

NP area get about 50 percent of their diet from animal matter as did the now extinct grizzlies that ranged on the eastern plains of Montana.[6]

The Montana Fish and Game Department continued grizzly bear surveys through the 1940s and 1950s. Major research in Montana was conducted in the 1970s with the Border Grizzly Bear Study led by Chuck Jonkel and the East Front Grizzly Bear Study led by Keith Aune. These were followed by the South Fork of the Flathead Grizzly study under Rick Mace and a study in the Mission Mountains by Chris Servheen.

*In 2007 the U.S. Fish and Wildlife Service announced that the Yellowstone grizzly bear population would be "delisted" or removed from "threatened status."*

John and Frank Craighead conducted landmark studies of grizzly bears in Yellowstone NP from 1959 to 1972. These studies and political efforts led to list the grizzly as a threatened species under the federal Endangered and Threatened Species Act (ESA), which was approved by congress in 1973 for the lower 48 states. The Interagency Grizzly Bear Study Team and management committee was established in 1975 to study the threatened population in and around Yellowstone NP. Committee members included representatives of the national forests surrounding the Park, the National Park Service, U.S. Fish and Wildlife Service and states of Montana, Idaho and Wyoming. Montana Fish and Game contributed services of its wildlife research laboratory in the study efforts. Ken Greer, the laboratory supervisor, collected data on hundreds of grizzly bears. His work resulted in probably the largest collection of grizzly bear skeletons in the world.

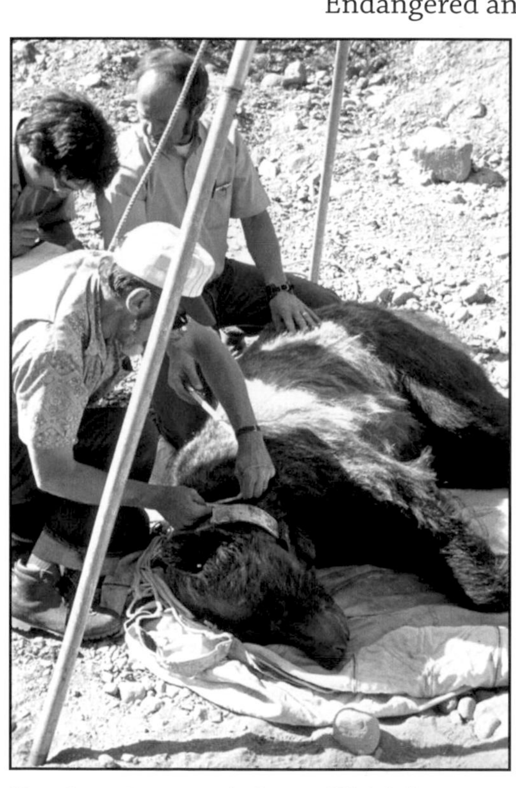

*Ken Greer, Montana's first wildlife laboratory supervisor, with assistants Dan Palmisciano and Dan Quillen collecting data and marking a grizzly bear near Yellowstone National Park. c. 1975. (Courtesy Kenneth R. Greer Photo Collection)*

Designations of critical habitat for grizzly bears followed the listing: The Yellowstone Ecosystem, the Northern Continental Divide and the Cabinet – Yaak Ecosystems in Montana. The Northern Continental Divide Ecosystem includes Glacier NP, Mission Mountains, Great Bear Wilderness, Bob Marshall Wilderness and Scapegoat Wilderness. The Cabinet – Yaak Ecosystem includes the Cabinet Mountains and Yaak River-Purcell Mountains area north to the Canadian border. The Bitterroot Mountains along the Montana-Idaho border are also designated but there has been considerable local opposition to re-introduction of grizzly bears into the area.

The Yellowstone Ecosystem has maintained its historical grizzly population. The population tripled in size and has expanded its range since protected under the ESA. In 2007 the U.S. Fish and Wildlife Service announced that the Yellowstone grizzly bear population would be "delisted" or removed from "threatened status." Kevin Frey was hired as a state bear damage control specialist to handle bear-human conflicts in the Montana portion of the ecosystem and to help with the recovery program.

The Northern Continental Divide Grizzly Bear Ecosystem has also maintained its historical grizzly population. Kate Kendall of the U.S. Geological Survey led the study in organizing a massive effort to use DNA technology to estimate the grizzly bear population size. Dan Carney and Art Soukkala worked on the Blackfoot and Flathead Indian Reservations. Rick Mace supervised work in the South Fork of the Flathead. Chris Servheen, the federal grizzly bear coordinator, also initiated some research. Grizzly bears have begun moving out on to the Great Plains and other areas of potential conflict with humans. Mike Madel, Tim Manley, Jamie Jonkel and Erik Wenum have served as state bear damage control specialists for this ecosystem.

*Grizzly bear cubs. c. 1966.* *(National Park Service photo, photographer unknown)*

The grizzly bear situation in the Cabinet-Yaak Ecosystem was unclear when the area was designated. In 1967, the U.S. Forest Service and Montana Fish and Game Department signed an interagency agreement to transplant grizzlies into the Cabinet Mountains to augment low numbers there. However, the Montana Fish and Game Commission took "a very dim view of a grizzly bear trapping and transplanting program" at their August 1967 meeting.[7] An effort to clarify the status of the grizzly bear in this area included private citizens, private industry, and state and federal agencies. In the 1970s the U.S. Forest Service had compiled a summary of reported sightings of grizzlies in the area although some of the sightings were questionable. The Amax Corporation started a silver mine in the area and the U.S. Borax and Chemical Company also was interested in mineral exploration. The president of the International Bear Association at that time, Cliff Martinka, suggested that U.S. Borax contact the senior author who hired Steve Martin as a consulting biologist to conduct a survey for fresh grizzly bear sign. He found some fresh grizzly tracks. This information provided the foundation needed to initialize a cooperative research project. U.S. Borax provided funds to start the project. Wayne Kasworm was transferred to the Cabinet area from the East Front Grizzly Project to serve as the principle

***. . .In 1967, the U.S. Forest Service and the Montana Fish and Game Department signed an interagency agreement to transplant grizzlies into the Cabinet Mountains because of their low numbers there. However the Montana Fish and Game Commission took "a very dim view of a grizzly bear trapping and transplanting program" at their August 1967 meeting.[7]***

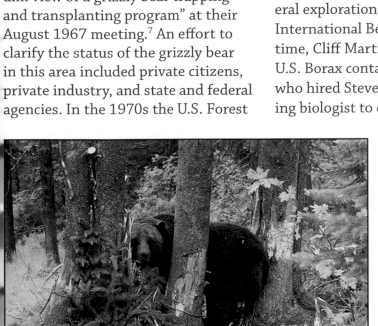

*Grizzly bear caught in a snare during the Northern Continental Divide Grizzly Bear Ecosystem study.* *(Montana Fish, Wildlife and Parks photo courtesy Rick Mace)*

*The grizzly queen of the Cabinet Mountains lived until she was 38 years old when she apparently was killed by a train.*

researcher. The U.S. Fish and Wildlife Service provided a pickup truck and other support as the federal contribution to the project. This joint state and federal effort led to trapping and radio collaring of a 28 year old sow in 1983 to get the ecosystem project underway. The population of the Cabinet-Yaak area was apparently quite low and would require supplementation if it was to prosper.

***A grizzly bear trapped from the North Fork of the Flathead River in British Columbia being released into the Cabinet Mountains. c. 1994.*** *(Photo courtesy Wayne Kasworm)*

The 28 year old female grizzly carried a radio collar until she reached an age of 34 years in 1989. In 1992 some claws were collected at the site of a bear and train collision. Blood and tissue samples taken in 1983 were compared to material on the claws using DNA analysis. The resulting DNA match suggested that the "queen" of the Cabinets lived until she was about 38 years old. In 1985 an old male grizzly was also captured as well as a young male. DNA analysis indicated that the "queen" and the old male had produced a son.[8]

*The grizzly bear population in the Yaak area north of the Cabinet range and extending to the Canadian border seems to be somewhat distinct from the Cabinet bears.*

From 1990 to 1994 four female grizzlies were trapped along the North Fork of the Flathead River in British Columbia. These were released in the Cabinet Mountains. One died during its first year in the Cabinets but in 2004 DNA from hair collected in a snare indicated that at least one of these bears still resided in the area. In 2005, another female from the North Fork of the Flathead drainage in Montana was transplanted to the Cabinets by Tim Manley and Jerry Brown of Montana Fish, Wildlife and Parks and in 2006 they moved another female grizzly from the South Fork of the Flathead to the Cabinets.

The grizzly bear population in the Yaak area north of the Cabinet range and extending to the Canadian border seems to be somewhat distinct from the Cabinet bears. The Yaak population is connected to the grizzly bear population in the Purcell Range across the border in Canada.[9]

***A historical grizzly bear photo from Montana Fish and Game files. c. 1950s.***

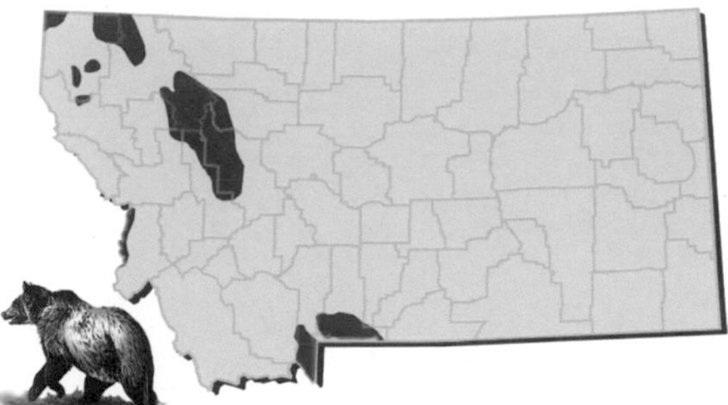

1942 Grizzly Bear Distribution

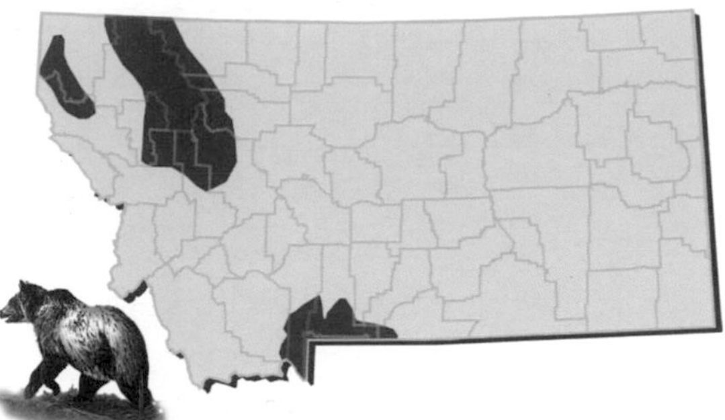

1970 Grizzly Bear Distribution

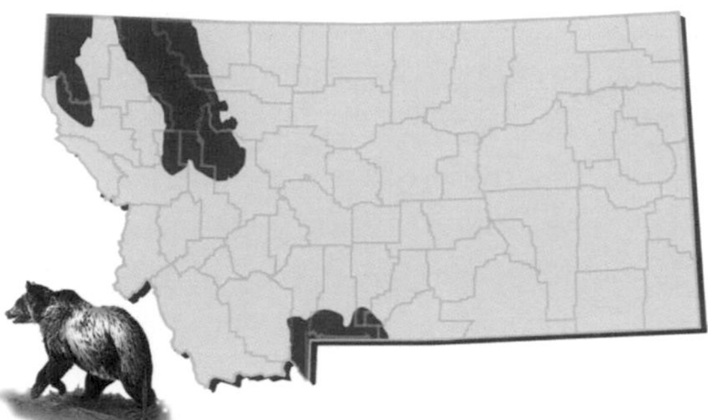

1985 Grizzly Bear Distribution

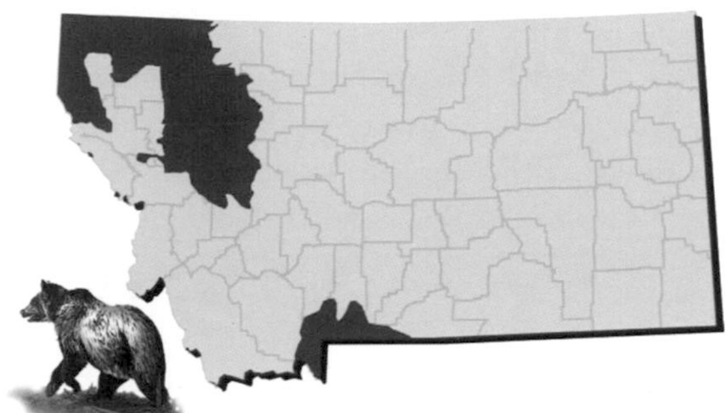

2008 Grizzly Bear Distribution

## BLACK BEAR

*(Ursus americanus)*

The American Black Bear is a species found only in North America. This native inhabits major forest areas of the continent from east to west and from Alaska to Mexico. Original distribution of black bears in Montana included mountainous areas and extended down the Missouri and Yellowstone River Valleys to the North Dakota border.[10]

Black bears mate in May or June, shortly after emerging from their winter dens. Female black bears usually become sexually mature by their fourth summer and give birth to between one and four cubs, with two being the most common. The interval between mating is from 2 to 4 years.

*Black bear - black color phase.* *(Photo courtesy Terry N. Lonner)*

***Black bear color phases were of considerable interest at the time of Lewis and Clark.***

Their pelage is predominantly black throughout most of their distribution across the continent. However, color patterns become more interesting in Montana as they encounter more variable climatic and ecological conditions. About 90 percent of the bears are black in the Canadian Province of Alberta, but this drops to 75 percent in the North Fork of the Flathead drainage and 60 percent in the Cabinet – Yaak area. The Rocky Mountain Front, west of Great Falls, has a frequency of 54 percent for the black color phase. The Beartooth Mountains of southern Montana and the Yellowstone NP area show the black color phase in the 40-55 percent range. In southern parts of Montana the brown color phase is the second most common at 30-41 percent, the blonde color phase occurs in 9-13 percent and the cinnamon color phase is least common at 3-6 percent.[11] Bears living in high altitude areas of the southern mountains also show a greater chest size than do those living in the lower elevations of northwestern Montana.[12]

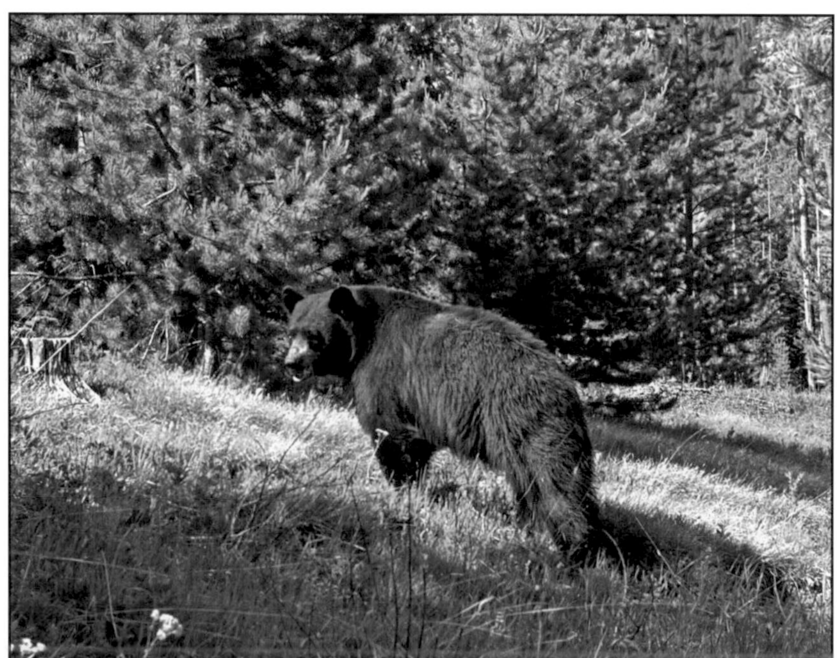

*Black bear - brown color phase.* *(Photo courtesy Terry N. Lonner)*

Black bear color phases were of considerable interest at the time of Lewis and Clark. The black phase was the most common phase in eastern deciduous forests of the United States where the men came from. Lewis gathered as much information as he could from Indians and incorporated it into his scientific knowledge base. The concept of biological species and subspecies was new at the time of their trip and was not fully defined in scientific terms. On May 31, 1806 Lewis wrote a lengthy discussion of black bears and grizzly bears,

> "(The Indians) ...said they [black bears] climbed the trees, had shorter nails and were not vicious, that they could pursue them with safety, they also affirmed that they were much smaller than the white bear. ... That the uniform reddish brown black &c of this neighbourhood are a species distinct from our black bear and from those of the Pacific coast...."[13]

Discussion about the biological status of the cinnamon color phase continued into the 20th century. Scientists and naturalists apparently were slow to recognize that black bears might have cubs of various colors in a litter. If litters contained several colors including cinnamon, then they were not a different species or subspecies. The Yellowstone Valley was noted as having the classic examples of cinnamon bears.[14] The "sun bear" or "silk bear" was a unique color phase reported from the Clarks Fork of the Yellowstone east to the Little Missouri River in North Dakota. This color phase was reported as being very light, almost white in color and having a coat of fine silky hair.[15] The historic term "sun bear" used here simply refers to a very light colored black bear and not to the true Sun bear which is a separate species found in Asia.

As forest dwellers, black bears feed primarily upon plants and insects. As omnivores they will also feed on animal carcasses and will kill prey animals if the opportunity presents itself. Domestic sheep sometimes become prey and bears can do considerable economic damage.

Black bears are common in mountainous areas of the state. Although moved frequently in damage control operations, they have never been transplanted either to maintain or reestablish populations in Montana. These inventive animals get into trouble when they raid bee yards, bird feeders, garbage cans and dumps or other locations where humans have carelessly left food accessible. Expanding suburbs have increased the number of "town" bears living close to humans where they often come into conflict. Black bears are occasionally seen in riparian forests of the lower Yellowstone valley but have not reclaimed their original range in Montana.

***Black bear sow with her cub raiding a garbage can.***
*(Courtesy Kenneth R. Greer Photo Collection)*

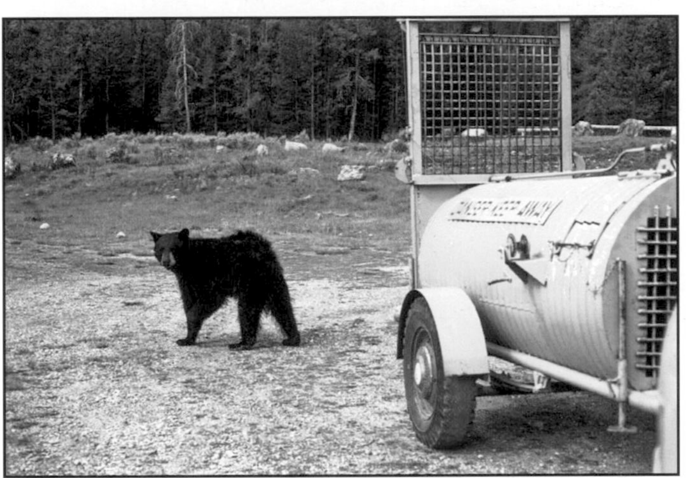

***A black bear being released in a remote area after being captured in a damage control operation.***
*(Courtesy Kenneth R. Greer Photo Collection)*

***A black bear in a Montana suburb looking for a garbage can.***
*(Photo courtesy Terry N. Lonner)*

Charles Jonkel of the Montana Fish and Game Department began black bear research in the forests of northwestern Montana.[16] Laboratory and several other field studies were carried out in years to follow. As the 21st century began these included use of DNA technology in a study by Rick Mace that encompassed much of the state.

*Charles Jonkel conducted one of the first comprehensive black bear studies in Montana. c. 1960.* *(Montana Fish and Game photo)*

*A snared black bear being administered oxygen while marking and taking blood samples.* *(Montana Fish, Wildlife and Parks photo courtesy Brent N. Lonner)*

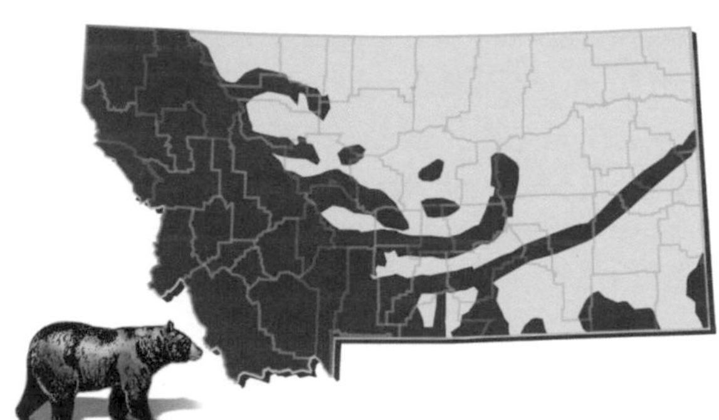

**Historic Black Bear Distribution**

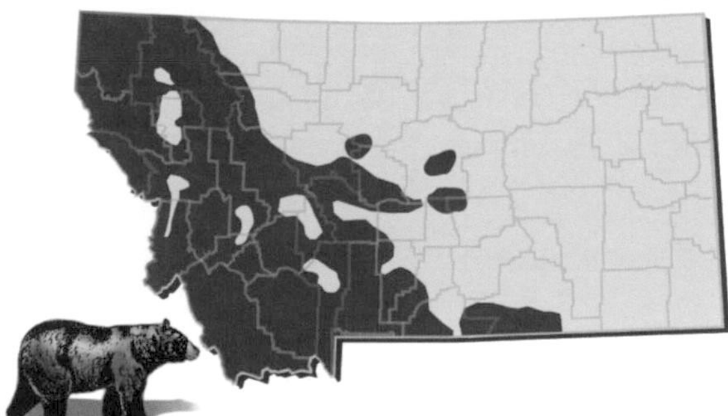

**1970 Black Bear Distribution**

*A station for acquiring black bear hair samples for DNA analyses.* *(Montana Fish, Wildlife and Parks photo courtesy Brent N. Lonner)*

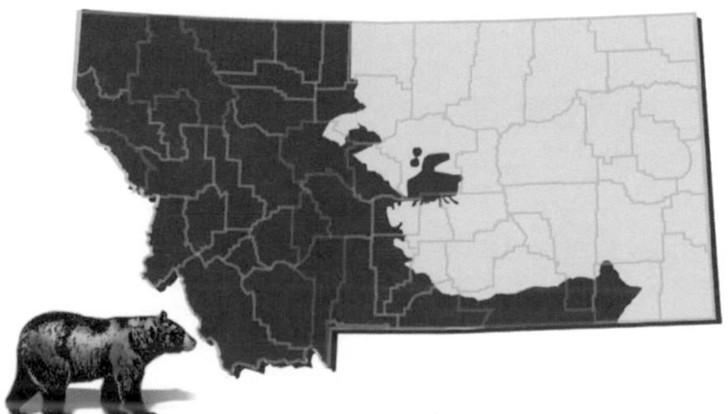

**2008 Black Bear Distribution**

# Footnotes

[1] Lewis, M. The journals of the Lewis and Clark Expedition: Gary E. Moulton, Editor. University of Nebraska Press, Lincoln. Volume 4:84-85.

[2] Ibid. Lewis M. Volume 4:338.

[3] Smithsonian specimen 202739. Number 60 on the Boone and Crockett list. Total length 460 mm. It is estimated to have been 11-15 years of age at death using the Palmisciano incisor tooth wear criteria.

[4] McDowell - Stonehocker, M. 2007. Videotaped interview with Terry Lonner and Harold Picton.

McDowell, L. Account of September 15, 1942. Typewritten account of the taking of the logo bear including a certification by R. Cooney.

[5] Cooney, R. F. 1941. Field notes for August 27, 1941 in the August 22 to August 31, 1941 notebook. Montana Fish and Game Department.

[6] Mowat, G. and D. C. Heard. 2006. Major components of grizzly bear diet across North America. Canadian Journal of Zoology. 84:473-489.

Hildebrand, G. V., S. D. Farley, C. T. Robbins, T. A. Hanley, K. Titus and C. Servheen. 1996. Use of stable isotopes to determine diets of living and extinct bears. Canadian Journal of Zoology. 74:2080-2088.

Robbins, C. T. , C. C, Schwartz , K. A. Gunther and C. Servheen. 2007. Grizzly bear nutrition and ecology studies in Yellowstone National Park. Yellowstone Discovery. 22(1):1-7.

[7] Dunkle, F. H. 1967. Memorandum and interagency cooperative agreement between the U.S. Forest Service and the Montana Fish and Game Department for transplanting grizzly bears into the Cabinet Mountains. Montana Fish and Game Department, Helena. 5 pp.

[8] Kasworm, W. F. 2006. Personal interview. February 8, 2006 with Harold Picton.

[9] Ibid.

[10] Hall, E. R. 1981. Mammals of North America. John Wiley, New York, NY 1181 pp.

Brown,M. H. and W. R. Felton. 1956. Before barbed wire. Beamhall House, New York. 256 pp.

Kelly, L. S. 1926. Yellowstone Kelly: The memoirs of Luther S. Kelly. University of Nebraska Press, Lincoln. 268 pp.

[11] Aune, K. and W. Kasworm. 1989. East Front grizzly study. Montana Fish, Wildlife and Parks. Helena. Final Report. 132 pp.

Mack, J. A. 1988. Ecology of black bears on the Beartooth Face, south-central Montana. M.S. Thesis, Montana State University, Bozeman, MT. 119 pp.

Cowen, I. M. 1938. Geographic distribution of color phases of the red fox and black bear in the Pacific Northwest. J. Mammalogy. 19:202-206.

Poelker, J. M. and H. D. Hartwell, 1973. Black bear of Washington. Washington State Game Dept., Olympia. Bulletin 14:108 pp.

[12] Swenson, J. E., W. E. Kasworm, S. T. Stewart, C. A. Simmons and K. Aune. 1987. Interpopulation applicability of equations to predict live weight in black bears. International Conference on Bear Research and Management. 7:244-246.

[13] Ibid. Lewis, M. Volume 7:313.

[14] Pelton, M. R. 2003. Black bear. Chapter 7 in Wild Mammals of North America: Edited by G. A. Fieldhammer, B. C. Thompson, and J. A. Chapman. Johns Hopkins University Press. 547-555.

Ibid. Hall, E. R. 1981.

# Footnotes, cont.

[15] Seton, E. T. 1953. Lives of game animals. Vol. 11 Part 1 Bears, Black Bear. C. T. Bradford, Boston, MA. 119-190.

Shields, G. O. 1888. Reprint 1988. Hunting in the great west, 1660-1882. John Willard Publisher, Billings, MT 170 pp.

Thompson, L. 1985. Montana's explorers: The pioneer naturalists. Chap. 8, John Palliser and Thomas Blakiston. Montana Magazine, Helena, MT. 72-79

Merriam, C. H. 1896. Preliminary synopsis of the American bears. Proceedings of the Biological Society of Washington D.C. X: 65-83. April 13.

[16] Jonkel, C. J. and I. M. Cowan. 1971. The black bear in the spruce-fir forest. Wildlife Monograph 27: 57

*Bison cow and newborn calf. (Photo courtesy Terry N. Lonner)*

# Chapter 14

## Some Other Big Animals

### SHIRAS MOOSE
(*Alces alces shirasi*)

Moose are the largest members of the deer family. However, moose in Montana are the smallest of three North American subspecies. Shiras moose occur along the Rocky Mountains from the Canadian border south to Utah. Some biologists believe that moose arrived in North America only as recently as 10,000 years ago and have undergone rapid evolution since their arrival.[1] The subspecies is named after George Shiras III, an early wildlife photographer and leader in conservation who had a special interest in moose and conducted the first moose survey of Yellowstone National Park. The Shiras subspecies appears adapted to patchy habitats and variable climates of the northern Rocky Mountain chain.

On May 10, 1805, Ordway, of the Corps of Discovery, reported seeing several moose near the mouth of the Milk River near present day Fort Peck. In 1832 a hunter killed a moose in the same area. On July 7, 1806, Captain oo and his companions were crossing what is now known as Lewis and Clark Pass in Lewis and Clark County, just north of the present highway connecting Great Falls and Missoula. He recorded the following comment,

***On May 10, 1805, Ordway, of the Corps of Discovery, reported seeing several moose near the mouth of the Milk River near present day Fort Peck. In 1832 a hunter killed a moose in the same area.***

*Moose are cold climate animals with an excellent ability to handle snow and the trials of winter. Their lack of ability to handle hot climates might limit their present distribution.[3]*

"Reubin Fields wounded a moos [sic] deer this morning near camp. My dog much worried."[2]

Moose are cold climate animals with an excellent ability to cope with snow and winter other conditions. Their lack of ability to handle hot climates might limit their present distribution.[3] In many areas, willow *(Salix spp.)* and wetland vegetation make up a major portion of their diet. They have sometimes been regarded as a "fire adapted species" that prosper following fires that open up forest allowing extensive stands of willows and other shrubs to develop.[4] However, research in the Yellowstone area indicated that moose also use mature sub-alpine fir *(Abies lasiocarpa)* forests extensively. These forests can take hundreds of years to regenerate after a fire, but can be critical to the survival of moose.[5] Thus, the concept of being a "fire adapted species" is not universally true. Although moose commonly have a single calf, they are capable of bearing and raising twins under conditions of excellent nutrition, as was observed in the Gravelly Mountains of southwestern Montana in the 1950s. A rapid increase in the moose population occurred there, but their diet differed from elsewhere consisting primarily of a tall growing plant called sticky geranium *(Geranium viscosissimum)*.[6]

Moose have never been transplanted in Montana. The U.S. Forest Service conducted surveys of moose populations beginning in the 1920s. Moose numbers in the upper Stillwater drainage in the south central part of the state were increasing and by 1935, were exhausting their food supply.[7]

After enactment of the Pittman-Robertson Act and formation of the state Wildlife Restoration Division, Lloyd McDowell and Marshall Moy began conducting moose surveys north of Yellowstone Park in 1942. In June to October they covered 341 miles on foot and 1,341 miles on horseback as they looked for moose. Bob Cooney surveyed the same area in 1943 and McDowell returned in 1944. The Slough Creek portion of the area was also surveyed in January.[8] After World War II, Joe Gaab was given the duty of conducting summer surveys of moose habitats. During 1947-1949 Joe traveled hundreds of miles on horseback to get a sense of the population.

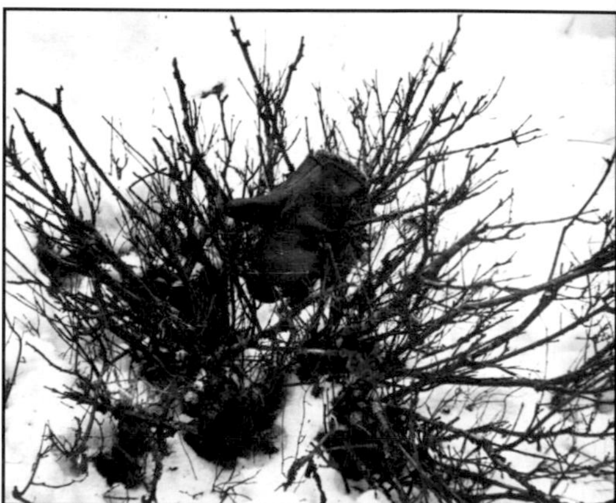

***Too many moose in an area cause a deteriation of their winter food supply.***
*(Courtesy Robert Cooney Photo Collection)*

***Bull moose feeding on smartweed (Polygonum hydropiper).***
*(Photo courtesy Terry N. Lonner)*

The first laws protecting moose in Montana closed the season from

*Joe Gaab conducted comprehensive summer moose surveys after WW II.* *(Courtesy Robert Cooney Photo Collection)*

*(Montana Fish and Game photos from Montana Wildlife, January 1962)*

*Making a paint bomb using a Christmas tree ornament to mark moose by dropping them on the animals from a helicopter.*

February 1 to August 15th and date back to about 1872. Numbers of moose appeared to have declined near the close of the 19th century. In 1910 there were an estimated 300 moose in Montana. A prohibition on moose hunting began in 1897 and continued until 1945.[9]

Lack of transplanting did not rule out moose adventures. Information was in great demand as the Gravelly Mountain population began to reach a peak and then decline.

Marking moose for research was a challenge in the era before tranquilizer and net guns. Ralph Rouse, LeRoy Ellig and Jim Mitchell filled Christmas tree ornaments with sheep marking paint and then dropped them on the animals from a helicopter. Their accuracy allowed them to mark 75 percent of the moose seen.[10] Moose calves were also tagged by teams working on horseback or sometimes by using a helicopter. Once a calf was located, crew members would dismount their horses and attach ear tags to the calf while other crew members would entice the infuriated and very protective cow moose to chase them while the tagging was done. The helicopter was sometimes used to help deter the anxious mother. Research studies paid off, providing a basis for moose management that would conserve this magnificent animal for the rest of the century.[11]

Moose populations have been negatively impacted by highway construction along streams and development of residential areas in stream side habitats. Moose succeeded in expanding their range during the 20th century even with the restoration of large predators.

***Moose populations have been negatively impacted by highway construction along streams and the development of residential areas in stream side habitats.***

*Moose calf with ear tags.* *(Montana Fish and Game photo by Terry N. Lonner)*

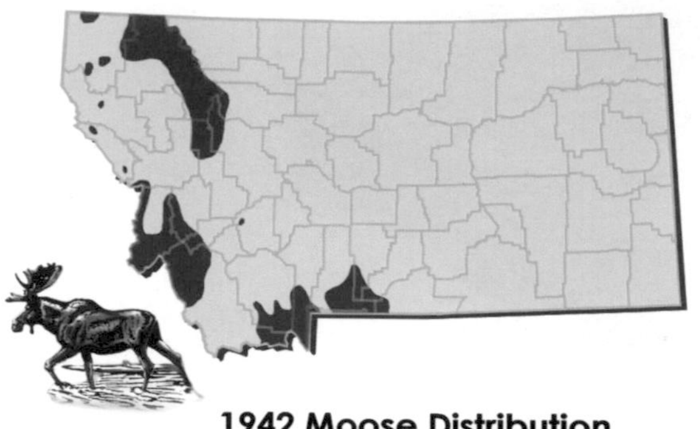


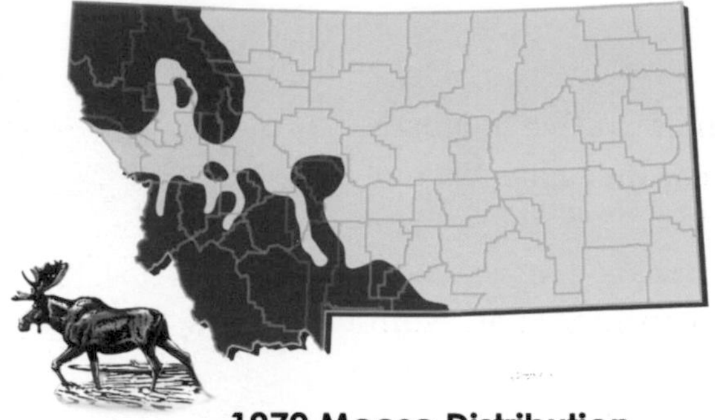


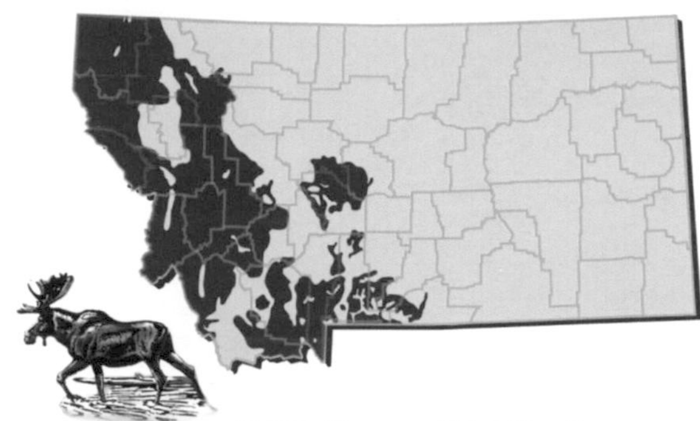


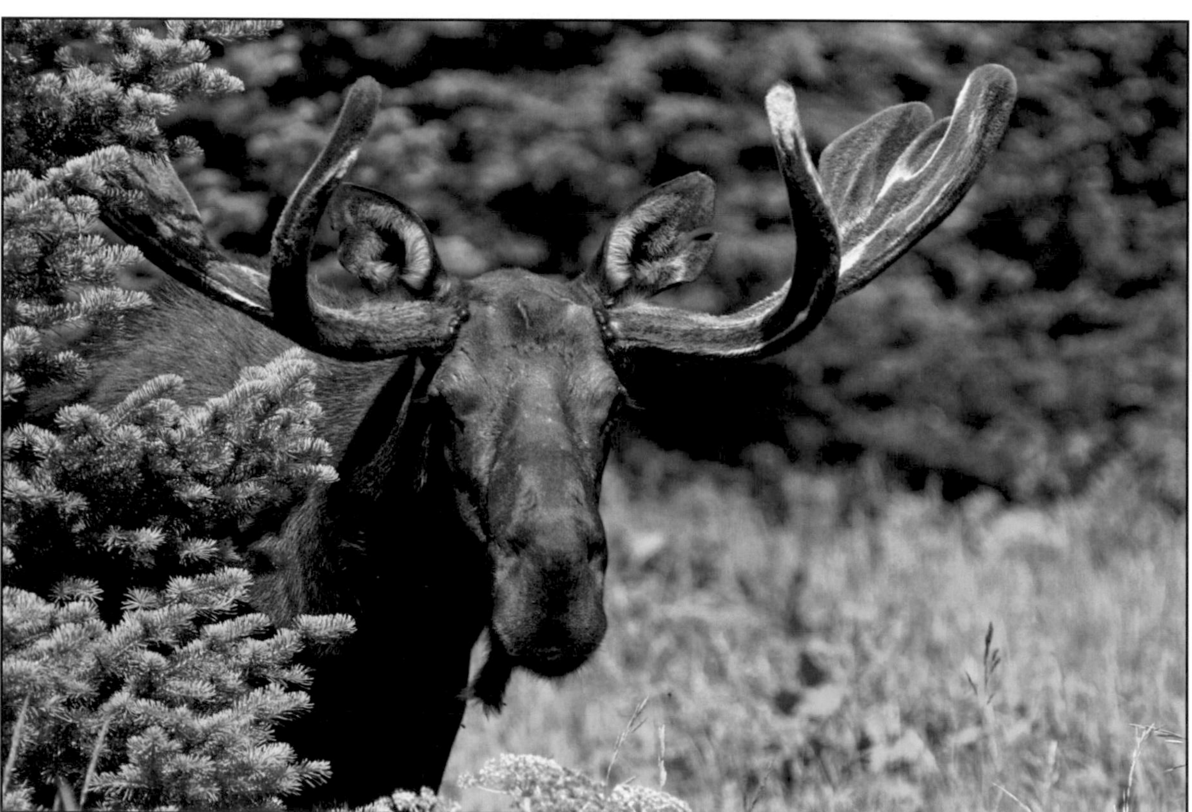

*Bull moose with antlers in velvet. (Photo courtesy Brent N. Lonner)*

## BISON

*(Bison bison* or *Bos bison)*

Bison are native to North America. They have been of legendary importance to humans since mankind first appeared on the continent and Montana has had a special place in the conservation of this species.

The first substantial herd conserved was that of Allard and Pablo in northwestern Montana. When the U.S. Congress forced a reduction in size of the Flathead reservation, most of the Allard-Pablo herd was sold to Canada. Eighteen bison from this herd were purchased and sent to Yellowstone National Park and 38 were purchased by Charles Conrad, a banker in Kalispell. Morton Elrod, head of the Biology Dept. at the University of Montana, led an effort by the American Bison Society to select a portion of the former reservation area to serve as a bison range. The selected land, near Moiese, was acquired and became the National Bison Range in 1908. Alicia Conrad, widow of Charles, sold 34 and donated 2 bison to populate the new enterprise. A barge trip across Flathead Lake and railroad ride transferred them from the Conrad ranch to the bison range. Another bison from the Goodnight herd in Texas was added to provide 37 bison for the startup population as the National Bison Range became real.[12] In 1910 three additional bison were added to the herd from the New Hampshire preserve of Austin Corbin. Some of the Corbin herd had come from the herd of "Buffalo" Jones in Kansas.

There has often been some commercial interest

***Roundup of the Michael Pablo buffalo herd for shipment to Canada. c. 1908.*** *(Courtesy Jim McLucas Photo Collection, photo by N. A. Forsyth)*

***Montana has had a special place in the conservation of bison... The first substantial herd conserved was that of Allard and Pablo in northwestern Montana.***

in bison which has led to its confusing legal status as both livestock and native wildlife. Some Indian tribes have reestablished herds on reservation lands in an effort to conserve bison as well as their culture. Commercial agricultural interest became intensified, particularly in the 1990s, to provide an alternate future for the species as livestock with all the potential genetic changes to refine the bison for domestication. Interest in making bison domestic livestock has led to many attempts to crossbreed them with cattle. This has left most bison herds with some cattle genes. Such breeding efforts can provide another route to extinction as happened to the auroch, a wild ancestor of cattle.

***Commercial agricultural interests have led to bison becoming an alternative to raising cattle.*** *(Photo courtesy Martha A. Lonner)*

***There has always been some commercial interest in bison which has led to its confusing legal status as both livestock and native wildlife.***

By 2006 the U.S. Fish and Wildlife Service was using genetic screening on its 4 bison ranges to build up herds with no detectable cattle genes.

The Yellowstone National Park herd was allowed to grow rapidly from the 1970s to present. The burgeoning herd began to vote with their feet to move outside the Park into Montana in large numbers during the 1980s. This movement has been the source of conflict ever since, because these bison carry the disease brucellosis.

Conflict between bison and cattle management has a long history. In 1871, 1,900 cattle were brought to Montana and grazed north of the Sun River. During winter of 1871-1872 the bison herd migrated south and cattlemen were forced to move their cattle to the south side of the Sun River and herd them to keep them from mingling with the bison.[13]

***The Bison population in Yellowstone National Park has increased from about 40 in 1890 to almost 5,000 in 2004. Missing data are because of incomplete counts during some years.*** *(Background photo courtesy Martha A. Lonner)*

Over the years many wildlife biologists and other citizens have expressed a desire to restore wild bison herds. Disease is regarded as the number one issue facing restoration of wild bison herds.[14] Brucellosis can infect humans, but perhaps of more immediate significance, can adversely affect the cattle industry. Much of the original genetic diversity of bison was lost during the 19th century decimation of herds by disease and market hunting. Existing brucellosis free herds have reduced genetic variability. The Yellowstone National Park herd does not contain cattle genes and could help increase genetic variability of other herds. However, at this time they cannot be used to enhance genetics of other herds because of the prevalence of brucellosis in Yellowstone. An experimental quarantine procedure to produce disease free individuals from the Yellowstone herd was commenced as the 21st century began.

*Bison in a quarantine facility just north of Yellowstone National Park in Park County, Montana. c. 2006.* (Photo courtesy Keith Aune)

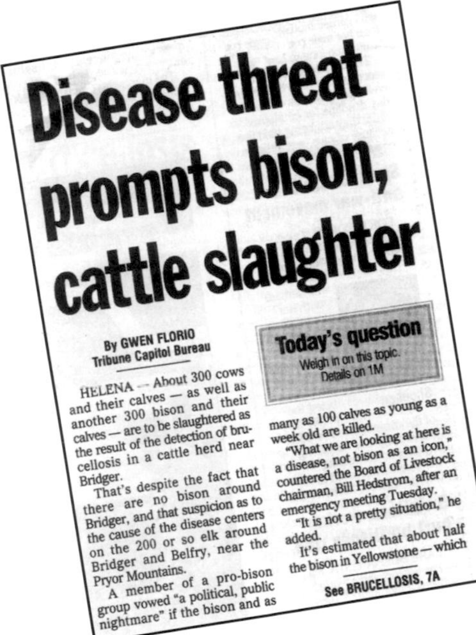

**Disease threat prompts bison, cattle slaughter**

By GWEN FLORIO
Tribune Capitol Bureau

**Today's question**
Weigh in on this topic.
Details on 1M

HELENA — About 300 cows and their calves — as well as another 300 bison and their calves — are to be slaughtered as the result of the detection of brucellosis in a cattle herd near Bridger.

That's despite the fact that there are no bison around Bridger, and that suspicion as to the cause of the disease centers on the 200 or so elk around Bridger and Belfry, near the Pryor Mountains.

A member of a pro-bison group vowed "a political, public nightmare" if the bison and as many as 100 calves as young as a week old are killed.

"What we are looking at here is a disease, not bison as an icon," countered the Board of Livestock chairman, Bill Hedstrom, after an emergency meeting Tuesday.

"It is not a pretty situation," he added.

It's estimated that about half the bison in Yellowstone — which

See BRUCELLOSIS, 7A

*Great Falls Tribune - May 30, 2007.*

Brucellosis is classified as a "bio-terror" or biological warfare agent. Because of this, some types of experiments necessary in development of new vaccines cannot be carried out on the Yellowstone herd. This increases costs and sometimes raises questions about using the vaccine in field situations.

***Disease is regarded as the number one problem in bison conservation.***

*Blood is drawn from a bison to test for diseases in a quarantine facility just north of Yellowstone National Park near Gardiner, Montana. c. 2006.* (Photo courtesy Keith Aune)

*Bison in Yellowstone National Park during winter 2005.* *(Photo courtesy Brent N. Lonner)*

"Where would you put them?" is a question sometimes asked by agricultural landowners when re-introduction of wild bison herds comes up. Indian reservations, Missouri River Breaks and the upper Yellowstone valley near Yellowstone NP are sites often suggested. A number of other sites have been suggested over the years. The question has been asked for each of the many species that have been restored over the years. Traditionally, people have stepped up, developed management techniques, plans and locations for re-introductions. Critics of bison re-introduction have said there are inherent problems. History tells us that most problems have solutions. Wild herds are desirable because if bison are to seize their heritage in Montana they must be allowed to evolve. There were over half a million commercially raised bison in North America as the 21st century began. There are only about 8,500 in the 13 managed "conservation herds" that seek to maintain the wild genome. The 3,000 plus Yellowstone Park herd (in 2008) obviously makes up a large part of this group.

The American Prairie Foundation and World Wildlife Fund are working to establish an area of wild or native prairie in Phillips County. The concept includes wildlife that are native to the prairie. Forty disease and cattle gene free bison from Wind Cave National Park in South Dakota have been added to the area and more will be added in the future. The bison were subject to genetic testing to ensure that they do not have cattle genes, at least as determined by the current quality of testing, which does not include the whole genome. Hunting access was provided on a portion of the 60,000 acres held by the Foundation in 2006. The privately owned bison are presently held in a ranching situations and are not part of the publicly owned wildlife resource.[15]

The American Bison Society was allowed to quietly die.[16] It has become apparent that the job of bison conservation is not over and the society has been revived. The Wildlife Conservation Society is now the legal holder of its legacy. North American bison conservation specialists have developed a conservation plan for bison restoration of North American bison.[17]

***Critics of bison re-introduction have said there are inherent problems. History tells us that most problems have solutions. Wild herds are desirable because if bison are to seize their heritage in Montana they must be allowed to evolve.***

## Caribou

*(Rangifer tarandus)*

Evidence indicates that Woodland (mountain) caribou are sometimes present in the Yaak River drainage, but "Very little is known about them".[18] These caribou are an isolated remnant population of probably under 100 that occupies the adjacent Selkirk area of Idaho, Washington and the Purcell Mountains of British Columbia as well as Montana.

***Both sexes of caribou have antlers. Cows weigh about 250 to 300 lbs. and bulls up to 500 lbs.***

Dark brown to grayish on the back with white undersides and rump, they have long legs and large hooves. Both sexes have antlers. Cows weigh about 250 to 300 lbs. and bulls 400 to 500 lbs. The species is anatomically the most primitive member of the Cervidae or deer family. They winter in cedar-hemlock forests and summer in the spruce – fir alpine zone. Food consists of a broad range of lichens, grasses, sedges, forbs and twigs of woody plants. Caribou are impacted by logging, fire, the encroachment of deer and moose populations and human disturbance.

Although generally considered of the Woodland subspecies *(Rangifer tarandus caribou)* genetic evidence suggest that this population is probably a southward extension of the Barren Ground subspecies *(Rangifer tarandus groenlandicus)* to the north. The caribou in Washington and Idaho are listed as endangered under the ESA of 1973, but in Montana they are classified as a game animal with a closed season. These are probably the only caribou that still exist south of the Canadian border. The small population is in jeopardy and requires the best efforts of both the U.S. and Canadian wildlife agencies if it is to survive.[19] Transplants to supplement the Montana population have occasionally been discussed but have not been carried out or definitely planned.

***Bull woodland or mountain caribou.*** *(Photo courtesy Doug Jury)*

***These caribou are an isolated remnant population of under 100 that occupies the adjacent Selkirk area of Idaho, Washington and the Purcell Mountains of British Columbia as well as Montana. . .and is probably the only caribou population that still exists south of the Canadian border.***

# Footnotes

[1] Bowyer, R. T., V. Van Ballenberge and J. G. Kie. 2003. Moose. Chapter 45 in Wild Mammals of North America, G. A. Feldhammer, B. C. Thompson and J. A. Chapman. Johns Hopkins University Press, Baltimore. 931-964.

Modern moose were present in "Beringia" (Alaska) prior to 15,500 years before present when the land connection with Asia still existed. As the continental ice sheets melted they could move south along an ice free corridor east of the Rocky Mountains between 15,000 and 10,000 years before present.

Lange, I. M. 2002. Ice age mammals of North America. Mountain Press, Missoula, MT. 226 pp.

Pielou, E. C. 1991. After the ice age. University of Chicago Press, Chicago. 366 pp.

[2] Cutright, P. R. 1969. Lewis and Clark: Pioneering naturalists. University of Nebraska Press, Lincoln. 439.

Stevens, D. 1971. Shiras moose. Chapter 9 in Game Management in Montana. T. W. Mussehl and F. W. Howell, editors. Montana Fish and Game Dept., Helena. 89-95.

Lewis, M. 1806. The definitive journals of Lewis and Clark: Over the Rockies to St. Louis. G. E. Moulton, editor. University of Nebraska Press, Lincoln. 8:95.

[3] Renecker, L. A. and R. J. Hudson. 1992. Thermoregulatory behavioral response of moose: Is large body size an adaptation or a constraint? Alces Supplement 1:52-64.

[4] Ibid.

[5] Tyers, D. 2003. Winter ecology of moose on the northern Yellowstone winter range. Ph.D. dissertation, Montana State University, Bozeman. 308 pp.

[6] Knowlton, F. F. 1960. Food habits, movements and populations of moose in the Gravelly Mountains, Montana. Journal of Wildlife Management 24:162-170.

Peek, J. M. 1962. Reproduction of moose in the Gravelly and Snowcrest Mountains, Montana. Journal of Wildlife Management. 26:360-365.

[7] Anon. 1942. Hellroaring-Slough Creek moose surveys. 1941-1942 Biennial Report, Montana Fish and Game Commission. Helena, MT. 44-45.

[8] McDowell, L. and various co-authors. 1942-1945. Montana moose surveys in the Slough Creek - Hellroaring Unit. Individual year reports. Montana Fish and Game Department, Helena.

Ibid. Tyers, D. 2003.

[9] Ibid. Stevens, D. 1971.

[10] Anon. 1962. Censusing moose by helicopter. Montana Wildlife, January. 24-25.

[11] Peek, J. 1962. "Moose! Largest of Montana's big game". Montana Wildlife, January. 26-29.

Ibid. Stevens, D. 1971.

Smith, N. S. 1962. The fall and winter ecology of the Shiras moose , *(Alces alces shirasi)* in the Rock Creek drainage, Granite County, Montana. M.S. Thesis, University of Montana, Missoula. 52 pp.

[12] Dary, D. A. 1989. The buffalo book. Ohio University Press. 384 pp.

Bigart, R. (Editor). 2001. Chapters 4,5,6, 7. and 8 in: "I will be meat for my Salish". Salish Kootenai College Press, Pablo, MT. 69-145.

[13] Vaughn, R. 1898. From the mines to the farm. Then and now or thirty-six years in the Rockies. Farcountry Press, Helena. 48-55.

[14] Reynolds, H. W., C. C. Gates and R. D. Glaholt. 2003. Bison. Chapter 29 in Wild Mammals of North America. G. A. Feldhammer, B.C. Thompson and J. A. Chapman, editors. Johns Hopkins University Press, Baltimore. 1009-1060.

[15] Pickett, K. 2007.The American prairie preserve: Serengeti of Montana? Great Falls Tribune July 1, 2007. 1, 6a,7a.

[16] Ibid. Dary, D. A. 1989.

[17] Redford, K. and E. Fearn. 2007. Vermejo statement of ecological restoration, Ecological future of bison in North America. A report from a multi-stakeholder, transboundary meeting. Wildlife Conservation Society Working Paper 30. 64 pp.

[18] Anon. 1958. Caribou on the Yaak. Montana Wildlife. August 2-3.

[19] Miller, F. 2003. Caribou. Chapter 46 in Wildlife Mammals of North America. G. A. Feldhamer, B. C. Thompson, and J. A. Chapman Editors. Johns Hopkins University Press, Baltimore. 965-977.

*Bison once roamed North America by the millions. "Herd of bison near Lake Jessie" in North Dakota, painting by John Mix Stanley from the 1855 Pacific Railway Survey Report. (Courtesy Merrill G. Burlingame Special Collections of the Montana State University Libraries)*

*Fur trapping has been an important part of Montana's wildlife heritage since the early part of the 19th century. (Photo taken at the Fort Benton Museum in Fort Benton, MT, courtesy Martha A. Lonner)*

Chapter 15

# Furbearers and the Like

Furbearing animals represent a separate legal category of wildlife species that Montana Fish, Wildlife and Parks is responsible for maintaining healthy populations and for recreational opportunities. Of the 10 species classified as furbearers only beaver *(Castor canadensis)*, fisher *(Martes pennanti)*, marten *(Martes americana)*, and swift fox *(Vulpes velox)* have been transplanted.

*Species legally classified as furbearers at this time are: Marten (sable), Muskrat, Mink, Beaver, Bobcat, Wolverine, Lynx (classified as a threatened and endangered species subject to special rules), River Otter, Fisher and Swift Fox (closed to trapping). Raccoon, Badger and Red Fox are nongame. Coyote, weasels (including the Long-tail, Short-tail [ermine] and Least weasel), and Skunks are classified as predators.*

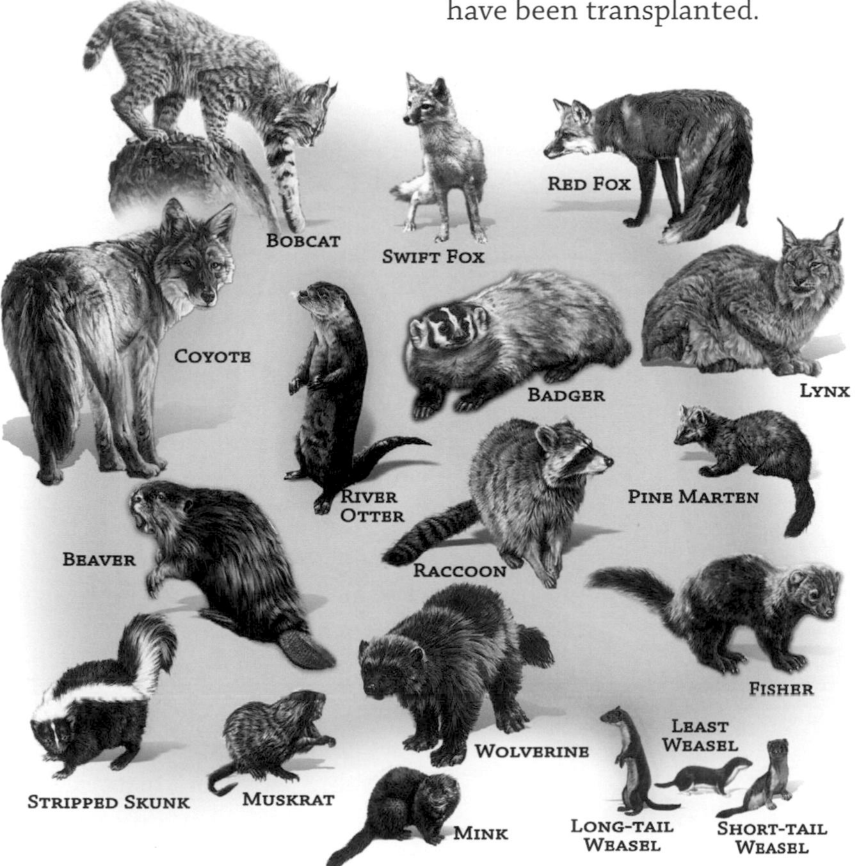

## BEAVER
*(Castor canadensis)*

Beaver are the largest North American rodent. Adults weigh from 30 to 60 pounds. A flattened tail is used for propulsion and to give warning slaps. Usually dark brown in color, colonies of "white" beaver have been found in Montana. Beaver construct lodges in wetland areas or burrows in banks of streams and build dams from vegetation and mud. Trees provide both construction materials and food. Beaver feed upon green under-bark of willow *(Salix spp.)* and deciduous trees. Winter food is stored by pushing sticks into bottoms of backwaters or ponds where it can be accessed under ice. Beaver breed during January-March, giving birth to between two and four "kits". Engineering activities of beaver often flood areas creating habitat for moose, fish, waterfowl and other wildlife. Engineering and logging skills of beaver often conflict with man when it involves such things as irrigation ditches and ornamental trees. Our propensity to create home sites along streams has exacerbated these conflicts.

***Our propensity to create home sites along streams has perpetuated these conflicts.***

Colonel A. J. Vaughn, the first Indian agent in Montana, made the first report of agricultural damage by beaver in 1858. He planted wheat when teaching Blackfeet Indians to farm at his agency on the Sun River. In a report to the War Department in Washington D.C. he said his wheat crop yielded 79 bushels per acre and beaver had eaten much of it. After considerable disbelief, he eventually convinced Washington bureaucrats that beaver did, in fact, eat wheat. They sent the 500 beaver traps he requested.[1]

***A typical beaver dam.*** *(Photo courtesy Dan Tyers)*

Beaver were legendary in the early history of Montana. Restoration efforts in later years received attention, probably because of historical interest as well as high economic value. During the 1920s, some beaver causing damage

***A beaver in its natural habitat.*** *(Photo courtesy Dan Tyers)*

to property were live-trapped by game wardens and moved to unoccupied habitats. Fur trappers during that period were allowed only to trap beaver causing damage. Increasing damage complaints reflected a steadily increasing beaver population. In 1921, 479 wild beaver were trapped for pelts in Montana and by 1926, the number increased to 9,714. High harvest levels were maintained for the remainder of the decade. The number of registered pelts declined to 4,574 in 1932 from impacts of severe drought.[2] Drought and Depression of the 1930s had a major effect upon beaver populations as habitat dried up and people trapping beaver for subsistence income.[3]

***Beaver Hut on the Missouri by Karl Bodmer***
*(Courtesy Rare Books Division, Special Collections, J. Willard Marriott Library, University of Utah)*

Another problem for beaver and muskrat populations occurred when an epizootic of tularemia raged across the state from 1939 to 1943. The epizootic appears to have been most intense in the southern part of the state and a number of human cases resulted from contact with furbearing animals.[4] Tularemia affecting beaver is often water-borne but also transmitted by blood sucking insects. This disease is fatal to beaver and other aquatic animals. Another variety of tularemia associated with domestic sheep, with severe consequences for humans, produced a number of cases in sheepherders.[5]

Rain and snow returned to Montana in the 1940s after the long drought. Passage of the P-R Act accelerated beaver re-introductions. Three transplanting crews aided by game wardens live trapped 168 beaver in 11 counties in 1941 and released them in 16 counties. In 1942, 68

***A dry creek bed with a remnant beaver dam depicting conditions during drought years of the 1930s.*** *(Photo courtesy Terry N. Lonner)*

***Fur farms were common in Montana from 1920 to 1945. The primary species raised on these farms were beaver, several varieties of red fox, and mink. An occasional effort was made to raise chinchilla, an exotic species from South America.[6]***

state beaver control trapper, found that even "white beaver" had returned to the state. He trapped several of these white-spotted or piebald beaver in the Big Hole River drainage of southwestern Montana.[8]

By that time enough agricultural damage was being done that game wardens and a newly hired damage control trapper were barely able to handle all of the complaints. Although public beaver trapping in Montana was illegal from 1941 to 1953 [9], in 1950-1951, 12,522 beaver pelts were recorded in Montana from damage control trapping for nuisance beaver causing property damage.[10] Floods along the Missouri and Mississippi rivers produced many disastrous situations for property owners in downstream

*Placing a beaver live trap, upper left. A beaver release on Moose Creek in the Pipestone Drainage. c. 1942. (Courtesy Robert Cooney Photo Collection)*

***By 1950, beaver had found a home in all major river drainages in the state.***

beaver were live trapped in 10 counties and moved to unoccupied habitat in 5 counties.[7] Live trapping continued throughout the war years and by 1944, the total number of beaver transplanted was 555. In 1946, the number had grown to 919 and by 1950, beaver had found a home in all major river drainages in the state. Howard Campbell, a

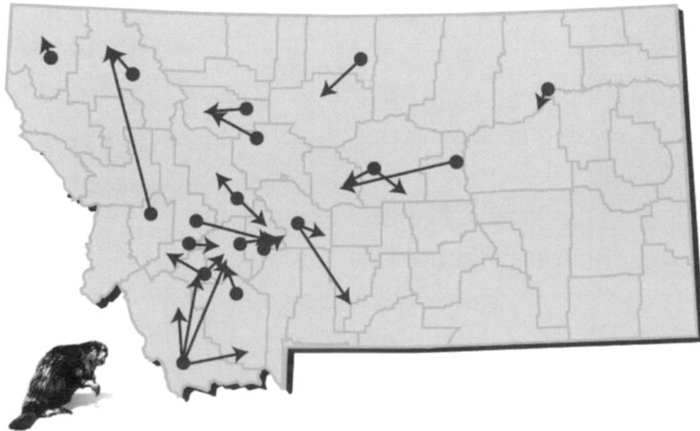

**1942 Beaver Transplants**

*Howard Campbell with the pelt of a "white" beaver trapped in the Big Hole Drainage of southwestern Montana. c. 1950. (Montana Fish & Game Photo)*

states. Flooding and a need to create jobs during the Depression triggered a great deal of interest in building large mainstream control dams on rivers.

After WW II this interest was once again mobilized to build large dams. Yellowtail Dam on the Big Horn, Tiber Dam on the Marias, Canyon Ferry on the Missouri, Hungry Horse on the South Fork of the Flathead, Libby Dam on the Kootenai and Noxon Rapids on the Clark's Fork of the Columbia Rivers were added to our state's collection of dams.

***Beaver dams near the head of a small drainage.*** *(Photo courtesy Dan Tyers)*

Opposition began to develop in the 1970s and enthusiasm for large dams and reservoirs began to wane. Glacier View Dam that would have flooded a beautiful portion of Glacier Park was defeated by local opposition. The Allen Spur Dam that would have flooded Paradise Valley of the Yellowstone River was defeated as were the Reichle Dam that would have flooded the Big Hole River[11] and the Sun Butte dam on the Sun River that would have intruded into the Bob Marshall Wilderness Area were also defeated. The Yellowstone River, except for a couple of small water diversion structures, remains the only free flowing river among Montana's larger rivers.

During this time the U.S. Soil Conservation Service (now the U.S. Natural Resources Conservation Service) and other organizations argued that small dams near head waters of major rivers could help control floods. This gave the hard working beaver, with their natural engineering skills, a strong element of charisma in the national public eye. This was magnified when Howard Campbell, the Montana state beaver trapper, helped the Walt Disney organization make its pioneering nature film "Beaver Valley". Filmed in Beaverhead County of southwestern Montana, movie makers drew upon knowledge and skills of Howard to make this film.

Charisma or not, beaver were causing problems and control efforts were straining department resources. Research by Joe Townsend and then Lloyd Casagranda[12] provided insight to get the situation under control and lay the groundwork to develop an official Montana beaver management program. Joe determined that counts of beaver dams and caches of winter food in major streams could provide fundamental population trend data necessary for management. This led to creation of probably the most nauseating data base ever devised. Innumerable cases of airsickness were produced as low flying airplanes pivoted, twisted and turned to follow each bend in major rivers of the state.[13] To the great relief of game

***. . . the U.S. Soil Conservation Service (now the U.S. Natural Resources Conservation Service) and other organizations argued that small dams near the head waters of major rivers could also help control floods.***

*Aerial photo taken during a beaver dam/cache count.*
*(Photo courtesy Dan Tyers)*

Fabich to furnish him with live trapped beaver that were caught in damage control efforts. The beaver were transported to Gardiner where they were loaded on pack horses along with an ice cake to keep them cool. Pack horses transported them to the wilderness area for release. A few more beaver got to hitchhike on fire fighting helicopters during the huge Yellowstone fires of 1988.

Tracking radios were implanted in 10 beaver. These provided information on movements and dispersal following release. The effort reestablished a

*Innumerable cases of airsickness were produced as low flying airplanes pivoted, twisted and turned to follow each bend in the major rivers of the state.*

wardens and biologists that flew as observers, the data base was finally complete and a management plan was put in place. With adjustments as needed, it has served well to the present day. The beaver management program has reduced beaver damage problems to more manageable levels while securing the future of beaver throughout the state. It has remained a tribute to the number of breakfasts lost while flying.

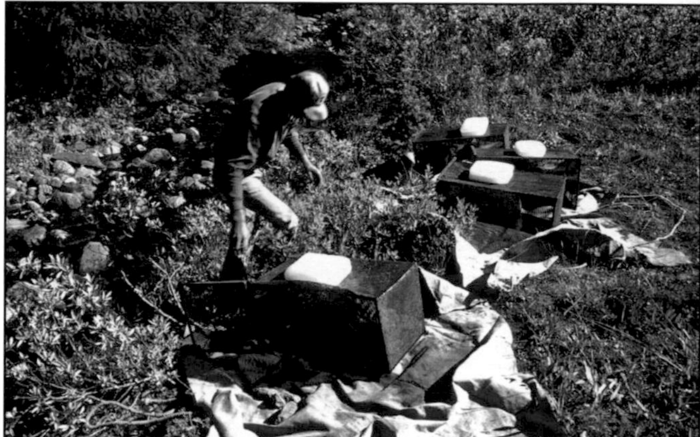

***Beaver in live traps with an ice cake to keep them cool before transplanting by horse. c. 1985.*** *(Photo Courtesy Dan Tyers)*

In the 1980s, Dan Tyers, a U.S. Forest Service wildlife biologist for the Gardiner Ranger District north of Yellowstone NP, evaluated habitat in the upper Boulder River drainage northeast of Gardiner in the Absaroka-Beartooth Wilderness. It had once been a prime source of beaver for trappers. Dan found excellent potential habitat in the area but devoid of beaver. He worked out an arrangement with state wildlife specialists Mike Ross and Harry Whitney along with state game warden Hank

*Once again these beaver engineers were free to build dams and habitat for fish, moose, waterfowl and other species in the area while enhancing the watershed.*

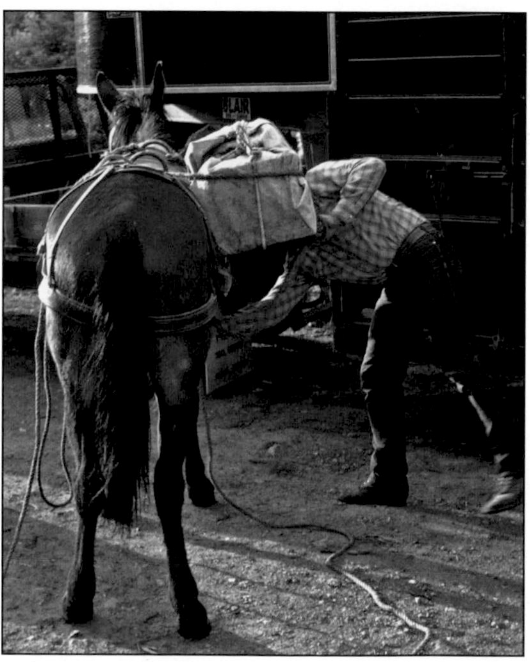

***Transplanting beaver by horse. c. 1985.***
*(Photo courtesy Dan Tyers)*

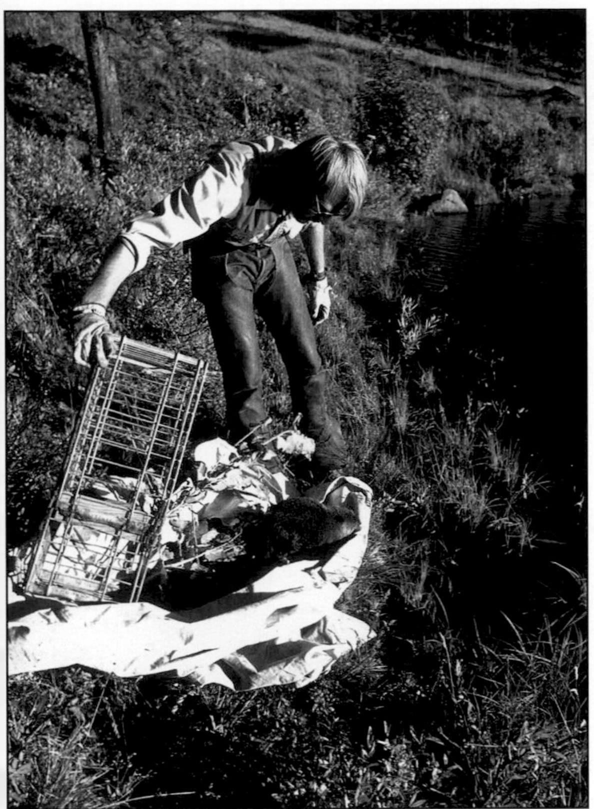

***Dan Tyers, U. S. Forest Service Biologist, releasing a beaver in the Absaroka-Beartooth Wilderness just north of Yellowstone National Park. c. 1985.***
*(Photo courtesy Dan Tyers)*

population in this area and radio transmitters showed a few dispersed to streams of northern Yellowstone NP, returning beaver to the northern winter range of the Park. Once again these wild engineers were free to build dams and habitat for fish, moose, waterfowl and other species in the area while enhancing the watershed.

## FISHER
*(Martes pennanti)*

Fisher, a member of the Mustelidae or weasel family, weighs in at 3 - 12 pounds, and inhabits dense coniferous forests of western Montana. It preys on animals up to the size of a snowshoe hare *(Lepus americanus)* and is legendary for its ability to prey upon porcupines (*Erethizon dorsatum*) without getting speared excessively by their quills. Although breeding occurs in April just after birth of 1 to 3 kits, the fertilized egg is not implanted in the uterus until February of the next year.[14] This phenomenon is called delayed implantation and is a trait found in all members of the weasel family as well as bears.

Although fishers are historical residents of Montana, their presence was not recorded between 1930 and 1959, a result perhaps of over-trapping and large scale forest fires. Catastrophic forest fires in Idaho and western Montana early in the 20th century may have separated the population along the west-central Montana-Idaho border from those farther north and east.[15] By the mid 20th century a population explosion of porcupines occurred resulting in timber damage in most forests of western Montana. The U.S. Forest Service became concerned and, after efforts to poison porcupines, planned to return fisher to its habitat where it could prey on them to keep their numbers down. A joint project between the U.S. Forest Service and Montana Fish and Game Department was established to re-introduce fisher. First year costs and part of those for the second year were paid for by the Forest Service. The state of Montana wildlife agency furnished transplanting expertise and personnel, and the British Columbia Game Branch agreed to participate. In the winters of 1958-1959 and 1959-1960, 40 fisher

***Fisher prey upon small animals up to the size of a snowshoe hare and is legendary for its ability to prey upon porcupines without getting speared excessively by their quills.***

*In the winters of 1958-1959 and 1959-1960 forty fisher were captured in British Columbia for transplanting to Montana.*

were captured in British Columbia for the project. Nine were released in the Pinkham Creek area south of Rexford in the northwest corner of the state; 15 were released in the Swan Mountain range at Holland Lake; and 12 were released in the Anaconda-Pintler Mountains southwest of Phillipsburg.[16] They have since re-colonized some of the forested areas of western Montana. Wisconsin and Minnesota also supplied 110 fisher for transplants made into the Cabinet Mountains between 1989 and 1991.[17] Fishers are legal to trap in Montana, but only in the northwestern part of the state and on a quota basis.

**1958-1960 and 1989-1991 Fisher Transplants**

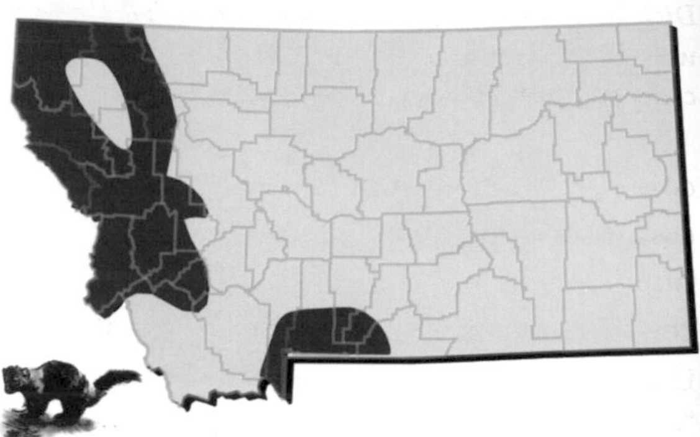

**2008 Fisher Distribution**

*Dick Weckworth, a pioneer Montana Fish & Game wildlife biologist, with a fisher from British Columbia for transplanting to northwestern Montana - 1959. (Courtesy Dick Weckworth Photo Collection)*

## MARTEN
*(Martes americana)*

Pine marten, or American sable, are another member of the weasel family. Typically weighing 1 - 2 pounds, Marten live in higher elevation coniferous forest habitats preying on voles *(Microtus spp.)*, squirrels (Sciuridae family) and other small mammals. Pelage varies in color across their range in western Montana.

Mating typically occurs during the first part of August followed by a period of delayed implantation. Fertilized eggs are not implanted until February followed by the birth of 1 to 5 young in March.

Marten are possibly the most valuable of Montana's furbearers. The highly valued dark brown or black

*Dick Weckworth, a pioneer Montana Fish & Game wildlife biologist, weighing a marten in a "handling cone". c. 1956. (Courtesy Dick Weckworth Photo Collection)*

color prized by trappers is the most common color phase of marten in northwestern Montana. In the south-central and southwestern portions of the state, the lighter yellowish or tan "canary" colors become more abundant.

Low populations were apparent in some areas after overharvesting during the 1930s. In 1944, 12 marten were captured in the northern Whitefish Range west of Glacier NP and released in the Anaconda-Pintler range in southwestern Montana. Marten ecology research projects carried out by Dick Weckworth, Chuck Jonkel and Vern Hawley working out of the Cooperative Wildlife Unit at the University of Montana[18] led to efforts to further expand marten range. Twenty-one marten live trapped along the North Fork of the Flathead River near Glacier Park were released in Lincoln County in the northwestern corner of the state in 1955.[19] Nine more marten from the northern Whitefish range were released in the Little Belt Mountains of Meagher County in 1956 and 1957. Thanks to these restoration efforts, marten are legal to trap today.

***Marten are possibly the most valuable of Montana's furbearers.***

***The highly valued dark brown or black color prized by trappers is the most common color phase of marten in the northwestern portion of the state.***

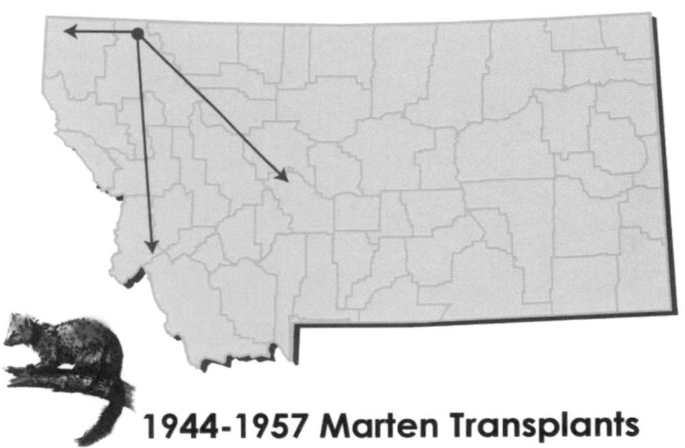

**1944-1957 Marten Transplants**

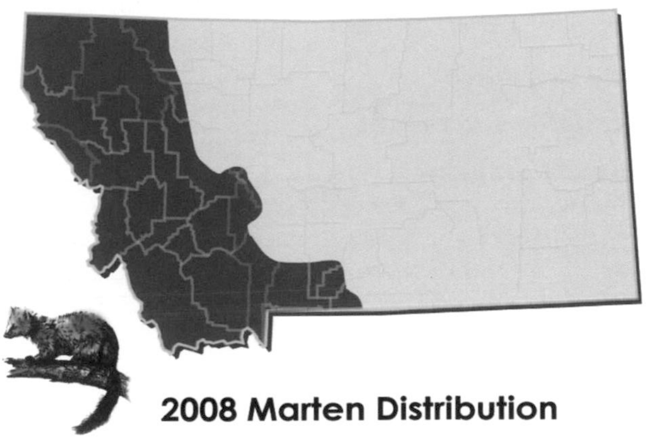

**2008 Marten Distribution**

*Marten in cages ready for transplanting from the Whitefish Range west of Glacier National Park to the Anaconda-Pintler Mountain Range. c. 1944. (Courtesy Robert Cooney Photo Collection)*

## SWIFT FOX

(*Vulpes velox*)

Swift fox are native to the northern and eastern Montana prairies. Although their scientific name has not been revised, recent DNA analysis has shown that swift fox may be closely related to arctic fox (*Alopex lagopus*).[20] The smallest fox in the state, they are classified as a furbearer with a closed season. Swift fox are about the size of a house cat and typically weigh 4 to 6 pounds. Their pelage is gray with yellowish or buff highlights on their neck and legs with black muzzle patches and a black -tipped tail. Swift fox spend most daylight hours in dens, coming out at night to hunt rodents and insects.[21] As inhabitants of the prairie, swift fox were negatively impacted by habitat loss from agriculture and sustained predator and rodent control programs. No sightings occurred in Montana between 1918 and 1978. In 1969 swift fox were officially listed as extinct in the state.[22]

***Although their scientific name has not been revised, recent DNA analysis has shown that swift fox may be closely related to arctic fox (Alopex lagopus).***[21]

***As inhabitants of the prairie, swift foxes were negatively impacted by habitat loss from agriculture and sustained predator and rodent control programs.***

Reduction in predator and rodent control programs provided an opportunity for these foxes to reclaim some of their original range in eastern Montana. A re-introduction program by wildlife officials and citizens in Alberta and Saskatchewan was begun in 1983. Some fox from this program colonized prairies of northern Montana providing a population of about 500. Another cooperative effort among Defenders of Wildlife, a swift fox breeding facility in Canada and the Blackfeet Nation led to successful re-introductions on tribal lands at the close of the 20th century.[23] In 2006 Les Bighorn and Allen Spotted Bull of the Assiniboine and Sioux tribal wildlife agency released swift foxes on the Fort Peck Reservation extending their range to northeastern Montana. The release was a joint project of the tribes, Defenders of Wildlife and Montana Fish, Wildlife and Parks under the auspices of the Montana Fish, Wildlife and Parks Commission.[24]

*Ryan Rauscher, a Montana Fish, Wildlife and Parks native species biologist, releasing an adult swift fox in northeast Montana. Only juveniles were used for translocation. c. 2005.* (Photo courtesy Ryan Rauscher)

## OTHER SPECIES

### Wolverine
*(Gulo gulo)*

The Wolverine is classified as a furberaer in Montana and is the largest terrestrial member of the weasel family (Mustelidae). Folklore about it has provided many intriguing stories. Wolverine weigh up to 35 pounds and are often described as resembling a small bear. Pelage colors range from medium brown to black with yellowish orange stripes along the side of the back. White or tan markings may occur on the chest or toes. White markings are common on wolverine from the Bridger Mountain Range and other "island" mountain ranges of central Montana. They breed during summer, have delayed implantation and give birth to one to five kits in February to April. Usually regarded as solitary animals recent studies using GPS collars have found they have a social side. Females have been observed admitting polygamous males into their dens and also males playing with kits.[25] Extensive home ranges of 200 to 400 square miles suggests low population densities.[26]

Lewis and Clark may have seen one near Great Falls and by the end of the 1920s wolverine were suspected to be near extinction in the state. Re-colonization occurred naturally from Canada, Glacier Park and wilderness areas. By the 1940s, wolverine had reclaimed much of their range in northwestern Montana but were not legally protected during this period. By the 1950s they occupied most forested mountain areas west of the Continental Divide and by the 1960s, wolverine were present in the Little Belt Mountains, Absaroka-Beartooth range and other major mountain ranges in the western, central and southern portions of the state.[27] In fact, Montana's wolverines represent the majority of the wolverine population in the lower 48 states.

***. . . Montana's wolverines represent the majority of the wolverine population in the lower 48 states.***

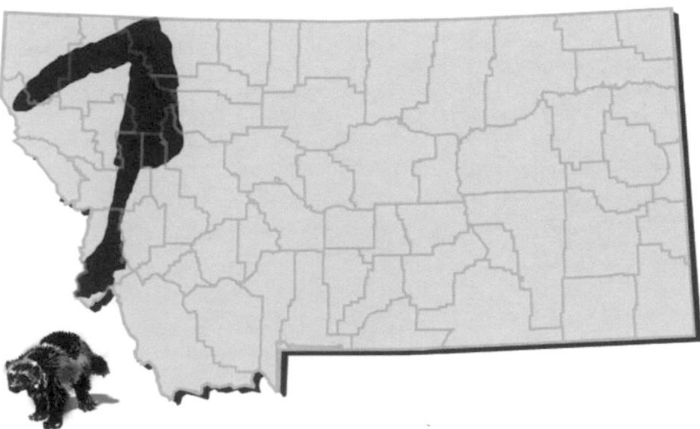

**1952 Wolverine Distribution**

*Wolverine. c. 1968. (National Park Service photo, photographer unknown)*

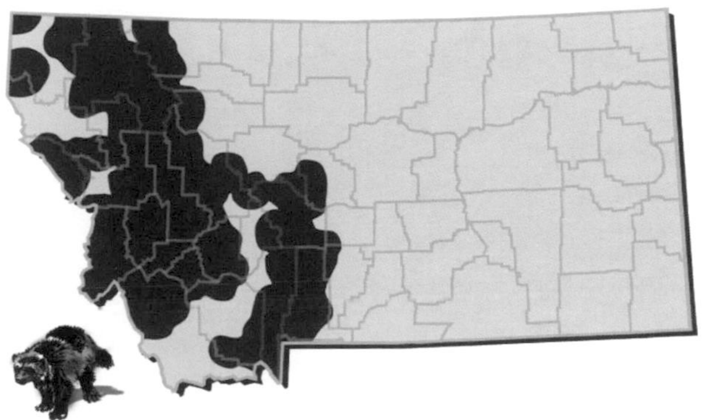

**2008 Wolverine Distribution**

## Muskrat and Mink

*(Ondatra zibethicus)* and *(Mustela vison)*

*Muskrat*

*Mink*

The Muskrat and Mink are classified as fubearers and have furnished the lions share of the furbearer harvest that provided pelts for the fur trade from Montana. Western Montana had about half the number of trappers producing about 40 percent of the pelts in the 1950s.[28] They still provide a large share of the harvest with about 50% of the furbearer pelts taken annually.[29]

***Western Montana had about half the number of trappers producing about 40 percent of the pelts in the 1950s.[26]***

## River Otter

*(Lutra canadensis)*

No trapping of River Otters had been allowed since the 1949-1950 season. Residents of northwestern Montana complained that increasing otters were responsible for poor fishing by reducing the number of fish in lakes and streams. Trappers accused otters of killing muskrat, beaver and mink reducing numbers of these highly preferred furbearers, but research by Ken Greer cleared the otters of the charges.[30] Otters are a managed furbearer in Montana with trapping allowed on a quota system.

*River Otter*

## Bobcats and Lynx

*(Lynx rufus)* and *(Lynx canadensis)*

*Bobcat*

Bobcats and Lynx are medium sized members of the Felidae or cat family. Like most cats their hunting strategy is primarily that of ambushing rather than the long distance pursuit of members of the dog family. Bobcats are widely distributed across the state in areas of lesser snowfall. Bobcats surpass coyotes in producing predator related problems in southeastern Montana.[31] The harvest of bobcats fluctuates with the market for long haired fur.

Lynx are a snow adapted species with large feet and prey primarily upon snowshoe hares *(Lepus americanus)*.

*Lynx*

During times of low hare populations they will switch to ruffed grouse and other smaller prey species. The major lynx population of the state is in the spruce-fir forests of the northwestern portion of the state. Winter track surveys for lynx are conducted each year by the Fish, Wildlife and Parks Department and the U.S. Forest Service has formally designated spruce-fir forests across the state as critical habitat for the species. Lynx do occur in the southwestern part of the state but are not common there. As clear-cut timber areas and burned areas regenerate they pass through a period of years when they become excellent snowshoe hare habitat providing an opportunity for lynx to prosper. One radio-tracked lynx in southwestern Montana is known to have travelled several hundred miles in the course of a month.

In early 2000, the U.S. Fish and Wildlife Service listed the Canada lynx as "threatened" under the federal Endangered Species Act. The listing covers 16 states, including Montana. As a federally threatened species, taking a lynx by trapping or shooting is prohibited. Although the lynx is now listed as a federally threatened species, winter snow track surveys show there are good numbers of lynx in Montana with the healthiest lynx population in the lower 48 states.

### Coyote
*(Canis latrans)*

As suggested by its name derived from the Aztec word coytl, the coyote has a rich folklore and history as an ultimate survivor and trickster. While coyotes have been known to kill deer and elk their primary food consists of small mammals, insects, berries seeds and some roots. Its efficiency in preying upon domestic sheep has often brought grief to sheep growers.[32] Always relatively abundant, coyotes

***Coyote***

***Coyote near her den with 8 pups.*** *(Photo courtesy Martha A. Lonner)*

***The coyote has a rich folklore and history as an ultimate survivor and trickster.***

were able to expand their role after wolves were eliminated from Montana in the early 20th century. The federal government had become heavily involved in wolf control on behalf of the livestock industry during the 19th century. As the number of sheepmen increased it was only natural to ask that the federal government also control the increasing number of coyotes.[33] Area control of the canid predators using poison injected into carcasses and shooting was carried out during most of the 20th century. The cyanide gun or "coyote getter" began to be used widely after WW II. During the war a new poisonous compound numbered 1080 was developed. This compound is highly toxic to canid predators, but other species were less sensitive to it. Carcasses injected with the poison were widely distributed across rangelands of the west during the 1950s giving a highly effective means of coyote control.

Striped Skunk

***Always relatively abundant, coyotes were able to expand their role after wolves were eliminated from Montana in the early 20th century.***

Raccoon

Coyote control efforts were funded by the U.S. Fish and Wildlife Service, the Montana Livestock Commission and the Montana Fish and Game Commission. Like many action programs this predator control effort was both very expensive and popular.[34] Questions concerning its effectiveness, side effects and cost benefits were never asked because of the "Millions for action, pennies for research" approach to problems. Reports of eagle, bear and particularly deaths of ranch dogs caused by the 1080 baits began to accumulate.

***The reduction in coyotes brought with it increased numbers of striped skunks, and badgers and raccoons increasing complaints about predation on smaller animals.***

**Striped Skunk, Badger and Racoon**
*(Mephitis mephitis), (Taxidae taxus)* and *(Procyon lotor)*

Badger

The reduction in coyotes brought with it increased numbers of skunks, badgers and raccoons, increasing complaints about predation on smaller animals. Two species of skunks occur in Montana, the Striped skunk (*Mephitis mephitis*) and western spotted skunk (*Spilogale gracilis*), although the latter only occurs incidentally. They are classified as predators and are a major wild reservoir for rabies. Additional skunk control efforts are made during years when skunk populations are high and there is a high incidence of rabies. Both badger and raccoon are classified as nongame in Montana.

Furbearer and predator research biologist Fletcher Newby found that skunks were the largest source of predatory losses, followed by bobcats, then coyotes and dogs. Although coyotes had been controlled for over a century they still were responsible for the greatest monetary loss.

A new program was started which targeted the specific animals causing the damage rather than just trying to eliminate a predator from the landscape. Training how to trap predators was offered to landowners.[35] The new approach proved to be highly successful. In the 1960s Arnold Rieder, rancher and legislator, led an effort to delete the category of predator from state law and instead classify the animals as furbearers and game animals. The bounties paid on predators was also abolished at this time. Fewer and fewer land owners gave permission for placement of federal 1080 baits on their land.

In 1972 President Nixon issued Executive Order 11643 banning the use of poisons to control predators on Federal lands. Shortly thereafter, the EPA issued PR Notice 72-2 that cancelled all registered predator control uses of sodium fluoroacetate, sodium cyanide, and strychnine. Despite the ban, pre-1972 stockpiles were never recalled or destroyed and this poison is still used today illegally to kill wolves, coyotes, and eagles. Effective site specific coyote control can reduce coyote predation on domestic animals to one-quarter or less of the loss under a completely uncontrolled situation. Most losses of domestic sheep are produced by other causes unrelated to predation. Both wolves and coyotes excel at cooperative hunting with other members of their species and sometimes even with other species such as badgers. Although they sometimes seem to behave like domestic dogs, behavioral and genetic research indicates that coyotes and wolves lack the inherent ability to interpret and respond appropriately to humans.[36] Treating these species as dogs has led to injury and death of humans.

### Red Fox
*(Vulpes vulpes)*

It was proposed that red fox was introduced from Europe in the 1700s and this led to the red fox populations of today. Although there was scientific debate about it, evidence has accumulated that red fox was present in North America before settlement. Captain Meriwether Lewis observed several color phases of red fox on his journey, including the cross fox.[37] They are currently classified as a nongame animal in Montana.

*Red Fox*

Red fox inhabit forested and mountainous areas as well as agricultural lands and it can be distinguished from swift fox by the white tip on its tail. Red fox vary considerably in color. The "cross fox" and cream colored "mountain fox" variants are found at elevations above 6,500 feet in the Beartooth Mountains and Yellowstone NP. Research indicates that these color phases are less wary than the most common red color phase.[38]

***Although there was scientific debate about it, evidence has accumulated that red fox was present in North America before settlement. Captain Meriwether Lewis observed several color phases of red fox on his journey, including the cross fox.*** [37]

*Red fox kits.* (Photo courtesy Terry N. Lonner)

## Long-tail, Short-tail, and Least Weasel

*(Mustela frenata), (Mustela erminea) and (Mustela nivalis)*

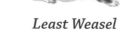

Weasels are classified as predators. Three species of weasel that live in the state are long-tail weasel, short-tail weasel or ermine and least weasel. The long-tail weasel is found throughout the state. The short-tail weasel (ermine), which turns white in the winter, inhabits mountains in the western third of the state and the least weasel lives in the northeastern area of the state.

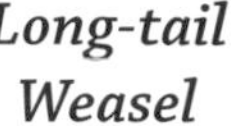

*Long-tail Weasel*

*Least Weasel*

*Short-tail Weasel*

*River Otters - pup and adult. c. 1996.* *(National Park Service photo, photographer Nathan Varley)*

*Badger. c. 1964.* *(National Park Service photo, photographer Bryan Harry)*

*Short-tail Weasel (ermine). c. Unk.* *(National Park Service photo, photographer unknown)*

*Striped Skunk . c. 2006.* *(Photo Courtesy Martha A. Lonner)*

# Footnotes

[1] Vaughn, R. 1900. Then and now, or thirty-six years in the Rockies. Farcountry Press, Helena. 442 pp.

[2] Atwater, M. M. 1932. Fur farming in Montana. 1931-1932 Biennial report, Montana Fish and Game Commission, Helena. 13.

[3] Anderson, R. 1986. Personal communication with Harold Picton.

[4] Jellison, W. L. 1970. Tularemia in Montana. Montana Wildlife. November. 6-25.

[5] Ibid, and Bell, J. F. and J. R. Reilly.1981. Tularemia. Chapter 18 in Infectious Diseases of Wild Mammals. Iowa State University Press, Ames. 213-231.

[6] Ibid. Atwater, M. M. 1932 and personal observations with Harold Picton.

[7] Biennial Report 1941-1942. Montana Fish and Game Commission. Helena. 74-75.

[8] Kurfiss, L. 1950. The return of the white beaver. Sporting Montana. Montana Fish and Game Department , Helena. Fall:11 and 22.

[9] Mussehl, T. W. and F. W. Howell. 1970. Game Management in Montana. Chapter 25 and 26. Furbearers and Predators. Montana Fish and Game Dept., Helena. 197-215.

[10] Biennial Report 1942-1943. Montana Fish and Game Commission, Helena. 6.

Biennial Report 1945-1946. Montana Fish and Game Commission, Helena. 15.

Biennial Report 1948-1949 and 1949-1950. Montana Fish and Game Commission, Helena. 12.

Biennial Report 1950-1952. Montana Fish and Game Commission, Helena. 27.

[11] Smith, Eldon. 1999. Videotaped interview with Harold Picton.

[12] Townsend, J. E. 1953. Beaver ecology in western Montana with special reference to movements. Journal of Mammalogy. 34:459-479.

Casagranda, L. G. 1955. A study of beaver-waterfowl relations in mountain streams of Beaverhead County, Montana. Master's thesis, Montana State University, Bozeman. 33 pp.

[13] Townsend, J. E. 1954. Beaver bank accounts. Montana Wildlife. 4(1):16-17.

[14] Powell, R. A., S. W. Buskirk and W. J. Zielinski. 2003. Fisher and marten. Chapter 29 in Wild Mammals of North America. Editors: G. A. Feldhammer, B. C. Thompson and J. A. Chapman. Johns Hopkins University Press, Baltimore. 635-649.

[15] Vinkey, R. S., M. K. Schwartz, K. S. McKelvey, K. R. Foresman, K. L. Pilgrim, B. J. Giddings and E. C. LoFroth. 2006. When reintroductions are augmentations: The genetic legacy of fishers (*Martes pennanti*) in Montana. Journal of Mammalogy. 87:265-271.

[16] Hawley, V. D. 1960. Fisher are returned to Montana forests. Montana Wildlife, July 1960. 16-18.

[17] Ibid. Vinkey, R. S., M. K. Schwartz, K.S. McKelvey, K. P. Foresman, K. L. Pilgrim, B. J. Giddings and E. C. LoFroth. 2006.

[18] Hawley, V. D. and F. N. Newby. 1957. Marten home ranges and population fluctuations. Journal of Mammalogy. 38(174-184).

Jonkel, C. J. and R. P. Weckworth. 1963. Sexual maturity and implantation of blastocysts in the wild pine marten. Journal of Wildlife Management. 27:93-98.

Weckworth, R. P. and V. D. Hawley. 1962. Marten food habits and population fluctuations in Montana. Journal of Wildlife Management 26:55-74.

[19] Biennial Report 1954-1956. Montana Fish and Game Commission, Helena. 43.

[20] Henry, J. David. 1998. Spirit of the Tundra. Natural History. 107(10):60-65.

# Footnotes, cont.

[21] Cypher, B. I. 2003. Foxes. Chapter 24 in Wild Mammals of North America. Feldhammer, G. A., B. C. Thompson and J. A. Chapman Editors. Johns Hopkins University Press, Baltimore, MD. 511-546.

[22] Ibid. Cypher, B. I. 2003. and conversation with Arnold Dood, Montana Fish, Wildlife and Parks Department, February 2006.

[23] Giddings, B. and C. J. Knowles. 1975. The current status of the swift fox in Montana. Pp. 101-120 in S. Allen, J. Whitsker Hoagland and F. David Stokel, editors. Report of the swift fox team. North Dakota Game and Fish Dept., Bismark. 170 pp.

[24] Curtis, S. 2007. Iktoni come home. Montana Quarterly 3(1) Spring. 74-80.

[25] Christofferson, A. 2007. Misunderstood and misrepresented: The story of the elusive wolverine. Yellowstone Discovery. 22(3):1-6.

Krebs, J., E. C. Lofroth, J. Copeland, V. Bandy, D. Cooley, H. Golden, A. Magoun, R. Mulders and B. Schults. 2004. Synthesis of survival rates and causes of mortality in North American wolverines. Journal of Wildlife Management. 68:493-502.

[26] Hornocker, M. G. and H. S. Hash. 1981. Ecology of the wolverine in northwestern Montana. Canadian Journal of Zoology 59:1286-1301.

[27] Newby, F. E. and P. L. Wright. 1955. Distribution and status of the wolverine in Montana. Journal of Mammalogy. 36:248-253.

Le Carcajou. 1956. Montana Wildlife. 6(1):1

Newby, F. E. and J. J. McDougal. 1964. Range extension of the wolverine in Montana. Journal of Mammalogy. 45:485-487.

[28] Newby, F. 1956. Fur production in Montana. Montana Wildlife. 6(1):7-13.

Newby, F. 1957. Montana's 1955-56 fur harvest. Montana Wildlife. February: 19-23.

[29] Giddings, B. 2008. Personal communication with Terry Lonner.

[30] Greer, K. 1955. The otter's diet - Good or bad? Montana Wildlife. 5(3):14-17.

Greer, K. R. 1955. Yearly food habits of the river otter in the Thompson Lakes region, northwestern Montana, as indicated by scat analysis. American Midland Naturalist. 54:299-313.

[31] Newby, F. 1958. A new approach to predator management in Montana. Montana Wildlife. August 22-27.

[32] Anon. 1967. Coyote. Montana Wildlife. 15-17.

[33] Ibid.

[34] Everin, W. 1954. Predator-enemy or friend. Montana Wildlife. 2(1) 18-22.

[35] Ibid. Newby, F. 1958.

Ibid. Mussehl, T. W. and F. W. Howell. 1970.

[36] Hare, B., B. Brown, C. Williamson and M. Tormasello. 2002. The domestication of social cognition in dogs. Science. 298: 1634-1636.

Jensen, P. 2007. The behavioral biology of dogs. CAB International London. 266 pp.

[37] Burroughs, R. D. 1995. The natural history of the Lewis and Clark expedition. Michigan State University Press, East Lansing. 340 pp.

[38] Ibid. Cypher, B. L. 2003.

Fuhrman, B. 2002. Tracking down Yellowstone's red fox: skis, satellites and historical sightings. Yellowstone Science. 10(1):8-15.

Keeler, C., T. Mellinger, E. Fromm and L. Wade. 1970. Melanin, adrenaline and the legacy of fear. Journal of Heredity. 61:81-88.

# Chapter 16

# More Mammals that Bite Other Mammals

## GRAY WOLF

(*Canis lupus*)

By the last third of the 20th century prey populations had recovered enough so the restoration of large predators could begin. Although the last resident gray wolf had been killed in the late 1920s, occasional lone wolves were reported in the state. Some of these visited the Glasgow area and other areas on the prairie while some turned up in the western mountains. An increase in wolf sightings in the North Fork of the Flathead River drainage occurred during the late 1960s and 1970s. In 1986, the first documented wolf den in Montana was found in Glacier National Park 50 years after their removal for predator control.[1] Called the "Magic Pack" it was discovered by Bob Ream, Diane Boyd and Dan Pletscher of the University of Montana. By the 1990s natural colonization had expanded to include the Missoula area as well as the Sun River area on the Rocky Mountain Front west of Augusta.

***In 1986, the first documented wolf den in Montana was found in Glacier National Park 50 years after their removal for predator control.[1]***

In the years before the last Montana wolf was killed in Judith Basin county during the late 1920s, people told a variety of experiences with wolves.

Roosevelt County Independent, July 18. 1921:[2]

"Infant Fondles Big Gray Wolf. Little Sarah Paulson, five-years old, is the baby daughter of Mr. & Mrs. Charles Paulson who live on the ranch just this side of Rocky Springs near

***Brown the Wolfer. c. unk.*** *(Photo by Evelyn Cameron, Courtesy Montana Historical Society, Helena)*

***"Mrs. Paulson was horrified to see her baby with its arms around the neck of a gray wolf."***

**—Roosevelt County Independent July 18, 1921.**

Miles City. One morning Sarah was playing a short distance from the house while her mother and an older child were washing the breakfast dishes. Paulson had ridden away only a short time before to look after some cattle. The mother and little brother heard the baby laugh as she kept repeating, "pretty doggy, pretty doggy."

The collie dog belonging to the family had accompanied Paulson, and Mrs. Paulson who was busy asked the little boy to look out and see what dog Sarah was playing with. Mrs. Paulson was horrified to see her baby with its arms around the neck of a gray wolf. She saw her baby remove its arms from around the animal's neck and pat it on the head. The great brute's lips were drawn up and its fangs showed white in a snarl. The wolf caressed the child with its lolling tongue and the baby gurgled in pleasure. Eventually the wolf was frightened away, the child running for a short distance alongside."

Other incidents were not so benign. Winnett Times, January 6, 1919:[3]

"Chouteau County Farmer is Winner in Mad Race with Death. Arthur Suredferger had been to Fort Benton for supplies. Early in dusk of the evening he started back toward his ranch. On the way he noticed far behind him, a pack of animals running toward him. He paid little attention to the wolves as he had no idea what they were and had no idea of danger. He was driving along at a leisurely pace when the hunger-maddened beasts caught up with him. Then he realized his danger. His attempts to frighten them off were without avail. One of the big wolves jumped at him and almost got a foothold on the car. Then he stepped on the gas and the race between him and death began..."

"According to the account, the farmer soon outdistanced the wolves, then turning to look for his pursuers, ran off the road. The road was muddy and some tense moments were spent while Suredferger was forced to put on his chains in order to get his car out of the ditch."

Wolves are the ancient ancestor of domestic dogs (*Canis lupus familiaris*) but thousands of years and generations of human selection have produced a very different wolf. The changes bred into dogs have given them a greater ability to interpret and communicate with humans making them much safer companions.[4]

In 1995 and 1996, 31 wolves from British Columbia and 10 wolves from Montana were released in Yellowstone NP by the U.S. Fish and Wildlife Service. The Montana wolves were the pack that had naturally colonized the Sun River area along the East Front of the Rockies near Augusta. The Yellowstone NP transplant has been highly successful and has produced several packs that now reside

*Releasing wolf #3 on Fishing Bridge service road in Yellowstone Park.* *(National Park Service photo by Jim Peaco; January 25, 1996)*

*Mike Ross, Montana Fish, Wildlife and Parks wolf management specialist, marking tranquilized wolves with radio transmitter collars in Madison Valley of southwest Montana .* *(Montana Fish, Wildlife and Parks photo by Sam Shepphard February, 2005)*

in Montana. Wolves also were transplanted to the remote Salmon River area of Idaho and have expanded their range into Montana. Montana Fish, Wildlife and Parks established a team of wolf management specialists in 2006 to manage potential problems involving this large carnivore. Because of the restoration success of wolves, the U.S. Fish and Wildlife Service delisted the wolf and turned their control and management over to the state in 2008. However the delisting is extremely controversial and is currently in an appeal process.

## MOUNTAIN LION

(*Puma concolor*)

***. . .lions were classified as predators that could be killed by any means at any time with a bounty paid on those killed.***

Mountain lion populations declined in the early 20th century as prey populations reached very low levels. Also known as cougar or puma, lions were classified as predators that could be killed by any means at any time and a bounty paid on those killed. This produced a population low that extended from the 1920s to the 1960s.[5]

As wild populations of prey rebounded in the 1950s, new opportunities became apparent. Large herds of domestic sheep that had been grazed

*Mountain lions taken during the bounty era. c. 1930s.*
*(Courtesy Hilger-McLucas Photo Collection)*

***The bounty paid on lions was terminated at the end of 1962.*[6]**

in many mountain areas were declining rapidly because of economic reasons. Cecil Garland, a lion hunter and wilderness advocate from Lincoln suggested that if mountain lions were given legal status as a game animal they could be controlled by recreational lion hunters. This might also allow lion populations to increase in areas where they were not in conflict with agriculture and humans.

*A "treed" mountain lion. c. 1987.* *(Photo courtesy Dave Pac taken by Bud Griffith)*

Les Pengelley, Wildlife Extension Specialist and Professor at the University of Montana picked up on the idea. He evaluated it as a wildlife management suggestion and believed it a good opportunity. He and Eldon Smith, Wildlife Extension Specialist at Montana State University, presented the idea in the public interest wildlife courses that they taught in many communities across the state. The concept developed a considerable following of lion hunters and people from "main-street." The bounty paid on lions was terminated at the end of 1962.[6]

A central Idaho mountain lion research project by Maurice Hornocker improved the understanding of the ecology of cougars. This led to lions being designated by the Montana Legislature as a trophy game animal in 1971.[7] Ken Greer, supervisor of Montana's wildlife research laboratory, began Montana's first mountain lion research project. Working in western Montana, Ken, along with other wildlife biologists and local houndsmen, combined forces to place neck collars on lions to gather dispersal and location of kill information on them as they showed up in harvests. Age and other information was gathered from skulls submitted to the wildlife laboratory. Ken and Maurice Hornocker assembled their information and presented it to the Fish and Game Commission leading to adoption of the quota based harvest system that we have today. By the late 20th century, mountain lions reclaimed most of their original range in the state occurring from border to border.

*A "problem" mountain lion being translocated. c. 1985.*
*(Montana Fish, Wildlife and Parks Photo by Mike Aderhold)*

Neil Anderson of the Montana Fish, Wildlife and Parks' wildlife laboratory developed and used a method of x-raying lion skulls to obtain population age structure information critical for management. Jim Williams filled in more parts of the lion story with research involving migratory elk and bighorn sheep in the Sun River area. Toni Ruth, as a student, addressed the interaction between cougars, wolves and grizzly bears in the vicinity of Glacier NP. Rich DeSimone of MFWP carried out long-term research of a hunted lion population in the Garnet Range between Helena and Missoula. Terry Enk examined the relationship

***. . .research projects have expanded knowledge of the ecology of the lion, and passionate houndsmen continue their enthusiastic support of the conservation of the "winter ghost."***

Deer are the major preferred food but they will kill elk as well as smaller prey species if deer are not available. Management by hunting has kept conflicts with humans to a minimum although wildlife control technicians occasionally must eliminate individual problem animals. This allows mountain lions to be in areas at population levels below the point at which they prey on livestock or have other conflicts with humans. Additional research projects have expanded knowledge of ecology of the lion and passionate houndsmen continue their enthusiastic support of the conservation of the "winter ghost."

The integration of large predators into the mosaic of human communities requires more than activists and lawsuits. Science and knowledge are required. The lion is a case in point. Kerry Murphy, a University of Montana graduate student continued lion research by investigating lions in the Missoula area.[8] Keith Aune and

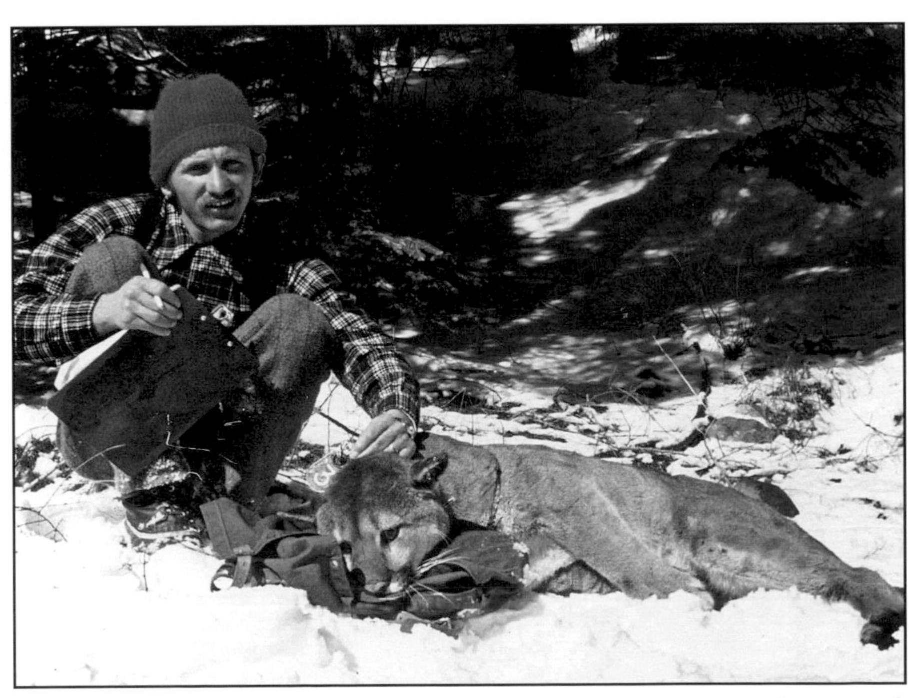

*Wildlife biologist Jerry Brown marking a mountain lion in 1976 near Bull Lake south of Troy for Montana's first lion research project supervised by Ken Greer, Montana 's Wildlife Lab Supervisor.* *(Montana Fish, Wildlife and Parks photo courtesy Jerry Brown)*

between big cats and a bighorn sheep population that was struggling to recover after a severe die-off. The bighorn sheep population trying to survive in the face of platinum mining in the Stillwater River canyon in south central Montana had its lion visitors put under scrutiny by Shawn Stewart, a state wildlife biologist at Red Lodge. One of the cats from this study showed up over 140 miles distant near Dubois, Wyoming. The knowledge derived from these research projects is the basis for an existing management strategy that has minimized conflict with humans. Montana wildlife professionals take large predators seriously and rely upon science and applied research as the way to maintain fully functional ecosystems that can meet a variety of challenges.

A Montana mountain lion turned up in St. Louis in one of those unusual movements that are sometimes seen in wildlife studies and stimulates a sense of wonder. Perhaps it was pursuing the same urges that a young bull elk from the Sweetgrass Hills north of Shelby had when it wondered its way to Kansas City, Missouri in the late 1980s.

***Black-footed ferrets are intimately tied to prairie dogs, both of which are subject to disease outbreaks that decimated them earlier in the 20th century.***

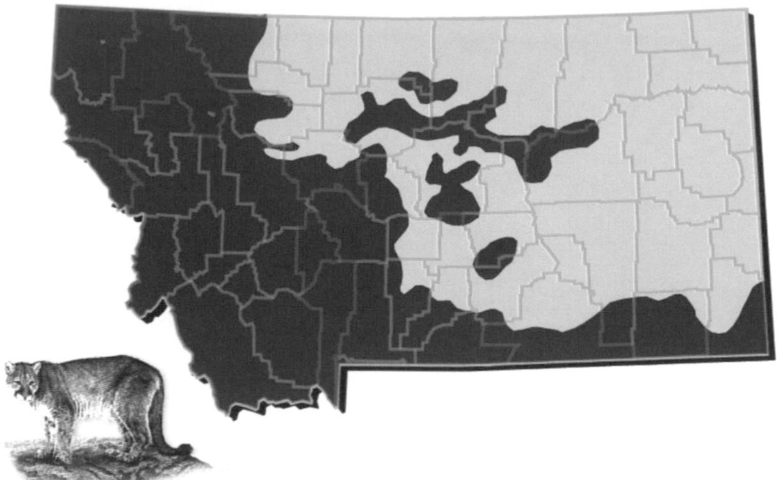

**2008 Mountain Lion Distribution**

### BLACK-FOOTED FERRET

*(Mustela nigripes)*

Black-footed ferrets were originally part of the Montana scene. This nocturnal member of the weasel family (Mustelidae) is directly tied to black-tailed prairie dogs *(Cynomys ludovicianus)* and native grassland. Poisoning of prairie dogs and crop cultivation eliminated much of its habitat. Both ferrets and prairie dogs are subject to the disease outbreaks that had decimated them early in the 20th century.[9]

Ferrets are very susceptible to canine distemper. Its food supply is also susceptible to sylvatic (bubonic) plague. Settlers and their domestic animals carried both of these diseases to North America.

Ferrets had been feared extinct for at least 20 years, but in 1964 a female ferret and kits were found in Mellette County in western South Dakota. They were considered the last black-footed ferrets in the world. Passage of the federal Threatened and Endangered Species Act in 1973 opened the door to possible restoration of this species. In 1979 a single ferret was sighted by a rancher in Carter County, MT and verified by an official from Montana Fish, Wildlife and Parks.[10] A second small population was discovered in Wyoming in 1981 but a multi-year attempt to find animals in Montana failed. Captive breeding programs were then established. In 1996 The U.S. Fish & Wildlife Service established a Black-footed Ferret Recovery Implementation Team to help guide recovery efforts. The U.S. Bureau of Land Management identified about

26,000 acres of prairie dog towns in south Phillips County of which approximately 18,000 acres were federal land.[11] In 1994-1996 a reintroduction team of federal and state agencies introduced black-footed ferrets into these prairie dog towns. This initial effort did not produce substantial success although some ferrets survived. By the end of 2006, more 500 captive-reared ferrets had been released and over 250 wild-born kits have been observed, but only 16 ferrets were known to have survived in the wild out of these numbers.[11]

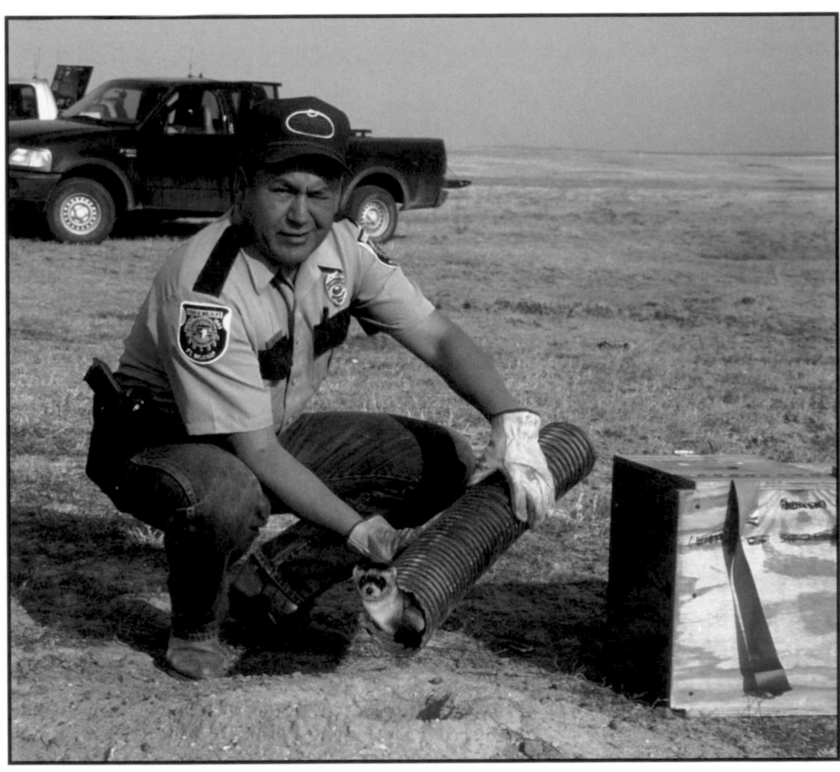

*Mike Fox with the Fort Belknap Indian Reservation in Montana releasing a Black-footed Ferret - 1999.* *(Photo courtesy Ronald P. Stoneberg)*

***Ferrets had been feared extinct for at least 20 years, but in 1964 a female ferret and kits were found in Mellette County in western South Dakota. At that time they were considered the last black-footed ferrets in the world. A second small population was discovered in Wyoming in 1981 but a multi-year attempt to find animals in Montana failed.***

# Footnotes

[1] Schullery, P. 1996. Gray wolf monitoring in Montana. Chapter 10 in The Yellowstone Wolf: A guide and source book. High Plains Publishing Co., Worland, WY. 103-107.

[2] Craig, V. 1961. Era of Lobo. This article contains this excerpt from the Roosevelt County Independent. Montana Wildlife, July. 20-25.

[3] Ibid. Excerpt from Winnett Times.

[4] Hare, B., B. Brown, C. Williamson and M. Tormasello. 2002. The domistication of social cognition in dogs. Science. 298 1634-1636.

Jensen, P. 2007. The behavioral biology of dogs. CAB International London. 266 pp.

[5] Biek, R., A. J. Drummond and M. Poss. 2006. A virus reveals population structure and recent demographic history of its carnivore host. Science 3ll(5760) Jan.27. 538-541.

[6] Smith, E. 1999. Videotaped interview with Harold Picton.

Mitchell, J. and K. R. Greer. 1970. Predators, Chapter 26 *in* Game Management in Montana. T. W. Mussehl and F. W. Howell Editors. Montana Fish and Game Department. 207-215.

[7] Hornocker, M. G. 1970. An analysis of mountain lion predation upon mule deer and elk in the Idaho Primitive Area. Wildlife Monograph. 39 pp.

[8] Murphy, K. M. 1983. Characteristics of a hunted population of mountain lions in western Montana. M. S. Thesis, University of Montana, Missoula. 48 pp.

Williams, J. S., J. J. McCarthy and H. D. Picton. 1995. Cougar habitat and food habits on the Rocky Mountain Front. Intermountain Journal of Science 1 (1): 16-28.

Murphy, K. M., G. S. Felzien, M. G. Hornocker and T. K. Ruth. 1998. Encounter competition between bears and cougars, some ecological implications. Proceedings of The International Conference on Bear Research and Management. 10.

Riley, Shawn. 1998. Integration of environmental, biological, and human dimensions for management of mountain lions (*Puma concolor*) in Montana. Ph.D. Dissertation, Cornell University, Ithaca, New York. 66 pp.

Enk, T. A. 1999. Population dynamics of bighorn sheep on the Beartooth Wildlife Management Area, Montana. Ph.D. Dissertation, Montana State University, Bozeman. 174 pp.

DeSimone, R. and B. Semmens. 2004. Garnet Mountains mountain lion research. Montana Fish, Wildlife and Parks progress report. January 2003 -December 2004. 16 pp.

[9] Richardson, R. 1992. The Ferret Experiment. Montana Outdoors. Vol. 23(2) 18-23.

[10] Weigand, J. P. 2008. Personal communication with Terry Lonner.

[11] Matchett, M. R., D. Biggs, V. Kopcso and T. Rocke. 2007. Does enzootic plague affect black-footed ferret survival? Intermountain Journal of Sciences. Vol. 13(4): 171-172.

# PART III

# Habitat and Humans

*Advance of Civilization N. P. Express. c. unk.*
*Photograph by L. A. Huffman*
*(Courtesy Montana Historical Society, Helena)*

**ARTICLE IX**

ENVIRONMENT AND NATURAL RESOURCES

---------------------

**Section 1. Protection and improvement.** (1) The state and each person shall maintain and improve a clean and healthful environment in Montana for present and future generations.

(2) The legislature shall provide for the administration and enforcement of this duty.

(3) The legislature shall provide adequate remedies for the protection of the environmental life support system from degradation and provide adequate remedies to prevent unreasonable depletion and degradation of natural resources.

*Snow geese at Freezout Wildlife Management Area.* *(Photo courtesy Brent N. Lonner)*

# Chapter 17

# Wastelands To Waterfowl

## FREEZOUT LAKE

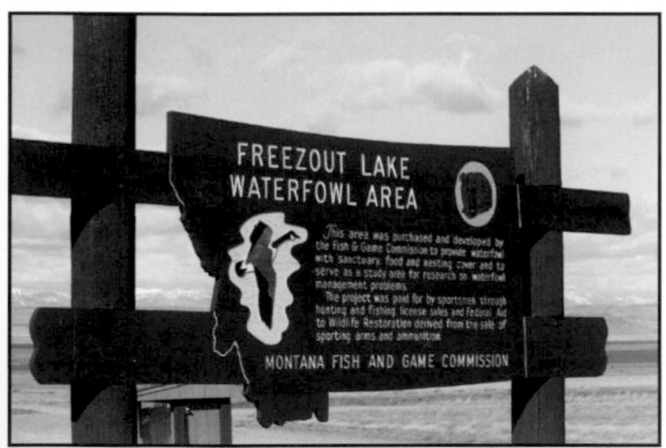


The federal wildlife refuge system initiated by Teddy Roosevelt, has expanded over the years and was mainly devoted to preserving remaining wildlife habitat. But people of Montana wished to restore wildlife to broad areas rather than confining it to limited areas provided by federal refuges. This sparked a desire to find ways of creating new habitat. One opportunity that appeared was an area just east of the Rocky Mountain Front in southern Teton County known as Freezout Lake. The Greenfields Irrigation Project, developed in the early 20th century, drained much of its wastewater into a basin that had no outlet forming Freezout Lake. Water in this lake gradually rose and began to flood the highway and railroad between Fairfield and Choteau. The lake attracted many waterfowl but also became loaded with alkaline salts. As happens in many western alkaline lakes, avian botulism developed during most years, killing thousands of waterfowl.

***Wastewater from the Greenfields Irrigation Project drained into a basin flooding parts of the highway and railroad between Choteau and Fairfield. The flooding was stopped by constructing a ditch connecting the basin to Priest's Lake and from there to the Teton River. This basin became known as Freezout Lake. c. 1954.*** *(Montana Fish and Game Photo)*

*Avian botulism can become a problem in ponds or lakes with poor drainage systems sometimes killing thousands of birds.* (Photo courtesy Robert Rothweiler)

In 1948, Wynn Freeman was in charge of the state waterfowl program and recognized an opportunity to do something positive with the situation in the early 1950s. Thus, the Fish and Game Department developed a plan to construct a drain for the lake via a ditch connecting it to nearby Priest's Lake, which also lacked an outlet, to the Teton River. Construction of 8 miles of drainage ditches began in 1953. When completed, the project lowered the level of Freezout Lake by 6 feet, saving the highway and railroad. This exposed grazing land but also allowed construction of a system of dikes and ponds to control water levels. These provided excellent waterfowl nesting habitat and a haven for migrating waterfowl. Perhaps, more importantly, ponds and dikes allowed control of water levels essential to minimizing avian botulism.[1] Montana hunters paid for the project through hunting license fees matched by P-R funds.

*A monument was placed at the Freezout Wildlife Management Area in honor of Wynn G. Freeman's pioneering work in Montana's wildlife conservation.* (Montana Fish, Wildlife and Parks photo courtesy Brent N. Lonner)

DEDICATED
TO THE MEMORY OF
WYNN G. FREEMAN
2/7/20 - 9/2/78
It was through his efforts during 30 years service as biologist, chief, and administrator of the Wildlife Division that this and several other Wildlife Management Areas in Montana exist today. May you use and enjoy it in the spirit which Wynn intended.


***The Montana wildlife agency continues to make payments in lieu of property taxes on state wildlife management areas.***

Agriculturalists of the Greenfields Irrigation District provided manpower, technical expertise and equipment for the extensive construction work. The 11,350-acre project included 6,040 acres covered by a long term lease of federally-owned land from the U.S. Bureau of Reclamation. Most of this leased land was flooded. The Montana Fish and Game Commission purchased private lands from willing sellers as were necessary for the project. It also continues to make payments to the county in lieu of taxes on these lands, as it does for all state wildlife management areas.[2] Three research studies of the Freezout project were completed as it matured. Knowledge gained contributed to the success of future habitat restoration projects.[3]

By the end of the 20th century over a million birds visit Freezout each year, giving testimony to the project's success. Some of these species spend their summers in the North American arctic. Some are resident waterfowl, which are hatched and raised in the wetlands. A few, like snow geese *(Chen caerulescens)* Ross's Goose *(Chen rossi)*, stop by on their way to and from the Siberian arctic. A captive breeding Canada Goose *(Branta Canadensis)* flock started by Dale Witt, an early manager of Freezout, resulted in resident nesters. Spring snow geese migrations through Freezout Lake from southern wintering areas (mostly from California) are truly one of the great wildlife spectacles of North America.

Freezout Lake basin has been accumulating salts since the ice age. Irrigation return water contains salts and fertilizers. Many of these materials are removed in the wetlands of Freezout and Priest's Lake. However, salt content of the outflow into the

*Snow geese nearby the Freezout Wildlife Management Area. c. 2006. (Photo courtesy Brent N. Lonner)*

***Tens of thousands of snow geese migrate through the Freezout Wildlife Management Area to the arctic each year and is truly one of the greatest wildlife spectacles of North America.***

Teton River is carefully monitored and adjusted several times a week to meet and maintain water quality standards for the river. The Teton River itself is impacted by water removal for irrigation and runoff from lands below the outflow from the Freezout project. Water flows in the lower river can also become critically low in drought years.[4]

## EASTERN PRAIRIES

The 1930s left water resources of eastern Montana in critical condition, so the U.S. Soil Conservation Service encouraged farmers and ranchers to build small reservoirs or stock ponds on their lands. The program was very popular and by the 1950s about 100,000 farm ponds had been constructed. Waterfowl immediately colonized this new habitat. These ponds provide nesting and rearing areas for species such as teal *(Anas spp.)*, mallard *(Anas platyrhynchos)*, pintail *(Anas acuta)*, redhead *(Aythya americana)* and American Coot *(Fulica americana)*. Band encounters of waterfowl raised on these ponds inspire amazement at the widespread national and international connections a pond can have. They also provide critical way stations for migrating waterfowl.[5]

***The U.S. Soil Conservation Service encouraged farmers and ranchers to build small reservoirs or stock ponds on their lands. . . Waterfowl immediately colonized this new habitat.***

*Melstone reservoir in Musselshell County used for livestock and waterfowl. c. 1940. (Montana Fish and Game photo from the 1941-42 Montana Fish and Game Commission Biennial Report)*

Efforts by private landowners contributed substantially to maintaining and expanding aquatic habitats as well as hunting opportunities in the state. Some of these ponds have brought usable water to semiarid areas, where Ferdinand Hayden was led to comment in 1860 that, "...one-third of the fluid we dignify by the name of water was buffalo urine."[6]

## CANYON FERRY RESERVOIR

*Dust storms were causing property damage and health problems in Townsend.*

Canyon Ferry dam on the Missouri River north of Townsend was built during the 1950s. As it filled and became an operating hydroelectric reservoir, water levels fluctuated considerably during the year. Low water of late summer and fall coincided with periods of strong winds as weather systems moved across the area. Wind tore soil from dried mud flats and produced severe dust storms in Townsend. Property damage and health problems from blowing dust led to considerable public anxiety.

The Federal Bureau of Reclamation, as operator of the dam, began looking for a solution. Discussions with the Montana Fish and Game Dept. and Robert Eng, a wildlife professor at Montana State University, led to a solution for the dust. This involved keeping the mud flats flooded and converting them into a waterfowl nesting area. Dikes were built to allow waterfowl habitats to remain flooded when the level of the reservoir dropped during its annual cycle. Dredging to build large dikes began in 1973. During winter months earth movers also dumped loads of gravel on the ice to produce nesting islands as the ice melted. Basic construction was completed in 1975. Professor Eng and helpers obtained and planted cuttings of aquatic vegetation and shrubs for the islands. Waterfowl began to use the new habitat immediately. Fledgling Canada

*Dike 4 construction at Canyon Ferry Project - April 1973.* *(Montana Fish and Game photo courtesy Tom Carlsen)*

*Dust storm from the dried mud flats at the south end of Canyon Ferry Reservoir c. 1973.* *(Montana Fish and Game photo courtesy Tom Carlsen)*

*A nesting Canada goose on one of the man-made islands at the south end of Canyon Ferry Reservoir.* *(Photo courtesy Robert Eng)*

geese were released on the ponds to take their first flights. As geese matured and migrated back to the islands to nest, they began a period of spectacular population growth. In a few short years nesting geese increased from 10 to a 100 and then to nearly a 1,000 birds.[7] Other species also colonized the new ecosystem. Osprey *(Pandion haliaetus)* began to seek out nesting sites. To accommodate them, Professor Eng teamed with The Montana Power Company to erect poles with "nesting" platforms away from power lines to serve as nesting substitutes for Osprey.[8] Cooperative efforts of the U.S. Bureau of Reclamation, Montana Fish, Wildlife and Parks, The Montana Power Company, Professor Eng, graduate students and volunteers had created a new productive component to enhance wildlife habitat out of a severe problem for human property and health.

***Contaminated mud flat on the Clark Fork of the Columbia River near Warm Springs, MT before cleanup. c. 1970.***
*(Montana Fish and Game photo courtesy Robert Greene)*

***Osprey with nest on top of a nonserviceable power pole. c. 2007.***
*(Photo courtesy Brent N. Lonner)*

## CLARK FORK RIVER

A century of mining and smelting heavily impacted and contaminated an area stretching from Butte to Anaconda and Warm Springs including the Clark Fork of the Columbia River. Montana adopted new water quality standards in 1967. The Anaconda Mining Company was given until 1972 to treat the wastes that it was dumping into Silver Bow Creek. The Atlantic Richfield Company acquired the Anaconda Copper Mining Company in 1977 after the mining company was forced into near bankruptcy by government seizure of its properties in Chile.

The mainstream Clark Fork was to meet a classification under the water quality act to allow for "growth and propagation of salmonid fish and associated aquatic life". Water treatment by the Anaconda Company began to improve water quality in the river.[9] Congress passed the Superfund Law for environmental cleanup in 1980. In 1982, the Environmental Protection Agency designated the Upper Clark Fork as

***A century of mining and smelting heavily impacted and contaminated an area stretching from Butte to Anaconda and Warm Springs including the Clark Fork of the Columbia River.***

*Settling ponds after cleanup of contaminated mud flats and tailings on the Clark Fork of the Columbia River near Warm Springs. c. 1990.* *(Montana Fish, Wildlife and Parks photo courtesy Robert Greene)*

***Cleanup of the nation's largest superfund site has created new waterfowl habitat, improved fish habitat and water quality for humans.***

the largest superfund cleanup site in the nation. The cleanup area extends 140 miles from the head waters of Silver Bow Creek above Butte to Milltown near Missoula. Silver Bow Creek and the Anaconda Smelter site were designated for priority cleanup in 1983.[10] Settling ponds that served to trap heavy metals were located near Warm Springs. Cleanup of these ponds was a priority for the project.

Jerry Gallagher and Bob Greene of Montana Fish, Wildlife and Parks began discussions with the Atlantic Richfield Company and Montana Highway Department that led to incorporation and construction of waterfowl ponds in the reclamation project design. The state of Montana had sued and after a 15 year court battle, won a settlement of $215 million from the Atlantic Richfield Company to resolve issues in the Clark Fork superfund area and pay for reclamation.[11] This resulted in creation of another productive waterfowl area out of a disaster site.

No. 38 — 114th Year gftribune@mcn.net 50¢

# Arco to pay state $215 million

## Settlement resolves key issues in Clark Fork Superfund suit

**By MIKE DENNISON**
**Tribune Capitol Bureau**

HELENA — The Atlantic Richfield Co. agreed Friday to pay Montana $215 million for cleanup and restoration of mining-ravaged areas in the upper Clark Fork River basin, apparently settling major portions of a 15-year-old lawsuit.

Attorney General Joe Mazurek announced the agreement at the Silver Bow County Courthouse in Butte Friday afternoon, calling it a big step toward fixing environmental damage caused by decades of mining and smelting in the 120-mile-long basin.

"This settlement accomplishes our main goal — restoring the river basin and its resources," he said. "I believe Montanans would rather see those benefits sooner, not later."

The settlement, filed Friday in U.S. District Court at Great Falls, culminates years of work on a lawsuit tied to the cleanup of multiple Superfund hazardous-waste sites stretching from Butte to Missoula.

A trial before U.S. District Judge Paul Hatfield began in March, but lawyers for the state and Arco officials had been engaged in court-ordered settlement talks for the past few months.

"It's been an incredible process," Mazurek told the Tribune. "We've spent thousands of hours over the last 16 months."

Gov. Marc Racicot, who ultimately authorized the settlement, said he was pleased that the state is about to achieve "what we have sought all along: The repair of damages to the Clark Fork basin from the persistent release of hazardous substances."

While Arco agreed to pay Montana $215 million in damages and cleanup costs, the settlement is not final and cleanup plans probably won't be completed until 2001.

John Wardell, Montana director of the U.S. Environmental Protection Agency, said his agency still has to approve the proposed cleanup plan

See ARCO, 4A

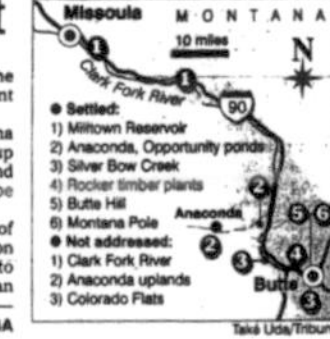


## AQUATIC ENVIRONMENTS AND OTHER SUPERFUND SITES

Reclamation of many damaged water resources and riparian sites continues in Montana and will affect miles of riparian zones benefiting waterfowl, raptors, fish, mammals as well as humans. Superfund and related cleanups represent a major industry for Montana. Cleanup of 14 federal superfund sites will cost over $1 billion. In addition, there are 211 state superfund sites and over 1,500 sites contaminated with petroleum. Most of the 71 projects seeking to improve water quality will directly benefit fish and wildlife as well as people.[12]

A century of mining left many old mines with waste piles and acid mine water drainages. An example is an area near Cooke City where mine drainage made miles of stream toxic extending into Yellowstone NP. Cleanup has enabled fish and other life to return. Belt Creek in the Little Belt Mountains and many other sites have shown that paying the environmental debt left by previous generations is well worthwhile. Restoration of upland mining dumps and strip mining sites is paying similar benefits for terrestrial life.

## PRESERVATION OF MONTANA'S STREAMS

Another effort to maintain healthy aquatic ecosystems so important to waterfowl and other wildlife began in the early 1960s. While involved in a fisheries research project Dick Graham, Head of the Cooperative Fisheries Unit at Montana State University, observed extensive use of bulldozers that were negatively impacting the stream bed of Rock Creek, north of Red Lodge. Lloyd Casagranda, the Montana Fish and Game Department's Information and Education person in Billings, and Perry Nelson, District Fisheries Manager, undertook an effort to insure a healthy future for Montana's waterways. They were joined by LeRoy Ellig, a Montana Fish and Game District Game Manager and Eldon Smith, Extension Wildlife Specialist from Montana State University, Dick Graham and Dick Munro, head of Montana Fish and Game's Information and Education Division. This group conceived legislation to at least prevent governmental agencies from destroying streams and aquatic habitats. They contacted the Montana Junior Chamber of Commerce (Jaycees) who made it their statewide project for that year. The dynamic campaign of the Jaycees encouraged sportsmen and other organizations to join in. In 1963 the Montana Legislature enacted the first Montana Stream Conservation Law.[13] This law encouraged cooperation

*This group conceived legislation to at least prevent governmental agencies from destroying streams and aquatic habitats. They contacted the Jaycees who made it their statewide project for that year. The dynamic campaign of the Jaycees encouraged sportsmen and other organizations to join in.*

*Rock Creek stream bed north of Red Lodge after irrigation channeling and highway construction.* (From Report of Biennial Activities in Montana Wildlife, Summer 1964)

his is a section of Flint Creek before highway construction.
the excellent cover of foliage.


A section of Flint Creek after adjacent highway construction.
—Photo by Jack Bailey

*Flint Creek stream bed before and after highway construction.* (*From Montana Wildlife, August 1958*)

between the State Highway Department and the Fish and Game Department. In its first year, it changed 22 projects out of 31 to reduce or prevent damage to aquatic habitats by highway construction.[14] A series of other laws were passed in the following legislative sessions. In 1973, the state was given the power to obtain water rights and leave water flowing in streams as a beneficial use of water.[15]

Water is the life-blood resource of western communities, human and natural. The effort to protect streams from bulldozers led to a broad protection of our aquatic resources and has provided a major economic resource through its positive affect upon fisheries and wildlife.

***In 1963 the Montana Legislature enacted the first Montana Stream Conservation Law.[15]. . . In its first year, it brought about changes in 22 projects out of 31 to reduce or prevent damage to aquatic habitats by highway construction.[16]***

**EDITORIAL:**

## Montana's Highway Commission Recognizes Wildlife Needs

Much of what we call "progress" has been made at the expense of our natural resources. Some of this has been inevitable, but a great deal of the waste and damage, particularly to wildlife habitat, could have been avoided by thoughtful planning.

In this respect, it should be most encouraging to conservasionists to learn of the action taken by the Montana State Highway Commission in response to a letter from the Montana Fish and Game Commission concerning the problems of destruction of fish and game habitat during highway construction.

The text of this resolution is reprinted in its entirety since this expression of cooperation in protecting wildlife might well be a pattern for other agencies and organizations to follow when their activities might endanger Montana's valuable wildlife resources.

**RESOLUTION**

"WHEREAS, the aims, objectives and undertakings of the State Fish and Game Commission of the State of Montana are of a nature and designed to add to the pleasure and well-being of all Montana people, and

WHEREAS, controlled abundance of fish and game adds materially to the economic wealth of our State, and

WHEREAS, the GREAT-OUT-OF-DOORS of which Montana so proudly boasts would lose its savor were her mountains, streams and valleys to become bare of their native inhabitants;

NOW, THEREFORE, BE IT RESOLVED, That the STATE HIGHWAY COMMISSION, incidental to its pre-construction, construction and maintenance activities, shall cooperate to the full in every practical way to assist the said STATE FISH AND GAME COMMISSION in carrying out its objectives.

BE IT FURTHER RESOLVED, That pre-construction, construction and maintenance department heads be given copies of this Resolution."

*From Montana Wildlife, Fall 1953. Vol. III No. 3. The above resolution took another decade to implement.*

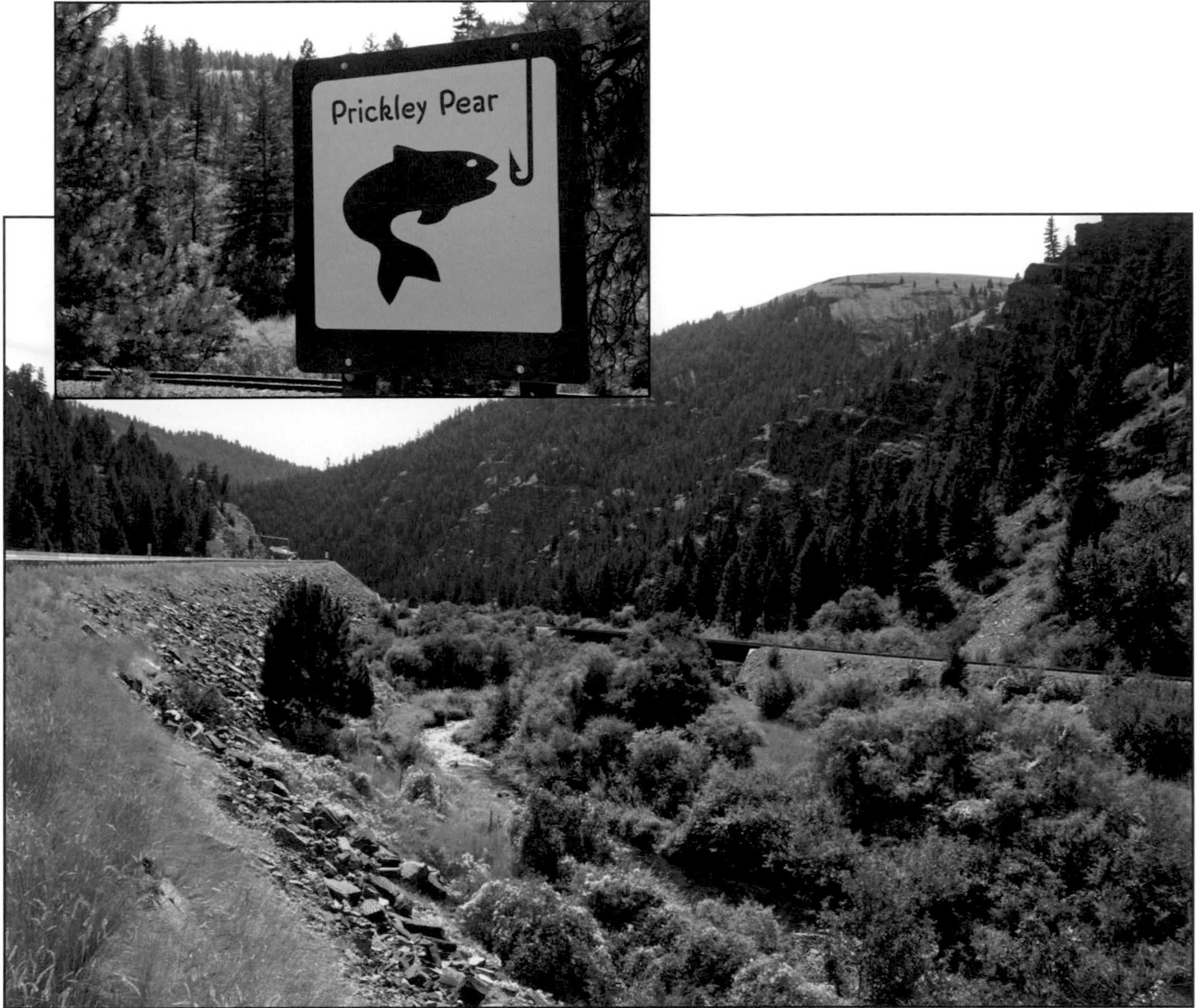


*This stretch of Little Prickley Pear creek along I-15 between Helena and Wolf Creek is one of the first reconstructed streams done under the Montana Stream Conservation Law during the mid 1960s. It is now healthy habitat for fish and wildlife. (Photos courtesy Brent N. Lonner , 2007)*

# Footnotes

[1] Avian botulism bacteria develop in snails and other aquatic animals killed by exposure due to falling water levels. If water levels rise due to late summer rains, waterfowl feed on contaminated food and develop botulism. Appropriate water level control either prevents a drop in water levels or prevents areas from re-flooding during late summer and early fall.

[2] Salinas, G. J. and R. W. Trueblood. 1954. Outlet for Freezout. Montana Wildlife. 4(3):22-24.

[3] Ellig, L. J. 1955. Waterfowl relationships to Greenfields Lake, Teton County, Montana. Technical Bulletin 1. Montana Fish and Game Dept., Helena. 35pp.

Knight, R. R. 1960. Vegetative characteristics and waterfowl usage of a Montana water area. Journal of Wildlife Management. 29:782-788.

Rothweiler, R. A. 1960. Food habits, movements and nesting of gulls on waterfowl area, Freezout Lake, Teton County, Montana. Master's Thesis, Montana State University, Bozeman. 29 pp.

[4] Gildart, B. 2004. Montana's avian spectacle. Montana Outdoors. Vol. 35(2):26-31.

Aderhold, M. 2006. Salinity isn't Teton River's only problem. Great Falls Tribune, January 5, 2006. Section 0, page 6.

Dickson, T. 2004. Controlling Freezout's weird water. Montana Outdoors. Vol. 35(2):31.

[5] Smith, R. H. 1952. More ducks for eastern Montana. Montana Wildlife. Vol. 2(3):10-11.

Smith, R. H. 1952. A study of waterfowl production on artificial reservoirs in eastern Montana. Journal of Wildlife Management 17:276-291.

[6] Thompson, L. S. 1985. Chapter 10: Ferdinand Vandiveer Hayden in Montana's explorers: The pioneer naturalists. Montana Geographic Series. Montana Magazine, Helena. 88-95.

[7]Carlsen, T. L. 1984. Waterfowl nesting on islands in two ponds of the Canyon Ferry Wildlife Management Area, Montana. M.S. Thesis, Montana State University, Bozeman. 91 pp.

[8] Grover, K. E. 1983. Ecology of the Osprey on the upper Missouri River, Montana. M.S. Thesis, Montana State University, Bozeman. 58 pp.

[9] Spence, L. 1987.Clark Fork Rx - Prescription for renewal? Montana Outdoors, Vol. 18(6) 2-6.

[10] Merrill, A. and J. Jacobson. 1997. Montana superfund sites. Montana Almanac. Falcon Publishing Co., Helena. 327-328.

[11] Dennison, M. 1998. Arco to pay state $215 million. Great Falls Tribune, June 20. 1 & 4a.

[12] Lee, S. 2005. State hits cleanup pay dirt. Great Falls Tribune. December 11, 2005. 1-4.

Lee, S. 2005. A mountain's hard to top.. Great Falls Tribune. December 12, 2005. 1 & 3a.

[13] Ellig, L. 2000. Videotaped interview with Harold Picton.

Smith, E. 1999. Videotaped interview with Harold Picton.

[14] Anon. 1964. Recommended legislation: Stream conservation law. Montana Wildlife. 3.

[15] Ibid. Spence, L. 1987.

Spence, L. 1990. Instream flow on the mighty Mo. Montana Outdoors. Vol. 21(4):2-6.

# Chapter 18

# Perils of Pesticides

Effects of pesticides on wildlife have long been a concern of Montana citizens. Many uses of pesticides early in the 20th century were directed at destroying rodents and grasshoppers. Poisons such as arsenic and strychnine were used to treat grain. Montana Game Warden J. L. DeHart tells of a trip in a 1920 report,

> "My own personal observations have been, when driving through the country where the use of poisoned grain had been indulged in, that in a distance of 100 miles where ordinarily robins and meadow larks could be found abundantly, I was not able to find a half a dozen birds all told."[1]

The view that poisoned grain would not harm birds was widely circulated at the time. In conflict with this viewpoint, cases of poisoning chickens, dogs, coyotes and even hogs were reported. Poisoned grain was often distributed as prairie sod was broken by the plow.

> "...the indiscriminate practice of gopher poisoning by the distribution of grain soaked in strychnine, and then distributed by the process of placing boys of 10 to 14 years of age upon the gentle old pony, usually found about the farm home, with a couple of nose bags hung upon either side of the pony, the boy receives instructions to ride about the farm and promiscuously throw the poisoned grain for the rodent family's use only, using the wireless, no doubt, to notify the feathered family to keep hands off."
>
> —J. L. DeHart, 1920.[2]

The climate disaster of the 1930s was severely compounded by outbreaks of hordes of migratory grasshoppers which brought grain poisoned with an arsenic and molasses mixture into heavy use. Distribution of the lethal material was not only by human hand but also mechanized equipment and aerial spreading. Grain-feeding birds were affected immediately. An

***"My own personal observations have been, when driving through the country, where the use of poisoned grain had been indulged in, that in a distance of 100 miles where ordinarily robins and meadow larks could be found abundantly, I was not able to find a half a dozen birds all told."[1]***

**— State Game Warden J. L. DeHart**

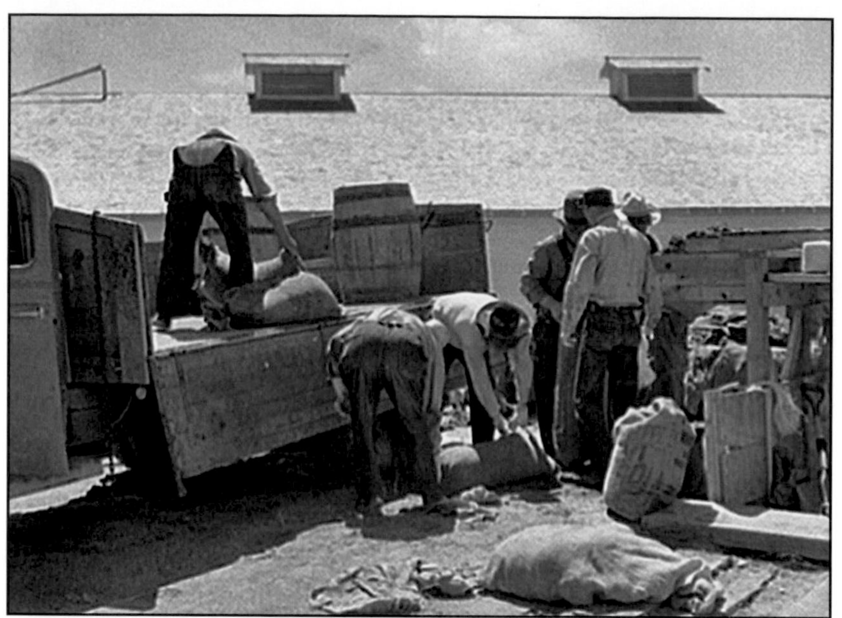

*Loading sacks of poison grasshopper bait. Forsyth, Montana June 1939.*
*(Photo by Arthur Rothstein. Library of Congress, Prints & Photographs Division, FSA/OWI Collection [LC-USF34-027817-D])*

***A new class of chemical insecticides was discovered and developed for use during World War II. DDT (dichlorodiphenyltrichloroethane), the first of these chlorinated hydrocarbon pesticides, saved millions of lives during the war by blocking typhus, malaria and the other insect-borne pestilences that have usually accompanied wars.***

ecological cascade to raptors and mammalian predators also occurred. Materials such as arsenic and strychnine persist in the environment subject to dilution only by the forces of wind and rain.

A new class of chemical insecticides was discovered and developed for use during World War II. DDT (dichlorodiphenyltrichloroethane), the first of these chlorinated hydrocarbon pesticides, saved millions of lives during the war by blocking typhus, malaria and other insect-borne pestilences that have usually accompanied wars. Paul Mueller, of Switzerland, received the Nobel Prize in 1948 for its discovery. DDT and its relatives were famed for their low toxicity to humans and other animals as well as their ability to kill insects for a month or two after application. This residual effect reduced the need for repeated application. Chlorinated hydrocarbons became agricultural chemicals after the war. The Montana Fish and Game Department was concerned about their impact and conducted a study of Chlordane and Aldrin in the early 1950s. These were widely used members of this chemical family that had been developed for agricultural use. The study showed little in the way of direct negative effects upon upland game birds.[3]

In the late 1950s a forest spraying project in the Hellroaring drainage north of Yellowstone NP as well as inside the Park resulted in a fish kill in the Yellowstone River. It was investigated by Dick Graham, then the fisheries biologist at the state fisheries laboratory. This incident as well as other reports nationally began to bring use of chlorinated hydrocarbon pesticides increasingly into question.

In the summer of 1963, Tom Mussehl, a Montana Fish and Game research biologist, led a blue grouse *(Dendragapus obscurus)* ecology study near Hamilton that was focused on effects of clear-cut logging on mountain grouse. A spruce budworm *(Choristoneura fumiferana)* outbreak was taking its toll on the forests of the Sapphire Mountain Range, location of the grouse study. The U.S. Forest Service began to spray the forest to quell the infestation. Mussehl and assistant research biologist Phil Schladweiler monitored spray deposition patterns as aircraft deposited DDT mixed with diesel fuel. Spray distribution monitoring cards and photographs of spray planes or helicopters showed that spray applications went into streams that supposedly were off limits. This information further inflamed an already intense local public opinion that strongly favored spraying operations. Of course insects that served as food for blue grouse using meadow areas were being killed, however no direct mortality of blue grouse due to spraying was found.[4]

*Spraying DDT over the forests of the Sapphire Mountain Range in western Montana. c. early 1960s.* *(Photo courtesy Tom Mussehl)*

Because grouse were eating insects contaminated with DDT, Mussehl and Schladweiler collected some grouse for laboratory analysis. DDT is fat soluble and thus accumulates in fat tissue. At that time, Dr. Bell and Dr. Clark of the Public Health Service's Rocky Mountain Laboratory in Hamilton also had an interest in wildlife. They obtained information concerning permissible levels of DDT in food from the U.S. Surgeon General. Some grouse showed levels of DDT in their tissues that exceeded levels for human food consumption by 10-30 times. The Surgeon General initially did not think this significant because people didn't eat much wild game. However, a Fish and Game Department survey showed that wild game (including fish) made up 70 to 90 percent of the diet of some Montana citizens. With this information the Surgeon General recommended that hunting seasons be closed in the area. Thus, DDT levels and the spray program that produced them became a public concern for human health.[5]

Lloyd Casagranda, a dynamic leader and head of the Information and Education Division of the Montana Fish and Game Department in the 1960s, took the contentious issue to leaders in Helena. With the help of Eldon Smith, a Wildlife Extension Specialist at Montana State College (MSU), a meeting of the Fish and Game Commission convened to consider the pesticide problem.[6] Information from Mussehl's study and the Surgeon General was presented. Others, as well as the senior author, testified. In 1964 the Montana Fish and Game Commission issued the first public policy statement in the nation protesting further use of chlorinated hydrocarbon insecticides on public lands. The statement went beyond insecticides and urged research on the effects of herbicides on wildlife habitat. They pointed out that pesticides were initially marketed on the basis of their effectiveness with little knowledge of long-term impacts. This was followed by widespread use during which problems with their use would typically appear.

*The DDT levels and the spray program that produced them became a concern for human health.[5]*

*The Montana Fish and Game Commission issued the first public policy statement in the nation against the use of chlorinated hydrocarbon pesticides.*

Field research began and the public became increasingly aware of the threats pesticides posed to wildlife and demanded that these compounds not

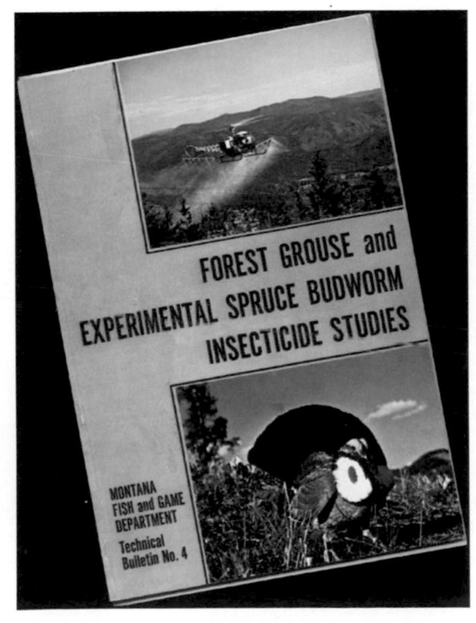

FOREST GROUSE and
EXPERIMENTAL SPRUCE BUDWORM
INSECTICIDE STUDIES

MONTANA
FISH and GAME
DEPARTMENT
Technical
Bulletin No. 4

**More pesticide control wanted**

be used.[7] This pattern, outlined by Montana officials, occurred with DDT. Finally, 8 years later the Federal Government banned use of DDT in 1972. It was this delay in recognizing adverse effects and taking action to correct the situation that particularly bothered the Commission. Before the DDT issue subsided another chemical issue arose.

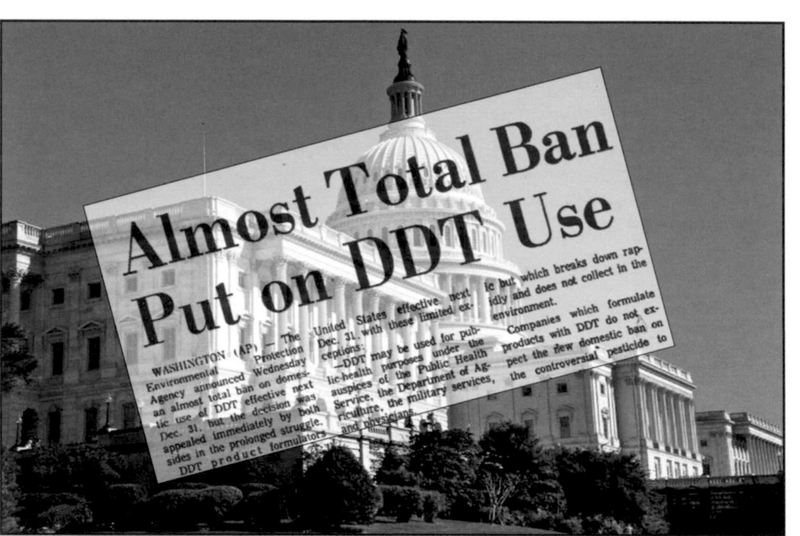

**Almost Total Ban Put on DDT Use**

WASHINGTON (AP) — The Environmental Protection Agency announced Wednesday an almost total ban on domestic use of DDT effective next Dec. 31, but the decision was appealed immediately by both sides in the prolonged struggle. DDT product formulators

United States effective next Dec. 31, with these limited exceptions:

—DDT may be used for public-health purposes under the auspices of the Public Health Service, the Department of Agriculture, the military services, and physicians

ic but which breaks down rapidly and does not collect in the environment.

Companies which formulate products with DDT do not expect the new domestic ban on the controversial pesticide to

*The public became aware of the problems in using DDT for pest control and the Federal Government finally banned its use in 1972.*

The element Mercury occurs throughout our environment. It is found in cinnabar (a reddish powder sometimes used as a red pigment for paint), coal and with metals like copper, lead and zinc. Processing or smelting of these materials releases the mercury which then concentrates in downstream or downwind paths.

***Mercury was found at higher levels in egg contents than eggshells, yet a decrease in partridge productivity was not found.***

Early miners used handfuls of mercury to "float" flecks of gold from screened gravel and the excess mercury got washed downstream. Manufacturers of mens' hats in the eastern U.S. used mercury in processing fur pelts. Workers making these hats developed mental disorders, hence the prase "Mad Hatters."

The Montana Fish and Game Department became concerned about potential for mercury in fish and in upland game birds because methylmercury, a commercial mercury-carbon fungicide, was used to treat most seed grains prior to planting in spring and fall. Unused treated seed was often dumped out in idle areas near grainfields and was an easy source of food for many kinds of grain-eating wildlife. It was not known if the mercury traveled through the developing plants to the harvested grain which would be eaten by both wildlife and people.

In October 1969 John Weigand, a Montana Fish and Game Department wildlife biologist researching Hungarian Partridge on farmlands near Choteau, collected samples of soil, treated seed grain, harvested grain, breast muscle, eggshells and contents of eggs of partridge over a 12 month period. All samples were tested for mercury levels at a private laboratory in Wisconsin.

Mercury-treated seed was found in partridge crops. Test results showed that mercury was at its highest level in breast muscle following spring seeding.[8] Mercury was found at higher levels in egg contents than eggshells, yet a decrease in partridge productivity

*Hatched eggs in a Hungarian Partridge nest.*
*(Photo courtesy John Weigand)*

was not found. Seventy-eight percent of partridge breast muscle contained mercury at levels exceeding the World Health Organization's guideline for human foods. Based on these findings and those coming in from other western states and Canada, the Montana Fish and Game Commission issued public health warnings to hunters not to eat the internal organs of game birds, to limit consumption of game bird meat, and pregnant or nursing women should not eat any game birds.

Wildlife scientists at an international, multidisciplinary conference in 1971 recommended banning the use of methylmercury fungicides as seed treatments.[9] Shortly after this conference a New Mexico farm worker and his family made national news. The worker had fed methylmercury-treated seed to his pigs. A short time after one of the pigs was eaten, his teenage son was hospitalized with blindness and a mental disorder, and there was serious concern for the health of his pregnant wife and their unborn child. This episode, plus mounting scientific evidence about human health risks from organic forms of mercury, resulted in a national ban on using these fungicide treatments.

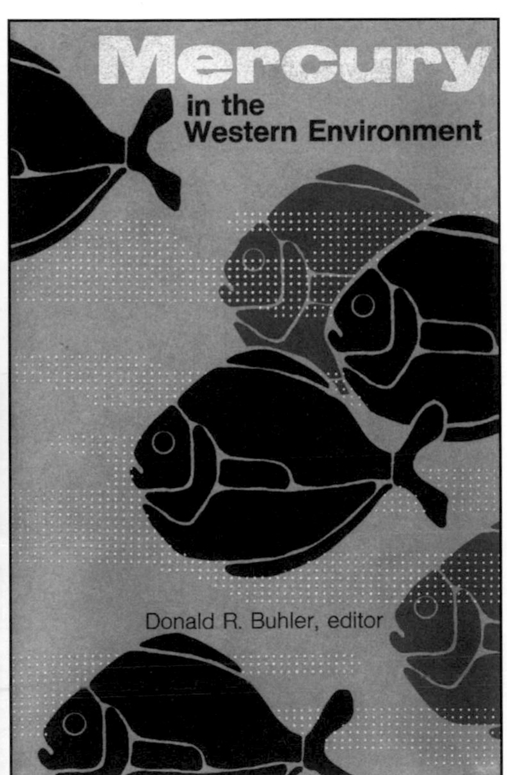

*Cover of the proceedings of a multidisciplinary conference in 1971 on the element Mercury and its effects on the environment.*

When the pesticide "cauldron" began to boil again in 1981, Montana Fish, Wildlife and Parks now had experts to address the issue.

*. . .mounting scientific evidence about human health risks from organic forms of mercury, resulted in a national ban on using these fungicide treatments.*

Grain farmers became worried that wheat stem sawfly *(Cephus cinctus)* would destroy grain crops. The recommended pesticide for fighting the sawfly was Endrin, another chlorinated hydrocarbon pesticide. Endrin is more toxic than DDT and most other chlorinated hydrocarbons. It also persists and accumulates in the environment. In addition to killing insects Endrin is also used as an avicide (bird poison) and as a rodenticide (rodent poison). It has killed pheasants, sharp-tailed grouse, mallards, jackrabbits, mule deer and fish.

*Grain farmers became worried that wheat stem sawfly (Cephus cinctus) would destroy grain crops. The recommended pesticide for fighting the sawfly was Endrin, another chlorinated hydrocarbon pesticide. Endrin is more toxic than DDT and most other chlorinated hydrocarbons.*

As applications began, residues from aerial crop spraying drifted into Sunday Creek near Miles City resulting in fish kills. Thus Montana Fish, Wildlife and Parks began to collect samples from fish, birds, deer and pronghorn.[10] Samples were split into three parts, one each going to separate federal, state and private laboratories. This was done because of the political obstacles posed by various interest groups in previous forest spraying battles. Once again, bearers of "bad news" were subjected to harsh treatment by various groups with economic interests. Laboratory results showed that consumption of waterfowl and other wildlife from affected areas were potentially hazardous to human health.

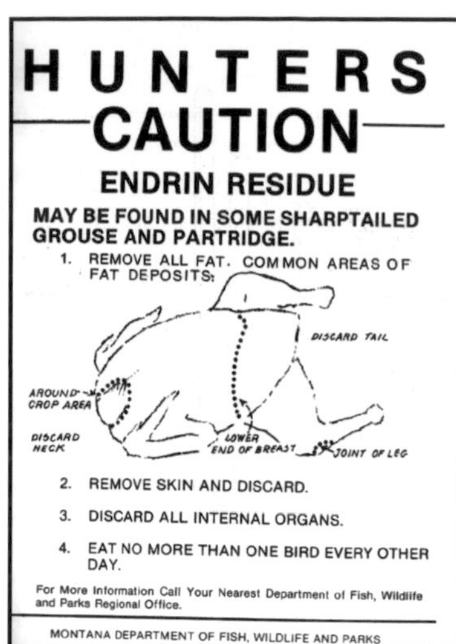

HUNTERS
CAUTION
ENDRIN RESIDUE
MAY BE FOUND IN SOME SHARPTAILED GROUSE AND PARTRIDGE.

1. REMOVE ALL FAT. COMMON AREAS OF FAT DEPOSITS:

DISCARD TAIL
AROUND CROP AREA
DISCARD NECK
LOWER END OF BREAST
JOINT OF LEG

2. REMOVE SKIN AND DISCARD.
3. DISCARD ALL INTERNAL ORGANS.
4. EAT NO MORE THAN ONE BIRD EVERY OTHER DAY.

For More Information Call Your Nearest Department of Fish, Wildlife and Parks Regional Office.

MONTANA DEPARTMENT OF FISH, WILDLIFE AND PARKS

The Commission again issued consumption advisories to waterfowl hunters in 1981. Once the threat to human health was made clear, use of Endrin became very restricted and eventually banned.[11]

Pesticide issues initially focused on human health but as research accumulated around the world, health of our total environment became more of a concern. Both laboratory and field research revealed a "thin eggshell syndrome" in some bird species. Chlorinated hydrocarbon pesticides and their break down products interfere with calcium metabolism of birds. This leads to production of very thin and fragile eggshells with dire consequences for reproduction of affected bird populations.

Toxic compounds accumulate to highest levels in predators as they move up the food chain. This contributed to listing the bald eagle *(Haliaeetus leucocephalus)* and peregrine falcon *(Falco peregrinus)* as endangered species under the federal ESA. During peak spraying years of the 1960s, 300 tons of DDT had been deposited annually in the Yellowstone ecosystem by aerial spraying to combat forest insects. DDT and its breakdown products persisted in the environment for many years.[12] Research in Yellowstone NP found depressed reproduction in both Bald Eagles and Osprey *(Pandion haliaetus)*. Evidence implicated the "thin eggshell syndrome".

"Spraying of DDT for forest insects by the U.S. Forest Service was likely an important negative factor for bald eagle populations. Reproduction, recruitment and population levels were depressed in sprayed areas, and the increase in population size after spraying ceased further implicated DDT as a population-depressing factor."[13]

***In 1980 methodical field surveys found only 13 successful bald eagle nests in Montana. Protection under the ESA was extended to bald eagles in 1978.[14] By 2006, there were 279 successful bald eagle nests counted in the state.[15]***

*Bald and golden eagles that died mostly from poisoning and other antrhopogenic causes. (Photo courtesy Al Harmata)*

Bald eagles usually nest within two miles of aquatic habitats. Thus, efforts to restore and maintain aquatic habitats that helped the restoration of waterfowl populations also provided the basis for eagle recovery as well. Even though they had been protected since 1940 under the Bald Eagle Protection Act they were impacted heavily by use of DDT and its relatives. In 1980 methodical field surveys found only 13 successful bald eagle nests in Montana. Protection under the ESA was extended to bald eagles in 1978.[14] By 2006, there were 279 successful bald eagle nests counted in the state.[15] Bald eagles were removed from the Federal endangered species list in June 2007, but they are still protected under the Federal Bald Eagle Protection Act.

*Number of successful Bald Eagle nests in Montana from 1980 to 2006.* *(Data courtesy Kristi DuBois, Montana Fish, Wildlife and Parks. Background photo courtesy Al Harmata)*

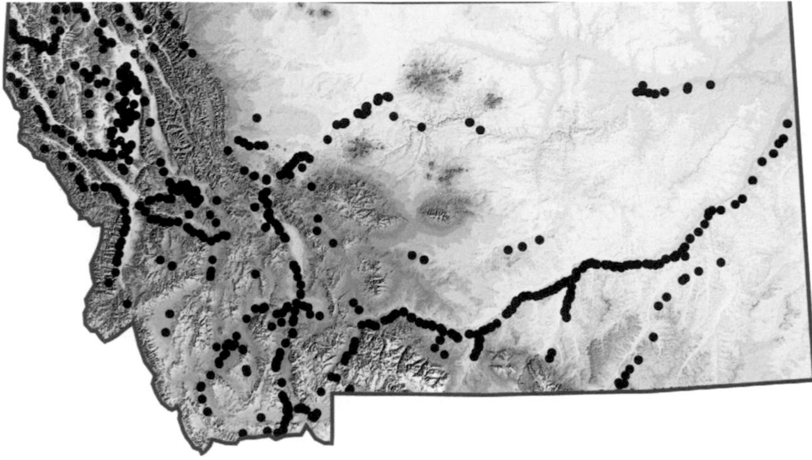

*Locations of Bald Eagle Nests in Montana as of 2006. Includes recent and historic nests.* *(Data courtesy Kristi DuBois, Montana Fish, Wildlife and Parks)*

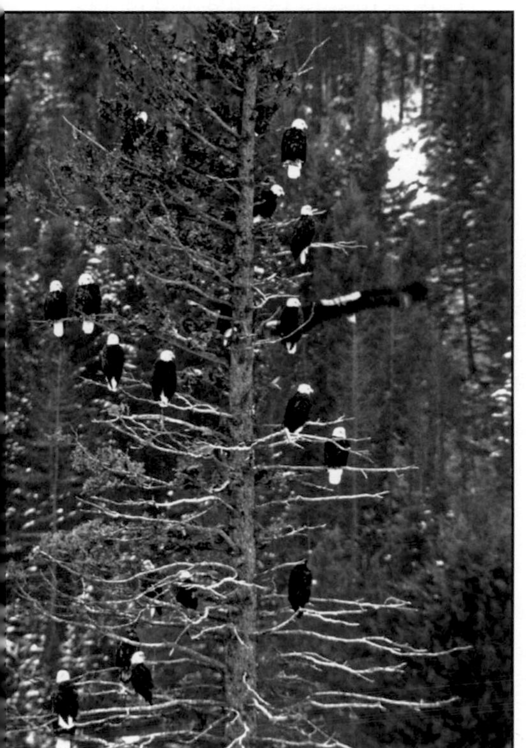

*Bald eagles perched along McDonald Creek in Glacier National Park watching for salmon to feed on. c. 1980.* *(Photo courtesy Riley McClelland)*

In addition to resident eagles, many migrate through the state each year. In the 1970s and 1980s these birds provided a great wildlife show as they gathered along McDonald Creek and the North Fork of the Flathead River to feed upon the salmon run from Flathead Lake. Large numbers of people traveled hundreds of miles to the southern edge of Glacier NP to see the show. When the salmon run collapsed, for reasons unconnected to eagles, the gathering of bald eagles ended as well. In the 1980s and 1990s another great eagle show occurred below Canyon Ferry Dam on the Missouri River. It also ended when the

***Providing habitat for the bald eagle, our national bird and symbol, requires maintaining stream flows and cottonwood trees (Populus spp.) along streams, limiting impact of roads and subdivisions in valleys as well as control of pesticides.***

salmon spawning in Hauser Reservoir ended.

Other environmental contaminants also affect eagles. Bald eagles feeding on ducks in the 1970s exposed them to lead shot picked up by ducks feeding on bottoms of marshes. This produced lead poisoning not only in ducks but also in eagles feeding on them. Steps to correct this situation included a nationwide campaign requiring waterfowl hunters to use steel shot or other types not containing lead in their shotgun shells.

***Seasonally, resident eagles in Montana have been shown to originate in Canada and analysis of blood and feathers of captured eagles outside of the nesting season suggests migrant eagles arrive in southwestern Montana more contaminated than their resident counterparts.***

Montana is home to many golden eagles *(Aquila chrysaetos)* and lies on the migratory pathway for hundreds more. These migrate annually through the Valley of the Eagles (the upper Shields River valley). Research led by Al Harmata from 1985 to 1993 found 86 percent of golden eagles and 56 percent of bald eagles carried toxic levels of lead in their systems.[16]

As the 21st century began, indications of mercury poisoning were found in a few eagles.[17] Considering early mining, smeltering and use of mercury fungicides reported by John Weigand,[18] this contamination is not surprising. This condition could become more common as pollution from other countries, forest fires and peat fires in the thawing arctic tundra increase with global climate changes with mercury released into the atmosphere. Coal-fired powerplants are also among the largest emitters of mercury, although they have to meet EPA standards.[19]

Detection rates and blood concentrations of contaminants tested suggest bald eagles residing in southwestern Montana, regardless of origin, are exposed to a variety of potentially toxic substances. However, low contaminant concentrations in nestling blood and feathers indicate bald eagles originating in southwestern Montana are living and producing young in a relatively clean environment. Migrant eagles in Montana have been shown to originate in Canada. Analysis of blood and feathers of captured migrants suggest these eagles arrive in southwestern Montana more contaminated than their resident counterparts. Further, declining detection rates and contaminant concentrations in eagles captured as autumn progressed through spring suggest local environments in the Madison-Missouri watershed provided clean foods that assisted in purging or at least reducing overall body burdens of deleterious chemicals and compounds.[20]

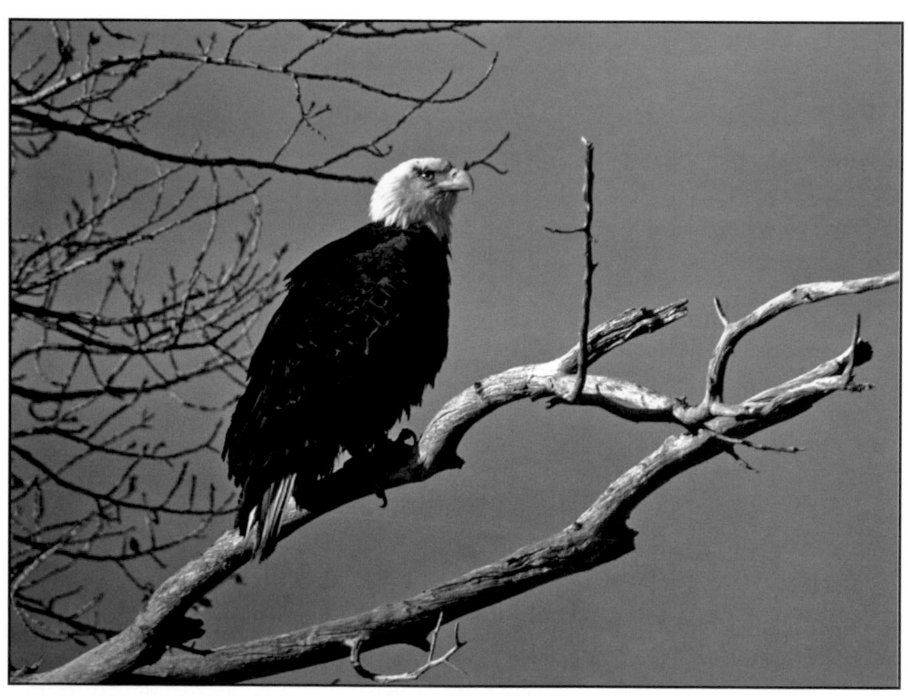

*The Bald Eagle (Haliaeetus leucocephalus) is a bird of prey found in North America that is most recognizable as the national bird and symbol of the United States of America.* (Photo courtesy Brent N. Lonner)

Peregrine falcons suffered a major population collapse during the period of heavy DDT use from 1950 to 1965. By 1975 it was extinct in Montana, Idaho and Wyoming as well as in the eastern

United States. This falcon is second in size to the gyrfalcon and is particularly noted for its very high speed dives. The peregrine usually has its young on cliffs along major watercourses. It hunts in open areas seeking its major food which are other birds.[21] Originally it occurred throughout the state along major rivers and migrating peregrines have been seen in all counties of the state.

Reintroduction began at the Red Rock Lakes National Wildlife Refuge in southeastern Beaverhead county during 1981. Prior to this reintroduction, precautions were taken to ensure the hatchling falcons were not going to be eating pesticide-contaminated prey. Samples of small birds and mammals from the area tested negative for chlorinated hydrocarbons.

Additional releases were made in southwestern Montana. The number of active nests or eyries increased slowly until 1999. More rapid population growth has been seen since then with 59 active eyries and at least 94 young being recorded for 2005.[22] The original recovery goal for Montana, when transplanting would cease, was 20 active eyries. In 1975 there were only 47 active eyries in the entire western United States.

Once again this success story represents the efforts of a broad range of groups including the Peregrine Fund, Indian tribes, Bureau of Land Management, U.S. Fish and Wildlife Service, U.S. Forest Service, National Park Service, Exxon-Mobil Corporation, private cooperators and Montana Fish, Wildlife and Parks.

*In 2005 Montana had more active nests of peregrine falcons than were in all of the western United States in 1975.*

The pesticide-pollutant story has been a case where wildlife research served as an early warning for impacts on human health. Although there were the usual attempts to suppress the test results for political reasons, the independence of researchers and Montana Fish, Wildlife and Parks was maintained for the benefit of both humans and wildlife. As John Weigand, retired Research and Technical Services Supervisor for Montana Fish, Wildlife and Parks, said in an interview—

"Research seeks to unveil the truth ...."[23]

The actions taken for the benefit of human health permitted many concerned citizens to bring about some vital restoration of several Montana wildlife species along with improving their habitat.

*The pesticide-pollutant story has been a case where wildlife research served as an early warning for impacts on human health.*

*"Hack box" with feeding tube used for a temporary home for young peregrine falcons prior to release.* (Photo courtesy Dennis Flath and the Peregrine Fund)

# Footnotes

[1] DeHart, J. L. 1920. What gopher poison has done. Biennial report of the Montana Fish and Game Commission, Helena. 40-44.

[2] Ibid.

[3] Eng, R. L. 1952. A two-summer study of the effects on bird populations of chlordane bait and aldrin spray as used for grasshopper control. Journal of Wildlife Management 16:326-337.

[4] Mussehl, T. W. and P. Schladweiler. 1969. Forest grouse - Experimental spruce budworm insecticide studies. Montana Fish and Game Dept., Helena. Technical Bulletin 4. 53 pp.

Mussehl, T. W. and R. B. Finley, Jr. 1967. Residues of DDT in forest grouse following spruce budworm spraying. Journal of Wildlife Management 31:270-287.

[5] Mussehl, T. W. 1999. Videotaped interview with Harold Picton.

[6] Smith, E. 1999. Videotaped interview with Harold Picton.

[7] Anon. 1964. Pesticide patterns and storm warnings. Montana Wildlife. Spring. 6-7. This action occurred before "Agent Orange" use during the Vietnam war cast suspicion upon herbicide use.

[8] Weigand, J. P. 1971. Mercury in Hungarian partridge and in their north central Montana environment. Proc. Mercury in the Western Environment. 171-185.

[9] Buhl, Don, editor. 1971. Mercury in the Western Environment. Oregon State Univ., Corvallis. 360 pp.

[10] Schladweiler, P. and J. P. Weigand. 1983. Relationships of endrin and other chlorinated hydrocarbon compounds to wildlife in Montana. Montana Fish, Wildlife and Parks, Helena. 230 pp.

[11] Weigand, J. 2000. Videotaped interview with Harold Picton.

Mussehl, T. 1999. Videotaped interview with Harold Picton.

[12] DDT and some related compounds were banned from use nationally in 1972.

[13] Swenson, J. E., K. L. Alt and R. L. Eng. 1986. Ecology of bald eagles in the Greater Yellowstone Ecosystem. Wildlife Monograph 95. 46 pp.

[14] Aderhold, M. 1988. Bald eagle. Montana Outdoors. Vol. 19(2):19-20.

[15] DuBois, K. 2006. Various reports and summaries concerning the bald eagle. Personal communication with Harold Picton.

[16] Harmata, A. and M. Restani. 1995. Environmental contaminants and cholinesterase in blood of vernal migrant bald and golden eagles in Montana. Intermountain Journal of Sciences Vol. 1(1): 1-15.

[17] Anon. 2006. BLM to study mercury in Montana bald eagles. Great Falls Tribune. August 30, 2006. M6.

[18] Ibid. Weigand, J. P. 1971.

[19] Perkins, S. 2006. Mercury rising. Science News. 170 (August 26, 2006):134.

Brown, M. 2008. Study finds pesticides in western national parks. Great Fall Tribune, Feb. 28, 2008. M6.

[20] Harmata, A. R. 2008. Monitoring mercury and other contaminants in bald eagles in southwestern Montana. Unpublished report to U.S. Fish & Wildlife Service, Migratory Bird Section, Denver, CO. Montana State University, Bozeman.

[21] Aderhold, M. 1988. American Peregrine Falcon. Montana Outdoors. Vol. 19(2):20-22.

[22] Dood, A. 2006. Background report. Personal communication to H. Picton. 1 pp.

[23] Ibid. Weigand, J. P. 2000.

Ibid. Mussehl, T. W. 1999.

# Chapter 19

# Land, Wildlife and People

Montana's land ownership is complex and varied. Wildlife often crosses multiple jurisdictions while exploiting habitat for seasonal use. As restored wildlife populations grew it was necessary to find ways to accommodate expanding herds of big game, especially elk. Because many national forest lands had relatively little winter range, elk would often move onto adjacent private lands during winter where conflict with land owners sometimes followed.

In March 1939, C. R. Rathbone killed an elk out of season on the Circle H Ranch in what is now the Sun River Wildlife Management Area. He contended the elk had damaged ranch property. A game warden investigated and Mr. Rathbone was subsequently cited and convicted. He appealed his case to the Montana Supreme Court. The Court reviewed the case and returned it to the lower court with some guidelines:

> "Montana is one of the few areas in the Nation where wild game abounds. It is regarded as one of the greatest of the State's natural resources, as well as the chief attraction for visitors. Wild game existed here long before the coming of man. One who acquires property in Montana does so with notice and knowledge of the presence of wild game and presumably is cognizant of its natural habits."

*"Montana is one of the few areas in the Nation where wild game abounds. . ."*

— Montana Supreme Court

*A sign on the Circle H Ranch (now the Sun River Wildlife Management Area) before the precendent setting Rathbone Supreme court decision about game damage complaints. c. late 1930s.* *(Photo courtesy Harold Picton)*

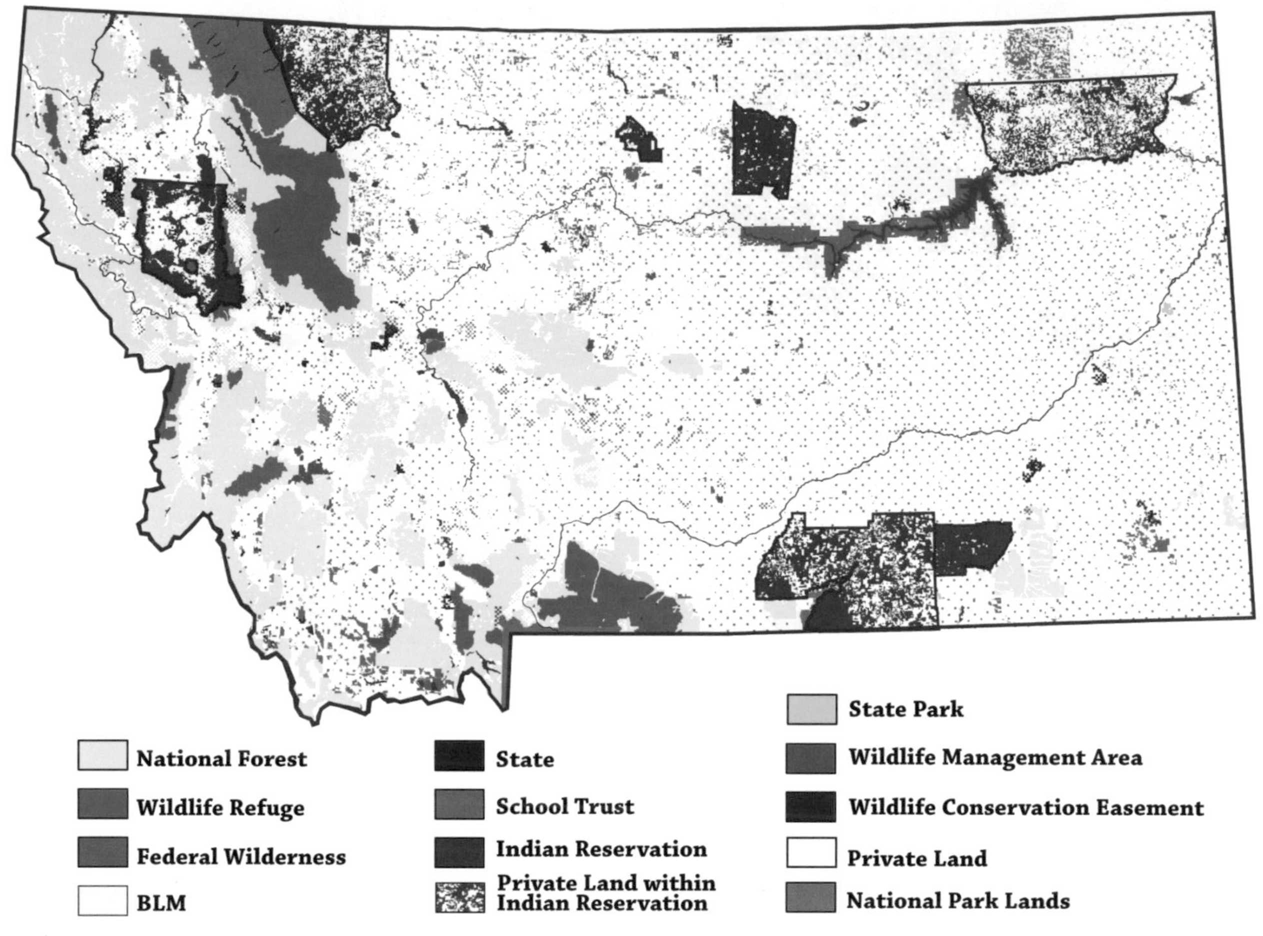


*Land Ownership in Montana - 2007. (Map Courtesy of Duane Lund, GIS specialist, Natural Resources Conservation System, Montana State Library, Helena)*

*Wildlife Management Areas or WMAs, were established to enable big game animals to maximize their use of public lands and reduce conflicts with private landowners.*[1]

This case established a legal precedent for game damage complaints. In short, the guidelines recognized both the State's right to preserve free ranging game animals and citizen's rights, under certain conditions, to protect their property. The conclusion was that each case be judged on its own merits. The case also inspired acquisition of big game winter ranges by the Montana Fish and Game Department.

To help resolve some conflicts, the Montana Fish and Game Department began purchasing select pieces of land for big game winter range with sportsmen's dollars generated under the P-R Act. The first of these vital acquisitions was in 1940 for elk in Pig Eye Basin of the Judith River drainage in central Montana. Other acquisitions followed in the Gallatin River, Sun River, Blackfoot River drainages and in many other areas throughout Montana. These areas (now called Wildlife Management Areas or WMAs) were established to enable big game to maximize use of public lands and reduce conflicts with private landowners.[1] In every case many people and organizations have been important in purchasing these areas. Some landowners wished to sell their land as WMAs because they loved their land and did not wish it to be subjected to real estate development; the Beartooth WMA south of Great Falls is an example.

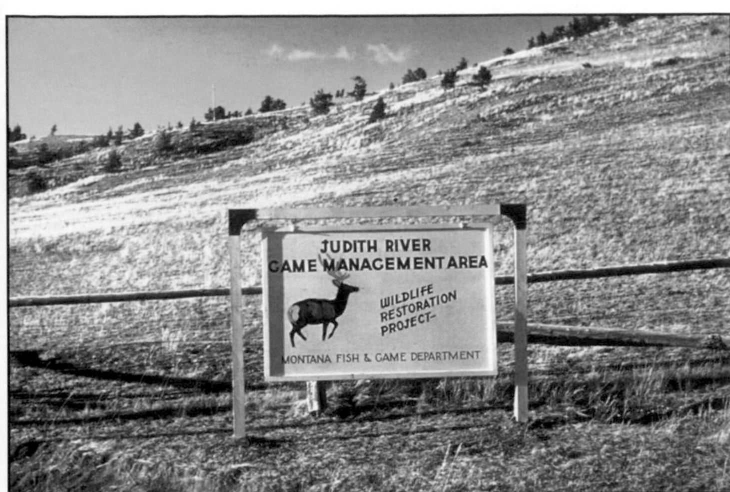


*The Judith River Game Management Area, established in 1940, was the first game range purchased by the Montana Fish and Game Department.* *(Photo Courtesy Gene Allen)*

## THE EAST FRONT

The Rathbone case also stimulated a complex and major effort to provide wildlife habitat on the East Front of the Rocky Mountains, particularly that portion from Glacier NP south to the Sun River. The Sun River WMA was purchased in 1948. This was to be the first in a long series of events that led to the protection of over 1,000 square miles of a complex wildlife ecosystem, traditional land uses and access for public recreation.

The state has sometimes needed financial help from willing citizens and organizations to purchase WMAs.

> "Late in 1947, Mr. Brucegard, an elderly rancher with land bordering the National Forest under Mt. Sawtooth, offered his land for sale to the Montana Fish and Game Department. The offer was made at 11 o'clock on a Saturday and the banks closed at 12. A certified check had to be delivered that day or the land would be sold to another buyer. The Department could not raise the money on such short notice so Mr. O'Claire, the State Game Warden, called Tom Messelt and Carl Malone in Great Falls who raised $10,000 between them and saved the land for the elk."[2]

In the 1950s oil and gas exploration companies began to show interest in this area where the sweep of the Great Plains meets the mountains. The Blackfeet tribe had declared the Badger-Two Medicine area immediately south of Glacier NP, a "Cultural District" under the National Antiquities Act, but the Bureau of Land Management manages mineral rights on federal lands and had leased some land in the area for oil drilling. A major public controversy arose and drilling was blocked.

***For the land that is the Sun River Wildlife Management Area, the Department could not raise the money on short notice. Tom Messelt and Carl Malone raised $10,000 between them and saved the land for the elk.***

The grizzly bear population centered in the Bob Marshall Wilderness

*Sawtooth Mountain on the Sun River Wildlife Management Area on the East Front.* *(Photo courtesy Brent N. Lonner)*

*Old Man of the Hills by Larry Zabel. A painting depicting where grizzly bear habitat transitions between the rugged peaks of the East Front and ranchlands of the plains.* (Courtesy Montana Fish, Wildlife and Parks Foundation)

***In 1997, Gloria Flora, supervisor of the Lewis and Clark National Forest, issued a moratorium on oil and gas development on national forest lands of the East Front.***

Area responded to a reduction in predator control efforts and began to move out on to the plains area west of Choteau. Charles Jonkel, of the University of Montana, included these bears in his research project.

The state acquired the Blackleaf WMA to provide winter range for elk in the northern portion of the Teton River drainage. Concern for the prairie grizzly population stimulated the Nature Conservancy to purchase Pine Butte Swamp Preserve in 1978. An exploratory oil well in the upper Teton River drainage caused concern for mountain goats, the population that had contributed significantly to the mountain goat transplant program in the early 1940s. Mike Thompson, a Montana State University graduate student, investigated the situation with a research project.[3] A little farther north, helicopters were being used to facilitate seismic oil exploration. Gayle Joslin, a Montana Fish, Wildlife and Parks wildlife biologist, was assigned to investigate impacts of these industrial efforts upon mountain goats.[4] Keith Aune, another MFWP biologist, began an East Front Grizzly Bear research project. Other research projects during this same time frame focused on mule deer and bighorn sheep.[5] These studies documented an area remarkably rich in wildlife and helped resolve desires of the public to see it protected. The Boone and Crockett club purchased Theodore Roosevelt Memorial Ranch near the mouth of Blackleaf Canyon to add to the protected wildlife habitat.

*Gas or Oil exploration rig on the east front near the Blackleaf Wildlife Management Area. c. 1981.* (Photo courtesy Gary Olson)

Data from research and routine management surveys were used by individuals and private organizations to oppose petroleum companies. In 1997, Gloria Flora, supervisor of the Lewis and Clark National Forest, issued a moratorium on oil and gas development on national forest land on the East Front. Drilling lease holders were given tax breaks if they sold their leases along the Front to nonprofit groups.

Since 2006, 63,374 acres of leases have been retired from 400,000 acres of federal lands along the East Front. In 2006, the Questar Corporation

HELENA INDEPENDENT RECORD

**Forest Service bans oil, gas leasing on Front**

Lewis and Clark National Forest issues final management plan

The New York Times

NEW YORK, THURSDAY, SEPTEMBER 25, 1997

**Forest Service Bans New Leases For Oil and Gas in Rockies Area**

GREAT FALLS TRIBUNE

WEDNESDAY March 8, 2000

**Oil, gas exploration ban stands**

donated several oil and gas drilling leases back to the Bureau of Land Management for retirement, and the Coalition to Protect The Rocky Mountain Front and the Wyss Foundation purchased 23,310 acres of federal, state and private leases from Startech Energy. In January 2007, the U.S. Congress enacted a ban on drilling on federal land along the Front. Legislation was key to resolving land-use conflicts that had been raging for almost 30 years. In April 2007, Trout Unlimited purchased 4,900 acres of drilling leases for retirement located in the Badger-Two Medicine area from Donald Epperson.[6] In addition, the Kohlman Co. donated 33,411 acres of oil and gas leases to Trout Unlimited for retirement. Ninety-one thousand acres of leases remain for possible development.[7]

“We finally got it done. We finally protected the Rocky Mountain Front forever. — *Sen. Max Baucus*”

**Drilling banned**

The U.S. Senate authorized a permanent ban on petroleum and mineral exploration along the Front in Montana on Saturday. The measure now goes to President Bush, who is expected to sign it. The Blackleaf Canyon area is shown here in 2005

**Congress permanently ends oil, gas leases**

By MARY CLARE JALONICK
Associated Press Writer
and RYAN HALL
Tribune Night City Editor

and other legislation that cleared Congress early Saturday. The legislation is now headed to President Bush, who must sign it for it to take

by a 79-9 vote.

"This is a major, major victory for Montana. We've been working to pass meaningful protections for the Rocky

finally protected the Rocky Mountain Front forever," he added. "Thirty years from now, our kids and grandchildren will thank us."

**Front lease agreement start of something good**

OUR OPINION

The incentives accompanying January's permanent ban on new leases on federal land along the Rocky Mountain Front are working.

Trout Unlimited announced last week that it had bought natural gas drilling leases on a couple of tracts in the Badger-Two Medicine area just south of Glacier National Park.

That makes Donald Epperson, a private developer from Helena, the first to take advantage of a law enacted by Congress in January banning new leases on federal land in the area.

In addition to the ban, the law also included a tax break for selling existing Front leases — a break equivalent to 25 percent of the value of the price received by the seller.

The TU-Epperson deal for an undisclosed price means 4,900 acres will be protected from further leasing.

It's the first deal since the law took effect, but it's not the first such deal.

In December, Startech Energy agreed to sell leases affecting more than 23,000 acres of federal state and private land to the Coalition to Protect the Rocky Mountain Front and the Wyss Foundation.

And last June, Questar Corp. donated a number of oil and gas leases on the Front to Trout Unlimited with the intention of returning them to the Bureau of Land Management where they'd be retired.

When leasing on the Front comes up in the news, the stories frequently focus on the political give and take, the technicalities of deals, and the dollars involved.

That's a necessity, of course, but it often leaves little room for the reasons behind the efforts of groups such as the coalition and behind legislation such as that passed in January.

Those reasons revolve around the area's uniqueness, unparalleled beauty, and superb habitat.

Animals big and small, peaceful and dangerous range along the Front, the eastern margins of the sprawling Bob Marshall Wilderness complex.

The rocky peaks are visible from a hundred miles away, and the lifestyle — including the ag and recreation industries — the area supports cannot be matched elsewhere.

Most important, once any of those values are lost, they are difficult if not impossible to restore.

We hope more such deals are in the offing.

Efforts to maintain the ecological value of over 1,000 square miles of mountain front habitat are a major contribution to Montana's culture. Over 170 ranchers and other private landowners have been willing to adjust land use practices to accommodate wildlife in this area. Assistance from the Bailey Wildlife Foundation and Defenders of Wildlife provided some compensation for predator damage to livestock.[8]

## SALT AND HABITAT USE

Not all efforts to manage wildlife use of habitats have been successful. Salt (sodium chloride) is used as a taste enhancer for humans and can also be used as a wildlife management tool as well as a special source of nutrition for domestic livestock and wild grazing animals. Salt dispersal was attempted as a technique to draw elk away from private lands during critical spring months to reduce conflict with private land owners. A salt distribution program was begun during World War II. Outfitters and others were given salt to distribute in back country areas.

***Salt dispersal was attempted as a technique to draw elk away from private lands during critical spring months to reduce conflict with private land owners.***

*Above - Loading salt into a Ford Tri-motor airplane. The plane would hold up to 60 blocks of salt weighing a ton and a half. Left - Merle Rognrud, a pioneer wildlife biologist, preparing to drop salt out of a Ford Tri-motor during early spring to help lure elk off of private land. (Courtesy Robert Cooney Photo Collection)*

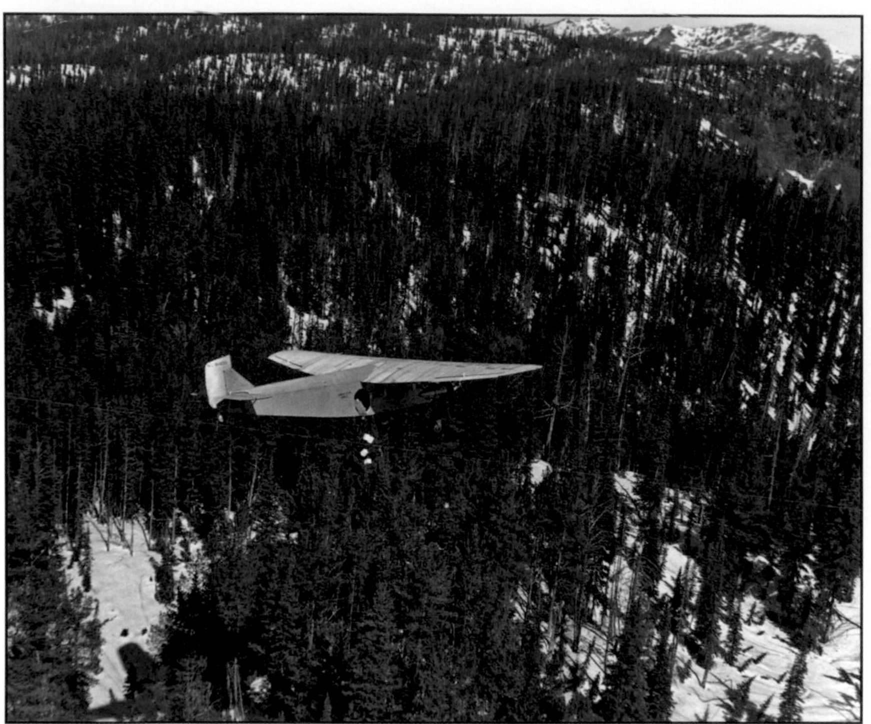

*Dropping salt blocks out of a Ford Tri-motor airplane during early spring to help disperse elk off of private land. c. 1948. This program was determined to be ineffective and was discontinued in the late 1950s. (Courtesy Robert Cooney Photo Collection)*

## ACCESS FOR THE ANIMALS

"As ranching interests in the valley became more intensified, there arose a serious conflict between big game and livestock use. ... A logical solution to the problem would have to be arrived at in one of two ways. Either the big game herds would have to be drastically reduced and kept at a minimum number that would be tolerated by ranchers, or essential winter range would have to be provided for big game where there would be no competition with livestock for available forage." — Comments made concerning the Blackfoot-Clearwater WMA.[11]

"Both proven and experimental practices of big game range management will be continued on the range. . . .In this manner the highest possible esthetic and sporting values will be realized by the people of Montana."[12]

*...there arose a serious conflict between big game and livestock use... Either the big game herds would have to be drastically reduced... or essential winter range would have to be provided for big game.*

A more spectacular effort was aerial distribution of salt by a Ford Tri-motor and other aircraft over mountainous areas. At its peak, 80 tons of salt were dropped at a cost of over $10,000 annually.[9] An evaluation of the program in the mid 1950s determined that elk did find and use the salt, but did not affect their distribution. The program was discontinued in the late 1950s.[10]

If elk and other wild grazing animals are provided with good range and access to a variety of plant species, they can easily satisfy their salt needs by eating small amounts of those plants that accumulate sodium in their tissues. However, natural salt licks occur and salt blocks distributed for livestock and those dropped from airplanes have started salt licks as rain and snow dissolved the salt into the ground. These are sometimes used by various wildlife species.

Research and innovation permitted some state WMAs to exert a broader influence than their acreage implies. Rest-rotation grazing plans that exchanged grazing by cattle have enhanced rangelands for elk and other species as well as expanding WMAs.[13] Examples of these grazing exchanges are found on WMAs such as Mount Fleecer and Mount Haggin. Funds from the P-R Act are also used to make payments to counties in lieu of county land taxes on State owned WMAs.

A major step in providing habitat for wildlife populations was taken toward the end of 20th century. Funds were made available through House Bill 526, known as Habitat Montana,

## Montana Fish, Wildlife and Parks
### Wildlife Management Areas as of 2008

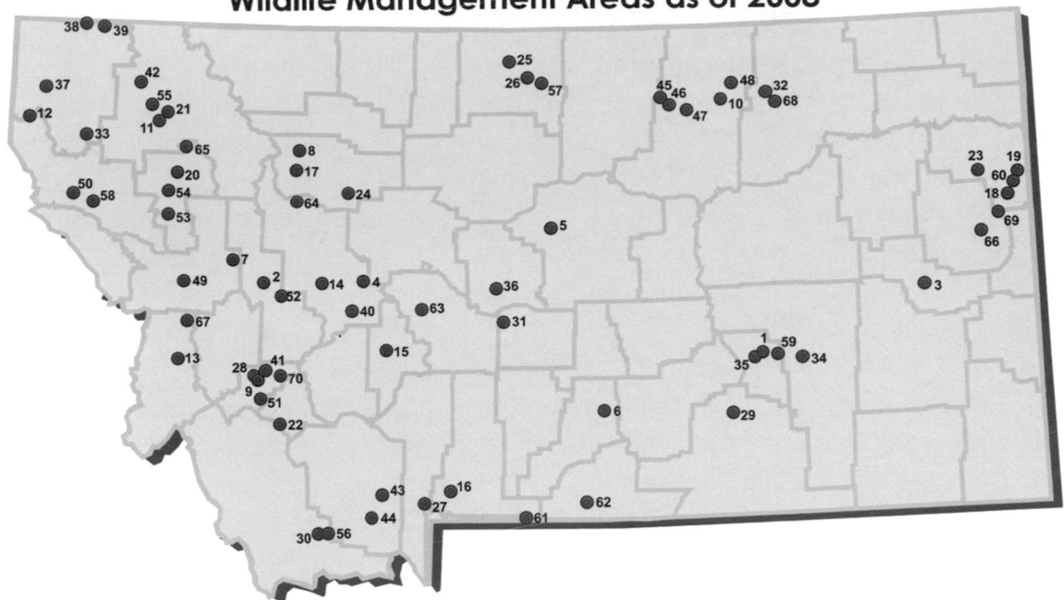

1 Amelia Island
2 Aunt Molly
3 Badlands
4 Beartooth
5 Beckman
6 Big Lake
7 Blackfoot-Clearwater
8 Blackleaf
9 Blue Eyed Nellie
10 Bowdoin
11 Buffalo Head Park
12 Bull River
13 Calf Creek
14 Canyon Creek
15 Canyon Ferry
16 Dome Mountain
17 Ear Mountain
18 Elk Island
19 F Island
20 Flathead Lake
21 Flathead River
22 Fleecer Mountain
23 Fox Lake
24 Freezout Lake
25 Fresno Reservoir
26 Fresno Tailwater
27 Gallatin
28 Garrity Mountain
29 Grant Marsh
30 Gravelly-Blacktail
31 Haymaker
32 Hinsdale
33 Horseshoe Lake
34 Howard Valley
35 Isaac Homestead
36 Judith River
37 Kootenai/Falls
38 Kootenai/West
39 Kootenai/Woods Ranch
40 Lake Helena
41 Lost Creek
42 Lower Stillwater Lake
43 Madison-Bear Creek
44 Madison-Wall Creek
45 Milk River - Dodson Creek
46 Milk River - Dodson Dam Unit
47 Milk River - Dodson S. Canal
48 Milk River - Sleeping Buffalo
49 Mount Jumbo
50 Mount Silcox
51 Mt. Haggin
52 Nevada Lake
53 Ninepipe
54 Pablo
55 Ray Kuhns
56 Robb-Ledford
57 Rookery
58 Roundhorn
59 Sanders
60 Seven Sisters
61 Silver Gate
62 Silver Run
63 Smith River
64 Sun River
65 Swan Lake
66 Three Mile
67 Threemile
68 Vandalia
69 War Dance Island
70 Warm Springs

*Research and innovative rest-rotation livestock grazing programs to enhance rangelands for elk and other wildlife were pioneered on the Mount Fleecer and Mount Haggin Wildlife Mangement Areas in the 1970s. (Small photo courtesy Martha A. Lonner and large photo courtesy Michael Frisina.)*

*Since 1940, 70 Wildlife Management Areas have been established by Montana Fish, Wildlife and Parks to maintain vital wildlife habitat for the protection of species and enjoyment by the public.*

approved by the Montana Legislature in 1987. Money from this program has been used primarily for purchase of voluntary conservation easements on private ranches. Cash payments to private landowners minimized the possibility that wildlife habitat could be destroyed by real estate development. Easements also provide access for hunters so big game numbers can be controlled.

***Conservation Easements also provide access for hunters so big game numbers can be controlled.***

On many easements, an important stipulation for maintaining habitat quality is implementing a rest-rotation grazing system developed by MFWP in cooperation with landowners. In 1994, the program started with the Fish, Wildlife and Parks Commission approving purchase of a complex conservation easement package involving three parcels of land in eastern Montana. The Page-Whitham Ranch was a key player in establishing these easements, which are on the Brewer, Tampico and South Ranches. This program has since expanded to many other areas.[14] Once again, cooperation among diverse segments of Montana's society is providing habitat for wildlife.

Nonprofit organizations such as local land trusts provide conservation easements to protect natural qualities of the landscape throughout the state. However, conservation easements administered by these nonprofit organizations usually don't provide public access for hunting and other public recreation.

## Montana Fish, Wildlife and Parks
### Conservation Easements as of 2008

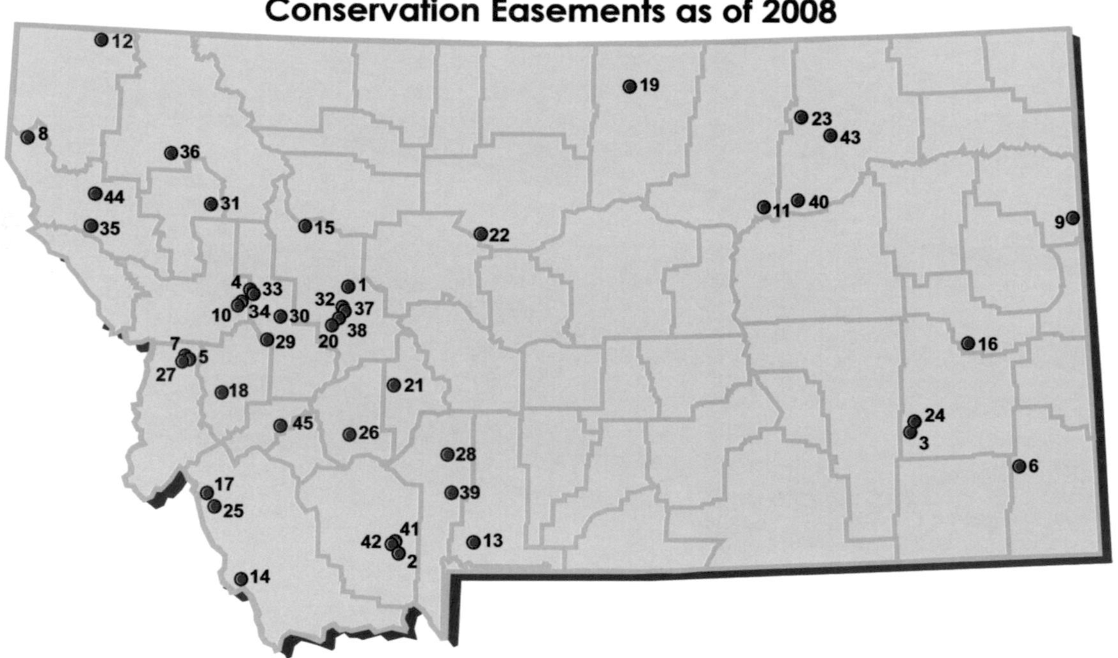


1. Bay Ranch
2. Bear Creek Angus
3. Bice
4. Blackfoot-Clearwater
5. Bolin Ranches
6. Brewer
7. Brown Valley
8. Bull River Vista
9. Buxbaum
10. Clearwater Junction
11. Cowell
12. Dancing Prairie
13. Dome Mountain
14. Dragging Y
15. Edwards
16. Fluss Ranch
11. Fred & Lynn Hirschy
18. Gillies Ranch
19. Gordon Cattle
20. Grady Ranches
21. Hahn
22. Harris Land & Cattle Co.
23. Hart
24. Hirsch Ranch
25. Jack Hirschy Livestock, Inc.
26. Keogh
27. Lewis Ranch
28. Maher
29. Manley Ranch
30. Mannix
31. North Swan Valley
32. O'Connell Lyons Creek
33. Opsata
34. Reinoehl
35. Roundhorn
36. Seabaugh Wylie Slough
37. Sieben Lyons Creek
38. Sieben Rattlesnake Creek
39. Sourdough Creek
40. South Ranch
41. Storey Ranch
42. Storey-Madison Ranch
43. Tampico Ranch
44. Thompson-Fisher
45. WH Ranch

## ACCESS FOR THE PEOPLE

Montana's wildlife resource belongs to the people of Montana. If they are to enjoy and utilize this resource they must have access to it. Another innovative program is called Block Management. Under this program Montana Fish, Wildlife and Parks (MFWP) compensates landowners for allowing hunters access to their land. MFWP also provides services to landowners to offset hunter related impacts and properly manage and regulate numbers of people who wish to hunt on their land.

Neil Martin, MFWP wildlife manager, initially began the program in southeastern Montana and it has now spread throughout the state.[15] This popular program was buttressed by legislation passed in 1995. As with most new ideas there was considerable discussion and weighing of alternatives before it was adopted.[16] These hunting and conservation programs have proven popular and receive strong public support.

Brewer Ranch. *(Photo courtesy Sam M. Espeland)*

*In 1994, Habitat Montana started with the Fish, Wildlife and Parks Commission approving purchase of a complex conservation easement package involving three parcels of land in eastern Montana. These easements are on the Brewer, Tampico and South Ranches.*

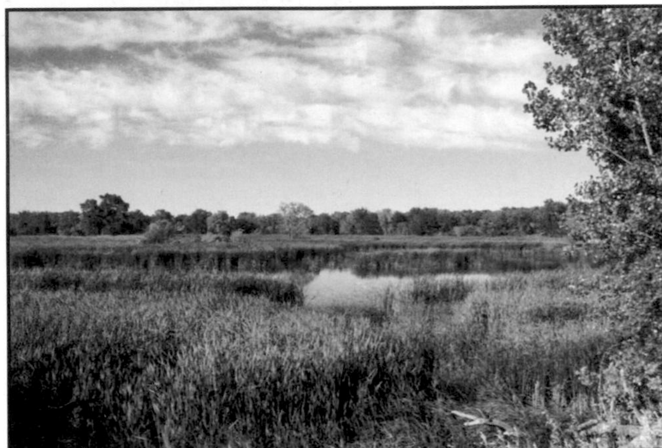

Tampico Ranch. *(Photo courtesy Sam M. Espeland)*

South Ranch. *(Photo courtesy Sam M. Espeland)*

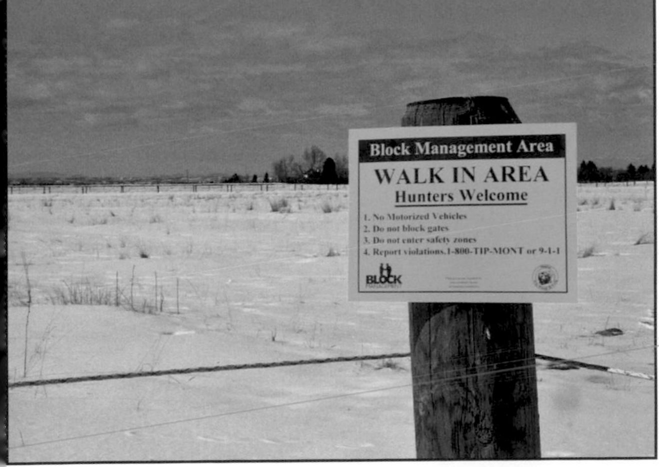


*Under the Block Management Program Montana Fish, Wildlife and Parks compensates land owners for allowing hunter access to their land.*

## Montana Upland Game Bird Enhancement Areas as of 2007

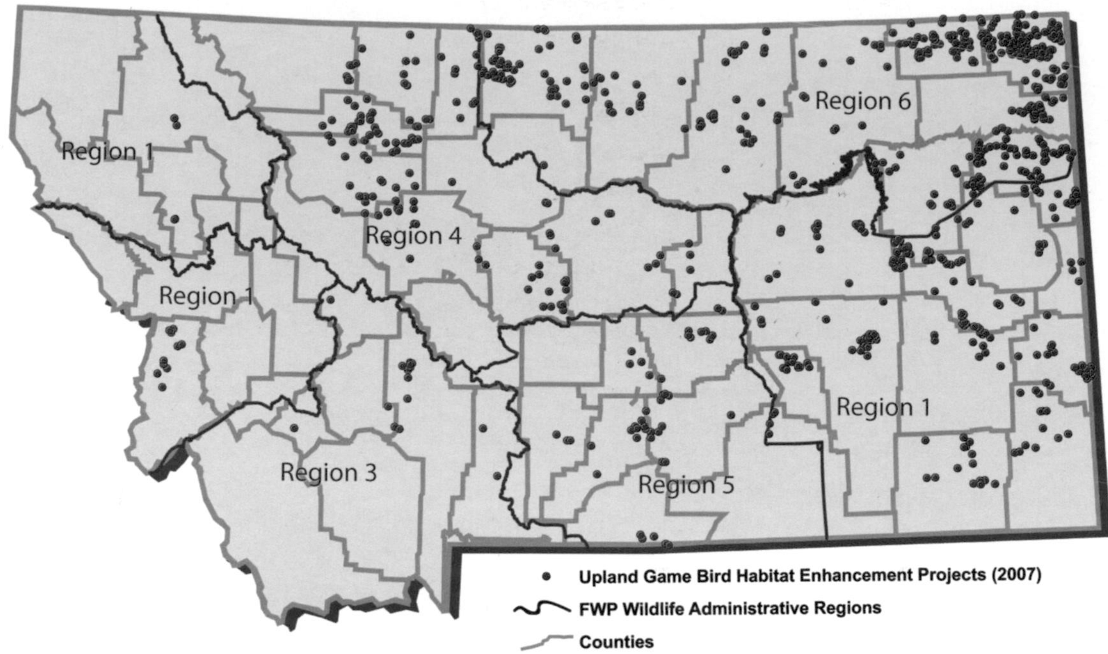


*Sometimes real estate purchases require "bridge money" or funds to make a payment to hold a land purchase until the complicated process of governmental financing can be completed.*

### BETTER HABITAT FOR UPLAND GAME BIRDS

An Upland Game Bird Enhancement Program, funded with hunter license dollars, has helped improve bird numbers and expand upland game bird hunting opportunities since 1987. Funds are available each spring for pheasant releases and year round for habitat-related projects including planting nesting cover, shelterbelts, food plots, or making grazing improvements. Each project funded includes a contract with a private landowner and an agreed upon level of public hunting.

### LAND FOR WILDLIFE IN THE YELLOWSTONE AREA

Sometimes real estate purchases require "bridge money" or funds to make a payment to hold a land purchase until the complicated process of governmental financing can be completed. Organizations like the Rocky Mountain Elk Foundation and the Nature Conservancy have helped provide "bridge" and supplemental financing. Supplemental financing is needed at times because government agencies can only pay appraised value while some parcels of land may sell for more. The U.S. Forest Service has been active in obtaining lands for wildlife near Yellowstone NP. Richard Denney (U.S. Forest Service) and Kurt Alt (MFWP), with heavy public support and involvement, succeeded in adding the checker-board "railroad grant" lands to the public portfolio in the Gallatin Land Trade.

The Dome Mountain WMA had been purchased by the state of Montana in the early 1980s to provide elk winter range. After the 1988 Yellowstone fires, private lands were obtained to protect the elk migration corridor from Yellowstone NP to this WMA about 25 miles north of the Park. Other efforts provided additions to northern Yellowstone winter range

*The nearly 5,000 acre Dome Mountain Wildlife Management Area just north of Gardiner, MT winters 60-70% of all elk migrating out of the northern portion of Yellowstone National Park. c. 2008. (Photo courtesy Terry N. Lonner)*

*Another controversy arose in the Bitterroot drainage of western Montana following battles over spraying forests with insecticides. . .people expressed concern about what massive clear-cut logging was doing to elk populations.*

areas. Efforts continue by the Forest Service, state of Montana and Rocky Mountain Elk Foundation to make more land bordering the Park available for better flexibility in bison management.

## LOGGING IN ELK HABITAT

Another controversy arose in the Bitterroot drainage of western Montana following battles over spraying forests with insecticides. The U.S. Forest Service then began clear-cut logging large areas, but this new forest management technique to regenerate forests often produced substantial soil erosion on steep slopes. Silting of the Bitterroot River and its tributaries generated major concern among local residents as well as faculty members at the School of Forestry at the University of Montana. Arnold Bolle, Dean of the School of Forestry, and other faculty members, produced a major report which criticized the U.S. Forest Service for their methods and clear-cutting was eventually stopped.[17] The U.S. Forest Service was under a mandate from Congress to become a "multiple use" agency to balance diverse land uses and arrive at some sort of an optimum pattern of use.

Another major concern about massive clear-cut logging arose in the 1960s when biologists throughout the

*Clearcut logging during the 1960s by the U. S. Forest in western Montana precipitated a congressional investigation and a major multiagency research effort to study the effects of clearcut logging on rivers, streams and elk. c. 1975. (Montana Fish and Game photo by Terry N. Lonner)*

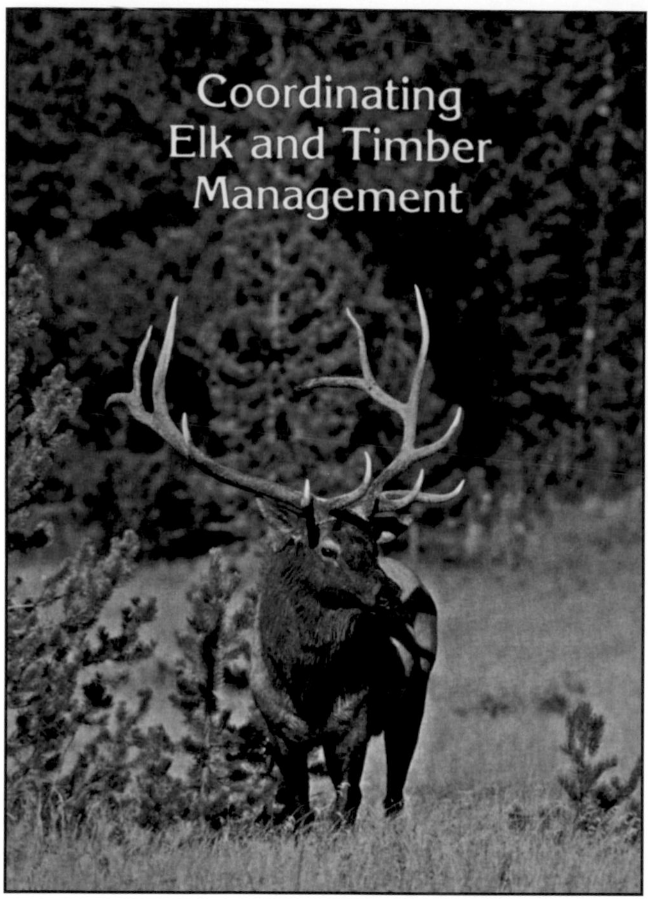


*Montana Cooperative Elk-Logging Study final report, 1985.*

west expressed concern about what this practice was doing to elk populations. In Montana the final impetus for action was provided by a proposed timber sale on the Middle Fork of the Judith River in the Little Belt Mountains, Lewis and Clark National Forest in the west central part of the state. Concerns were so strong about the negative effects this sale may have on elk that it led to initiation of a cooperative elk-logging study begun in 1970 involving seven separate study areas in western Montana. This cooperative effort by the U.S. Forest Service, Montana Fish, Wildlife and Parks, University of Montana, U.S. Bureau of Land Management and Plum Creek Timber Company, Inc. extended over 15 years and involved efforts of nearly 200 people. A final report was published in 1985 and provided several management recommendations to assist wildlife and timber managers with improving coordination between elk and timber management.[18]

***A long-term cooperative elk-logging study was begun in 1970 involving seven separate study areas in western Montana.***

## SAGEBRUSH AND HABITAT

Sagebrush *(Artemisia spp)* grassland covers extensive areas in Montana. Humans often describe it as a dull and monotonous landscape but critters of lesser size recognize it as a diverse forest. Sagebrush provides homes for sage grouse, pronghorn antelope and many other wildlife species. It also provides winter range for mule deer and elk. A commonly held belief was that its presence was detrimental to cattle range and an indicator of declining range

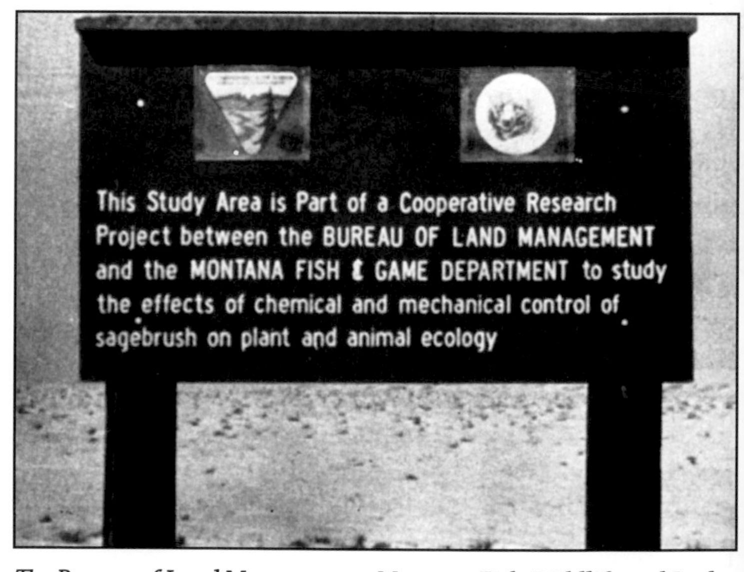


*The Bureau of Land Management, Montana Fish, Wildlife and Parks and Montana State University joined in a cooperative research project to investigate the effects of various types of sagebrush control and the role of sagebrush in grasslands.*

conditions. Subsequently sagebrush was controlled or removed from large areas in several western states by spraying with herbicides, burning or flailing it with large mechanical beaters.

Research in the 1950s and early 1960s cast doubt on widespread negative attitudes about sagebrush. Congress gave the Bureau of Land Management and U.S. Forest Service broader responsibilities as multiple use agencies and they responded to a growing body of scientific information. The Bureau of Land Management, U.S. Forest Service, Montana Fish, Wildlife and Parks and Montana State University joined in a cooperative research investigation of the effects of various types of sagebrush control and the role of sagebrush in grasslands.

Research concluded that in most situations sagebrush removal was detrimental to wildlife. Sagebrush plays an important role in grasslands and its removal often is harmful to virtually all aspects of the system.[19] As it builds soil it brings minerals and sometimes water to the surface which other plants use. As a result of this research, Montana now avoids conversion of sagebrush grasslands to the explosively fire prone cheatgrass *(Bromus tectorum)* ranges extensively present in other western states.

Late in the 20th century the prospect of widespread coal bed methane development again brought concerns for sagebrush habitats. While leks of sage grouse often become the focus of concerns about land use impacts, it is important to realize that winter and summer habitats are also required. Sagebrush is important in the biology of many species year round.

***Spraying sagebrush with herbicides. c. 1960s.*** *(Photo courtesy Tom Mussehl)*

## LEARNING FROM DEER

Life means constant change and we can never be complacent about our knowledge. Montana has invested heavily in research to help take some of the uncertainty from its management actions and to try and determine where management activities might go wrong before they do. Scientific research projects have been undertaken on most species to separate facts of their biology from myth and folklore. This has certainly been the case with the 50+ year effort to understand deer across our broad state. This research was carried out by Montana Fish, Wildlife and Parks in cooperation with Montana State University, the University of Montana and the Montana Cooperative Wildlife Research Unit.

Mule deer were subjects of the first research projects and focus was on their reproductive biology.[20] Other early projects examined food habits and ecology of mule deer in southwestern Montana, the Little Belt Mountains and Bridger Mountain Range.[21] Wild animals that feed on plants typically

***. . .research concluded that in most situations sagebrush removal was detrimental to wildlife. Sagebrush plays an important role in grasslands and its removal often is harmful to virtually all aspects of the system.[19]***

*Long-term deer research efforts started in the early 1950s and were first conducted on mule deer in mountain ranges such as the Bridgers in south central Montana.* (Photo courtesy Terry N. Lonner)

feed on only 10 or 15 percent of plant species growing in their home ranges. They also are very specific about parts of plants they eat and time of the year they eat them. This complexity means that detailed knowledge of their food habits must be known before an understanding of how they use the habitat in which they live. Deer studies were extended to the Missouri Breaks and other areas. Some projects examined how domestic livestock and deer used areas together. By the early 1960s white-tailed deer were beginning their recovery and research was begun on them. Widespread hunter interest in deer maintained a high research presence.

***The long term studies built an unprecedented body of knowledge that extends into the 21st century.[23] It lends a deeper understanding to the more routine types of biological information collected by the management biologists across the state.***

Richard J. Mackie, professor of wildlife management at Montana State University, was contracted by the Montana Fish and Game Dept. in 1970 to coordinate statewide deer research. He assigned graduate students to initially assist him with evaluating deer habitat.[22] Then in the mid-1970s, a full time team of research biologists was formed to conduct comprehensive long-term studies on deer. This included MFWP biologists Ken Hamlin, who continued work on mule deer in the Missouri River Breaks and Dave Pac on mule deer in the Bridger Mountains. Gary Dusek worked on white-tailed deer in both the Glendive area of the lower Yellowstone River and in northwest Montana. Henry Jorgensen, a plant ecologist, assisted with all of these efforts. Another MFWP biologist, John Mundinger, focused on questions about deer and logging in northwestern Montana. Radio-tracking provided detailed information on movements and insights into social biology of deer. These aspects have a great deal to do with how deer use habitat and to define qualities of deer habitat.

The long-term studies built an unprecedented body of knowledge that

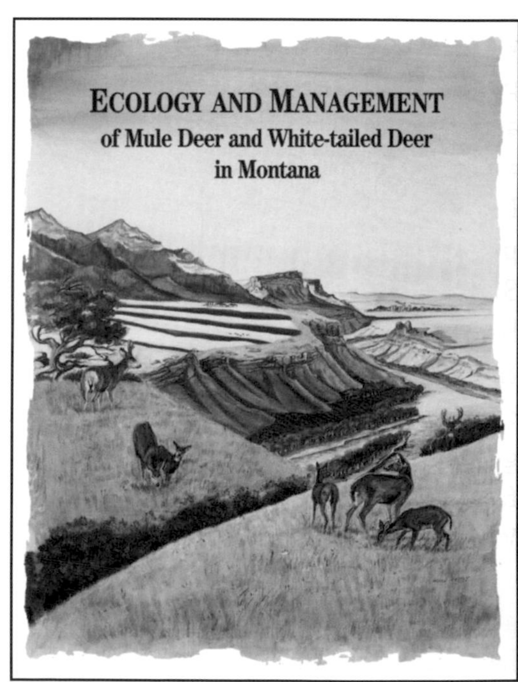

ECOLOGY AND MANAGEMENT
of Mule Deer and White-tailed Deer
in Montana


*Final report of nearly 50 years of research on mule and white-tailed deer in Montana, 1998.*

continues to be used today.[23] It lends a deeper understanding to the more routine types of biological information collected by management biologists across the state.

As the 21st century neared, the threat of Chronic Wasting Disease (CWD) loomed ever closer to Montana's borders. A deer study was begun in the southeastern corner of the state to obtain background information critical to control CWD, if it ever crosses the border into Montana. This was in addition to the statewide disease monitoring program participated in by biologists, hunters and the Wildlife Research Laboratory.

*Participants of the Montana Conservation Council's fourth annual wilderness trail ride into the Bob Marshall Area, July 1962. Some women went on this trip including a young Dorothy Bradley, one of Montana's pioneering female conservationists - she is in front with her hands on the sign.* *(Courtesy Robert Cooney Photo Collection)*

## A WIDENING DOOR FOR WOMEN

Society is dynamic and has undergone changes in public attitudes and interests. Women have always been involved to some extent in the wildlife scene, especially the wives of wildlife professionals who provided so much support. They were also involved as hunters, sportsmen club members, members of the Montana Wildlife Federation, participants in the Wilderness Society of Montana and members of the Montana Chapter of the Wildlife Society. However, employment as field workers was generally denied. Economics of family life changed dramatically after World War II.

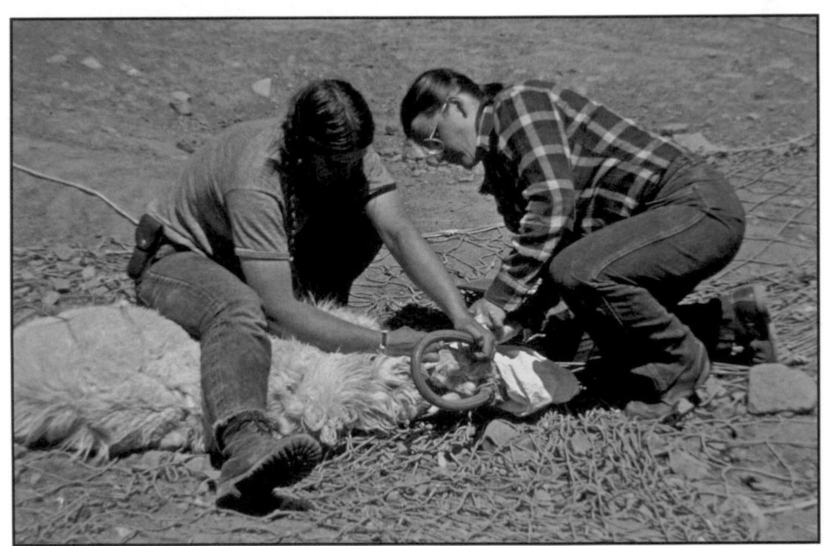

*Gayle Joslin (right) with her assistant Helga Ishle (left) marking a mountain goat on the Rocky Mountain Front. Gayle was the first woman wildlife biologist hired by the Montana Fish and Game Department in 1975.* *(Great Falls Tribune photo by Wayne Arnst)*

In the 1950s Mary Barraclough and Ramona Holt were fish and wildlife graduate students at Montana's universities.[24] As civil rights legislation took effect in the 1960s women began professional wildlife careers in federal agencies. Then in the mid-1970s Gayle Joslin, Heidi Youmans and Kristi Dubois became the first female full-time wildlife biologists in the Montana Fish and Game Department. Women continue to bring their skills and dedication to todays wildlife resources.

***Women have always been involved to some extent in the wildlife scene, especially the wives of wildlife professionals who provided so much support.***

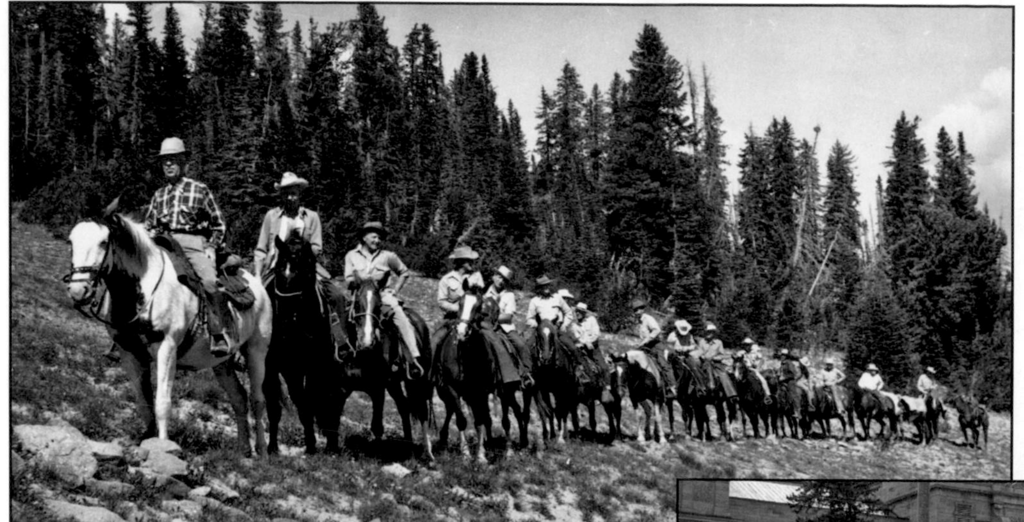

*Left - Gallatin County Conservation Committee led by Fred Williams. c. 1940s.* *(Courtesy Robert Cooney Photo Collection)*

*Below - Citizen activists on the Capitol lawn in Helena protesting bison slaughtered after they migrate out of Yellowstone Park into Montana. c. 2004.* *(Photo courtesy Martha A. Lonner)*

## CHANGING SOCIETY

Other societal changes brought modifications to the work environment. Many of Montana's environmental policies became law during the 1960s and 1970s. These have produced a more formal working environment and increased documentation of all actions. The network of sportsmen's clubs with links to business, farming, ranching and general citizens, which generated "Main Street" support for many wildlife management actions, became less influential. They were replaced with a large number of more narrowly focused interest groups often with conflicting demands. Humans are part of the natural community and their activities and attitudes certainly affect wildlife and its habitat. Jim Posewitz summed up the situation,

> "... while you couldn't get our society to hate the environment you could get them to hate the environmentalist and so when we took resource protection, also known as environmentalism, off of main street, when we took it out of the rod and gun club network, which was main street and your community and we put it into cells of activists within a community rather than the community itself, we've been fighting a defensive political battle ever since."[25]

Some of these conflicts are being worked out in some areas by such groups as the Devils Kitchen Management Team in the Big Belt Mountains. By involving representatives of all interests in an area, conflicts can be solved in much the same fashion as they formerly were in local rod and gun clubs.

*. . .when we took resource protection, also known as environmentalism, off of main street, when we took it out of the rod and gun club network, which was main street and your community and we put it into cells of activists within a community rather than the community itself, we've been fighting a defensive political battle ever since."[25]*

GREAT FALLS TRIBUNE • WWW.GREATFALLSTRIBUNE.COM

ELECTION 2000 2000 Wednesday,

**Voters approve initiative to ban new game farms**

Other ballot measures also OK'd

By SHANNON DININNY
Associated Press Writer

censes and the shooting of game

By a nearly 3-to-1 margin, voters approved the measure, 74 percent to 26 percent, according to early returns.

Opponents of the bill also said repealing their right to operate would negatively impact local economies where game farms are located.

more than 800 people each year and has been estimated to bring in about $12 million annually.

Supporters of the bill to repeal the

*Artificial feeding of big game animals on public land has been banned in Montana for several decades.*

Other activities, such as artificial feeding of wildlife, have to be regulated because of their negative effects upon wildlife. Artificial feeding of big game animals on public land has been banned in Montana for several decades.[26] When we see problems in controlling diseases such as brucellosis, bovine tuberculosis and chronic wasting disease, the wisdom of this long established ban

*Artificial feeding of big game animals on public lands in Montana has been banned for several decades.* (Courtesy Jim McLucas Photo Collection)

is much appreciated. Banning private game farms in the state by a citizen's ballot initiative (I-143) in 2000 was done for the same fundamental reasons as banning artificial feeding on public land and was a major step forward in maintaining the health of our environment and its wildlife.

Costs of Montana's wildlife restoration and its habitat have been repaid many times over. The $5/elk contribution made by sportsmen early in the 20th century for elk transplants represent one of the best investments ever made to the state.

## DEDICATED PEOPLE AND OTHER COSTS OF WILDLIFE RESTORATION

Not all costs of wildlife restoration and management have been financial and these costs cannot ever be repaid. They are sacrifices by wildlife workers. As quoted earlier, in 1948 Secretary of State Sam Mitchell commented upon giving approval to purchase the state's first airplane, "Well young man, I hope you don't kill yourself." The hope remains valid, but unfortunately our hopes have not always been met. Eight people, four pilots and four biologists, dedicated to wildlife work have been killed in airplane crashes while flying wildlife surveys in Montana.

Ralph Rouse, wildlife biologist and pilot Henry Meine crashed and died while flying an elk survey in the Madison Mountain Range in 1962.[27] In 1963 a pilot was killed while flying an antelope survey and the biologist was severely injured.[28] Terry McCoy and pilot Fred Cooper were killed while radio-tracking elk in the Sapphire Range during 1974.[29] Ken Lorang,

*Banning private game farms in the state by a citizen's ballot initiative (I-143) in 2000 was done for the same fundamental reasons as banning artificial feeding on public land and was a major step forward in maintaining the health of our environment and its wildlife.*

*Eight people, four pilots and four biologists, dedicated to wildlife work have been killed in airplane crashes while flying wildlife surveys in Montana.*

wildlife biologist and Game Warden pilot Delbert Bloom crashed and died while flying a waterfowl nesting survey along the Marias River in 1979.[30] Frank Gjersing, wildlife biologist, died in a crash while flying a deer survey along the Missouri River in 1983.[31]

There have been a number of other, less severe crashes resulting in broken backs, broken limbs and other injures as well as accidents from which the parties were able to walk away. One of these occurred in sub-zero cold.

Special flying skills are needed to safely provide the judgment of local weather conditions and for low level flights over plains and rugged mountainous terrain. A professional society of wildlife biologists, The Montana Chapter of The Wildlife Society, has honored some of these pilots including Jim Stradley, Dave Hoerner and Roger Stradley for their many thousands of hours of safe wildlife aerial surveys.

Go Slow—Live

The Montana Standard
And
The Butte Daily Post

Powell County Award Upheld
— Right-of-Way, Page 3

Vol. LXXXVI—No. 221 Established 1876 Butte-Anaconda, Montana, Friday Morning, March 9, 1962 Home Edition Price 10 Cents

Plane Crash Near Ennis Kills 2

Dillon Pilot, Sheridan Game Biologist Victims

Great Falls TRIB

Great Falls, Montana, Monday, June 4, 1979

Two killed in plane crash north of Loma

Two state Fish and Game Department employees whose light plane went down during a goose survey Saturday were found dead early Sunday morning about 20 miles northwest of Loma, officials said.

Delbert Bloom ... and Kenneth Da...

...teau, apparently were killed instantly when their Piper Supercub ... into cottonwood trees ... 500 yards ...

Saturday

Great Falls TRIBUNE

June 11, 1983 Great Falls, Montana 25 cents No. 29—98th Year

Biologist dies in plane crash

By FRED MILLER III
Tribune Correspondent

High-tension transmission lines stretch from the wreckage of the single-engine FWP plane. (Tribune Photo by Stuart S. White)

See CRASH, 1-A

*There have been a number of other, less severe crashes resulting in broken backs, broken limbs and other injures as well as accidents from which the parties were able to walk away.*

*Special flying skills are needed to safely provide the judgment of local weather conditions and for low level flights over plains and rugged mountainous terrain.*

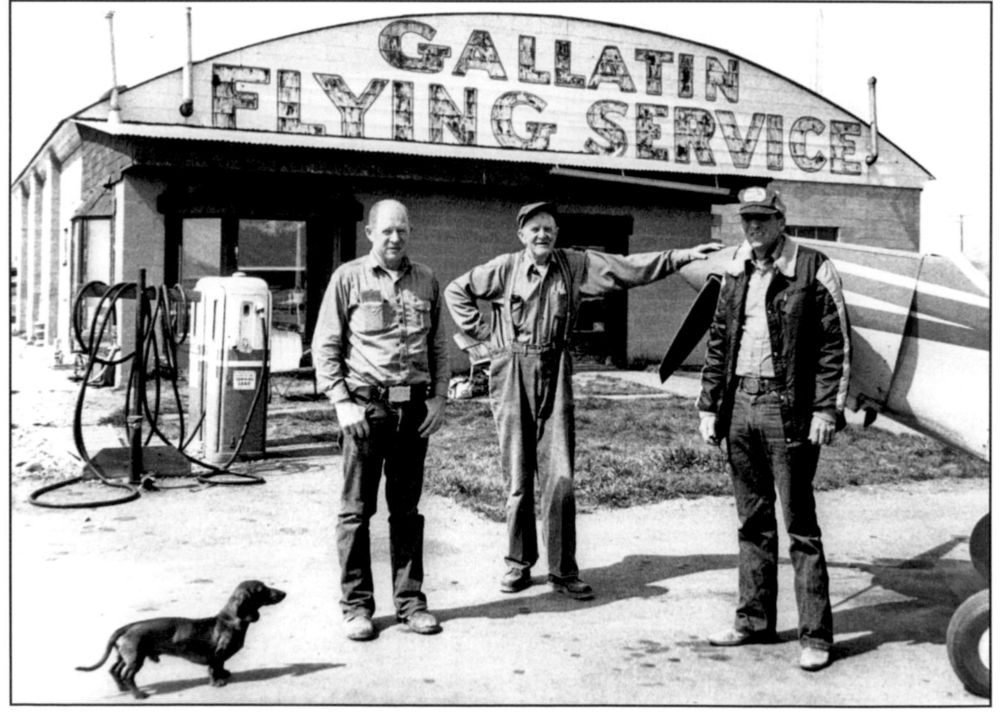


*The Flying Stradleys. Jim pioneered aerial wildlife surveys in the 1940s and his two sons, Roger (left) and Dave (right), continued his legacy. Jim flew enough hours (miles) to equal 4 round trips to the moon.* (Photo courtesy the Stradley Family)

# Footnotes

[1] Books, D. 2000. Dedicated to Wildlife. A century of conservation. Montana Outdoors. Vol. 31(6): 19.

[2] Picton, H. D. and I. E. Picton 1975. Saga of the Sun. Montana Fish and Game Department, Helena. 55 pp.

[3] Thompson, M. J. 1981. Mountain goat distribution, population characteristics and habitat use in the Sawtooth Range. M.S. Thesis, Montana State University, Bozeman. 79 pp.

[4] Joslin, G. 1986. Rocky mountain goat investigations Rocky Mountain Front. Final report. Montana Fish Wildlife and Parks, Helena. 283 pp.

[5] Aune, K. T., T. Stivers, and M. Madel. 1984. Rocky Mountain Front grizzly bear monitoring and investigations. Montana Fish, Wildlife and Parks, Helena. 239 pp.

Kasworm, W. F. 1981. Distribution and population characteristics of mule deer along the East Front, northcentral Montana. M.S. Thesis, Montana State University, Bozeman. 73 pp.

Ihsle, H. B. 1982. Population ecology of mule deer with emphasis on potential impacts of oil and gas development along the east slope of the Rocky Mountains, northcentral Montana. M.S. Thesis, Montana State University, Bozeman. 85 pp.

Andryk, T. A. 1983. Ecology of bighorn sheep in relation to oil and gas development along the east slope of the Rocky Mountains in northcentral Montana. M.S. Thesis, Montana State University, Bozeman. 100 pp.

[6] Peterson, R. 2007. Trout Unlimited buys 4,900 acres on the Rocky Mountain Front. Great Falls Tribune April 13, 2007. 1-2M.

[7] Pucket, K. 2008. Energy company cedes its oil, gas leases along front. Great Falls Tribune, March 5, 2008. 1&3A.

[8] Vollertson, J. A. 2005. Using multiple regression analysis to associate education levels and financial compensation with livestock producers tolerance for grizzly bears in the Northern Continental Divide Ecosystem. PhD dissertation, Montana State University, Bozeman. 150 pp.

[9] Cooney, R. 1953. Salting Montana's big game. Sporting Montana. 1(3)20-23.

[10] Rognrud, M. 1999. Videotaped interview with Harold Picton.

Janson, R. 1957. A partial evaluation of artificial salting for elk management in the vicinity of the Sun River Game Preserve. Typewritten report. Montana Fish and Game Dept., Helena. 3 pp.

Goodman, B. 1957, Further notes on the effect of salting on elk distribution. Typewritten report. Montana Fish and Game Dept. 2 pp.

Rognrud, M. 1959. Evaluation of big game salt as a management tool. Typewritten report. Montana Fish and Game Dept., Helena. 3 pp.

[11] Geis, A., W. Woodgerd, M. Rognrud and R. L. Hodder. 1955. The Blackfoot-Clearwater game range survey. Game range pre-development survey. Montana Fish and Game Commission, Helena. 56 pp.

[12] Hodder, R. L. 1955. The Sun River game range survey. Game Range Pre-development survey. Montana Fish and Game Commission, Helena. 46 pp.

[13] Frisina, M. R. and F. G. Morin. 1991. Grazing private and public land to improve the Fleecer elk winter range. Rangelands 13: 291-294.

Frisina, M. R. 1992. Elk habitat use within a rest-rotation grazing system. Rangelands 14: 93-96.

Frisina, M. R. and R. B. Kiegley. 2004. Habitat Changes - Mount Haggin Wildlife Management Area. Rangelands 26: 3-13.

[14] Gunderson, P. 1994. Lands Legacy - Good Deeds without Deeds. Montana Outdoors Vol. 25(1):17-21.

# Footnotes, cont.

Martin, N. 2000. Videotaped interview with Harold Picton.

[15] Ibid.

[16] Cada, J. D. 2000. Videotaped interview with Harold Picton.

Ellig, L. 2000. Videotaped interview with Harold Picton.

T. Messelt. 1971. A layman and wildlife and a layman and wilderness. Montana Stationary Company, Great Falls, Montana.

[17] Bolle, Arnold W., R. W. Behan, G. Browder, T. Payne, W. L. Pengelly, R. E. Shannon and R. F. Wambach. 1970. A University View of the Forest Service. Washington, DC: U.S. Senate Document No. 115, 92st Congress, 2nd Session. The "Bolle Report" on the Bitterroot National Forest in Montana. Same as the original report entitled "A Select Committee of the University of Montana Presents its Report on the Bitterroot National Forest," Missoula, MT: University of Montana.

[18] Lyon, L. J., T. N. Lonner, J. P. Weigand, C. L. Marcum, W. D.. Edge, J. D. Jones, D. W. McCleerey and L. L. Hicks. 1985. Coordinating elk and timber management. Final Report of the Montana Cooperative elk-logging study. Montana Fish, Wildlife and Parks, Helena. 53 pp.

[19] Peterson, J. G. 1995. Sagebrush: Ecological implications of sagebrush manipulation. Montana Fish, Wildlife and Parks, Helena. 49 pp.

Pyrah, D. 2000. Videotaped Interview with Harold Picton.

[20] Sears, H. 1955. Certain aspects of the reproductive physiology of the female mule deer. M. S. Thesis, University of Montana, Missoula. 82 pp.

Hudson, P. 1956. The morphology of the embryonic and fetal development of the Rocky Mountain mule deer. M. S. Thesis, University of Montana, Missoula. 61 pp.

[21] Wilkins, B. T. 1956. Range use, food habits and agricultural relationships of the mule deer, Bridger Mountains, Montana. M. S. Thesis, Montana State University, Bozeman. 34 pp.

South, P. R. 1957. Food habits and range use of the mule deer in the Scudder Creek area, Beaverhead County, Montana. M. S. Thesis, Montana State University, Bozeman. 34 pp.

Lovaas, A. L. 1957. Mule deer food habits and range use in the Little Belt mountains, Montana. M. S. Thesis, Montana State University, Bozeman. 43 pp.

[22] Lonner, T. N. 1972. Age distributions and some relationships of key browse plants on big game ranges in Montana. M. S. Thesis, Mont. State University, Bozeman. 79 pp.

Martin, P. R. 1972. Ecology of skunkbush sumac *(Rhus trilobata* Nutt.*)* in Montana with special reference to use by mule deer. M. S. Thesis, Mont. State University, Bozeman. 97 pp.

Schwarzkoph, W. F. 1973. Range use and relationships of mule deer on the west slope of the Bridger Mountains, MT. M. S. Thesis, Mont. State University, Bozeman. 65 pp.

Bucsis, R. A. 1974. Ecological characteristics of the Armstrong mule deer winter range, Bridger Mountains, MT. M. S. Thesis, Mont. State University, Bozeman. 104 pp.

Hamlin, K. L. 1974. Ecological relationships of mule deer in the Bridger Mountains, MT, with special reference to daily and seasonal movements. M. S. Thesis, Mont. State University, Bozeman. 65 pp.

[23] Mackie, R. J., D. F. Pac, K. L. Hamlin and G. L. Dusek. 1998. Ecology and management of mule deer and white-tailed deer in Montana. Montana Fish, Wildlife and Parks, Helena. 180 pp.

Dusek, G. L., A. Wood, S. Hockman, C. Sime and J. Morgan. 2006. Ecology of white-tailed deer in the Salish mountains, northwest Montana. Montana Fish, Wildlife and Parks, Helena. 263 pp.

Dusek, G. L., R. J. Mackie, J. D. Herriges Jr. and B. B. Compton. 1989. Population ecology of white-tailed deer along the lower Yellowstone River. Wildlife Monographs 104:68 pp.

[24] Barraclough, M. E. 1954. Biology of Canada geese *(Branta canadensis moffitti)* in the Flathead Valley of Montana. M. S. Thesis, University of Montana, Missoula. 91 pp.

Holt, R. D. 1955. Comparative morphology of the Rocky Mountain whitefish *(Prosopium williamsoni)*. M. S. Thesis, Mont. State University, Bozeman. 20 pp.

[25] Lonner, T. N. (Producer) 2005. Back from the brink - Montana's Wildlife Legacy. DVD and Montana PBS televvision documentary, Montana Fish, Wildlife and Parks Foundation, Helena. ***www.mfwpfoundation.org***

[26] Weigand, J. P. and R. J. Mackie. 1985. A review of winter feeding of big game animals and potential applications in Montana. Special. Research Rept., Montana Dept. of Fish, Wildlife and Parks, Helena. 26 pp.

[27] Anon. 1962. Plane crash near Ennis kills 2. The Montana Standard, Butte. March 9, 1962.

Sasse, D. B. 2003. Job-related mortality of wildlife workers in the United States, 1937-2000. Wildlife Society Bulletin 31(4):1015-1020.

[28] The authors were unable to find the name of the pilot who was killed while searching in government documents and newspapers. The biologist, Joe Townsend, recovered from a broken back suffered in the crash. He passed away before this project began.

[29] Ibid. Lyon, L. J., T. N. Lonner, J. P. Weigand, C. L. Marcum, W. D. Edge, J. D. Jones, D. W. McCleerey and L. L. Hicks. 1985.

[30] Anon. 1983. Two killed in plane crash north of Loma. Great Falls Tribune. June 4, 1979. 1.

[31] Anon. 1983. Biologist dies in plane crash. Great Falls Tribune. June 11, 1983. 1.

Anon. 1983. Great Falls Tribune. June 15, 1983. 1 and 2a.

***Montana is a land of diverse landscapes - the Rocky Mountain East Front exemplifies these landscapes where the mountains meet the prairie. c. 2007.*** *(Photo courtesy Brent N. Lonner)*

*Sportsman Knudson helping band a nesting Canada goose on Goose Island, Flathead Lake north of Polson, Montana. c. 1948.*
*(Courtesy Merle Rognrud Photo Collection)*

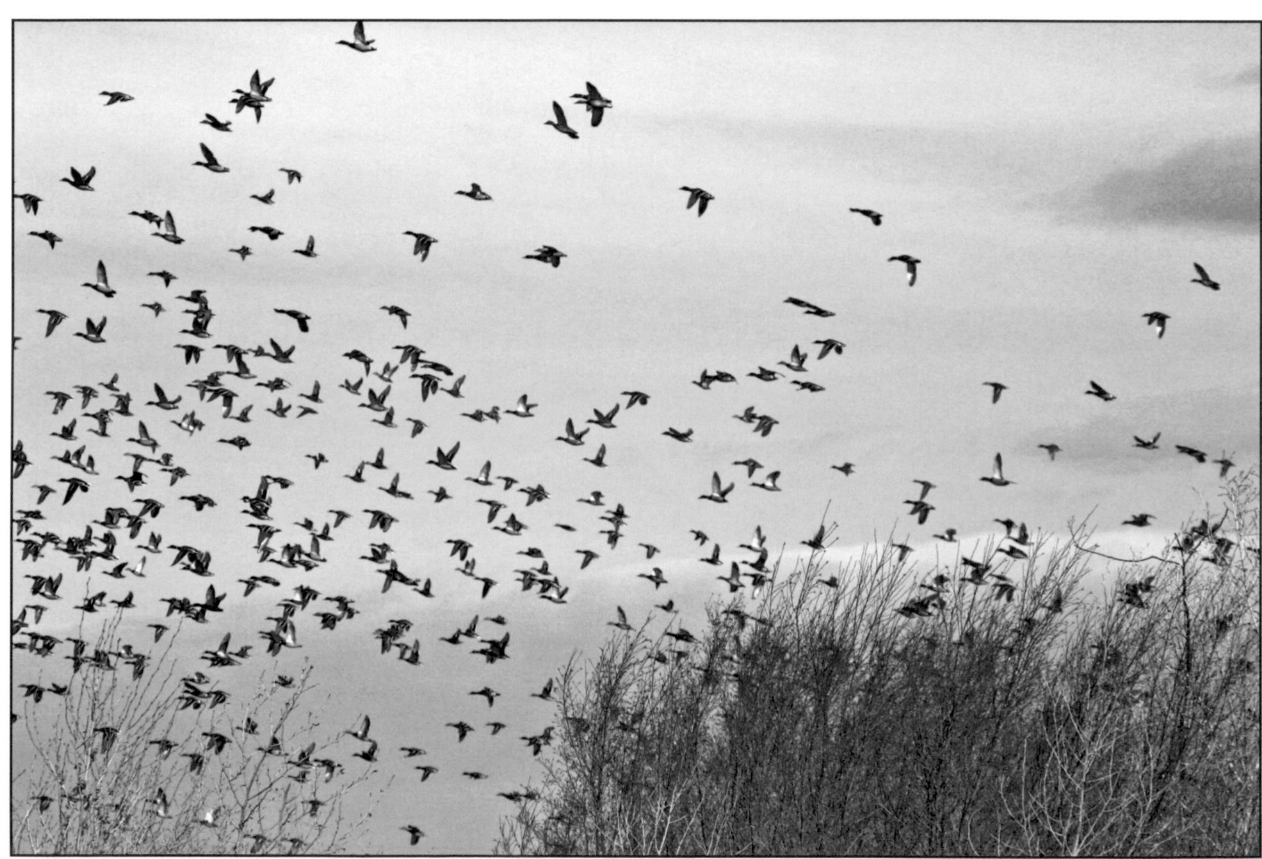

*Since the middle of the 20th century waterfowl, especially Canada Geese, have benefited dramatically from many wetland conservation and research projects in Montana. c. 2007. (Photo courtesy Terry N. Lonner)*

Chapter 20

# Past and Future

A trip into the past is like a visit to a foreign land. Travelers see different things and visit different places. We have taken some less traveled paths and talked to people not documented before. This has left us with a remarkable story of people trying to build a better life and also a better environment. It gives us some feeling for why the 1972 Montana Constitution makes a clean and healthful environment a fundamental right of Montanans. We have found that wildlife resources are a unique contribution of Montana's culture to the nation. Decimation of some wildlife resources to near extinction has been a common theme for mankind throughout history. Restoration to where wildlife is a common feature of the land, not just in a few refuges or zoos, is uncommon.

Twenty-one thousand years ago Montana was a very different place. Twenty-five to 30 percent of the state was covered by glaciers. Another 5 or 6 percent was covered by large lakes including Lake Glendive, Lake Circle, Lake Jordan, Lake Musselshell, Lake Cut Bank, Lake Great Falls and Lake Missoula. The Missouri river flowed through an alternate channel, now dry, called the Shonkin Sag east of Great Falls near the Highwood Mountains.[1] A very robust and complex ecosystem was present. This ecosystem had persisted for hundreds of thousands of years through many climate changes.

***The Missouri river flowed through an alternate channel, now dry, called the Shonkin Sag.[1]***

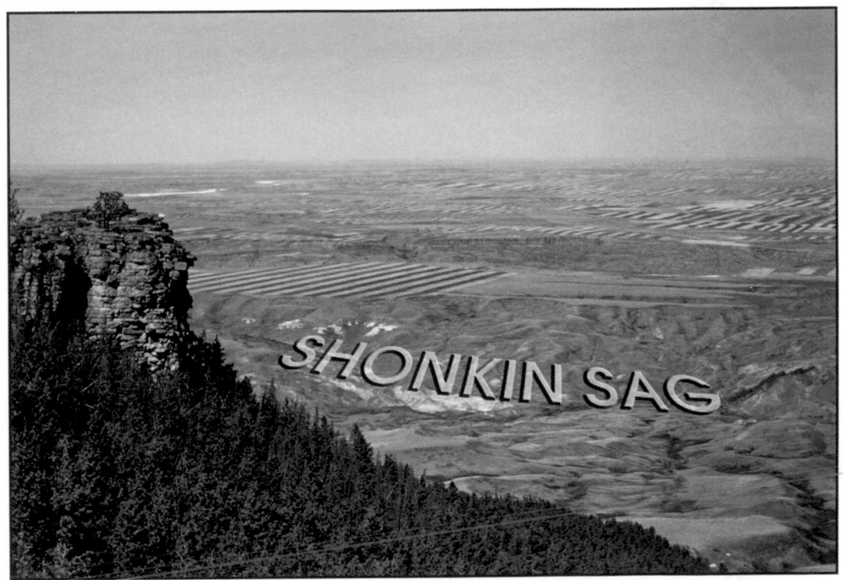


*Square Butte near the Highwood Mountains overlooks the geologically famous Shonkin Sag, the channel that carried the outlet river from Glacial Lake Great Falls during the Bull Lake glaciation 130,000 years ago - Illinoian Ice Age. (Photo courtesy Harold Picton)*

*Paintings of ice age animals similar to this rendition by Rudolph F. Zallinger have been found on the walls of caves around the world. Primitive man painted such pictures , anthropologists believe, not merely to adorn the cave, but to propitiate the spirits of animals and thus assure mastery over them in hunting. (Illustration courtesy Time-Life Books, Inc. by Montana Outdoors)*

Then this ecosystem changed dramatically. The American Cheetah vanished about 17,000 years before present and the giant short-faced bear dropped out 12,000 years ago. Horses and camels disappeared 8,000 or 9,000 years before present. Mammoths saw their end in Montana about 8,000 years ago, although they may have lingered on in other areas of North America for another 1,000 years.[2]

A new ecosystem began to develop about 11,000 to 12,000 years before present. Although many animal species in it were modified versions of surviving ice age animals, an entirely new element was added, MAN THE HUNTER. The new ecosystem developed into robust stature with human hunting as one of the selective forces.

Arrival of horses on the northern plains in the 1700s made it possible for native peoples to more thoroughly exploit the wildlife cornucopia of the plains of eastern Montana. Human hunting migrations of a 1,000 round trip miles were made from what is now eastern Washington to the plains.[3] Lewis and Clark treked across Montana to the Pacific Ocean. Explorations of David Thompson in 1808 set up the geopolitical conflict between Britain and the new United States over land and its wildlife resources. Montana was a major economic battleground in this conflict.[4]

Hunting expeditions of native Americans continued through the 1870s when a few soldiers (from the less than 600 U.S. Army personnel stationed in Montana) were assigned to escort them so they could pass safely by scattered settlements springing up across Montana. This was done to ease tensions and prevent conflicts. During this time hunts in eastern Montana were highly profitable for the Indians. One account of a party of 600 Salish-Kootenai peoples from northwest Montana and northern Idaho tells of them killing an estimated 6,000 bison (equivalent to 3,240,000 pounds of beef) in a single hunt in 1875.[5]

The wildlife resource was overwhelmed in the last half of the 19th century. Decimating factors included arrival of diseases introduced

*The Buffalo Hunt by Charles M. Russell.* *(Oil on canvas, 1919 [No. 39] , Courtesy Amon Carter Museum, Fort Worth, Texas)*

*A pile of buffalo skulls waiting to be made into fertilizer. c. 1880. (Courtesy Burton Historical Collection, Detroit Public Library)*

*One account of a party of 600 Salish-Kootenai peoples from northwest Montana and northern Idaho tells of them killing an estimated 6,000 bison (equivalent to 3,240,000 pounds of beef) in a single hunt in 1875.[5]*

with livestock, subsistence hunting by people residing in the state and arrival of industrial hide hunters who linked the wildlife resource to the industrial market economies of the United States and Europe. Buffalo were gone by 1884 and welfare of most other species was precarious.

*The Family of John Harshenberger - three generations, Sheridan County Montana. November 1937. (Photo by Lee Russell. Library of Congress, Prints & Photographs Division, FSA/OWI Collection [LC-USF34-030923-D])*

Montana residents became concerned about the status of their wildlife and took action. The predecessor of the Montana Fish and Game Department was formed before the national conservation movement succeeded in forming the U.S. Forest Service, national wildlife refuges or National Park Service. By 1910, Montana citizens were raising donations for restoring elk. This spontaneous conservation by the people of Montana has continued through five generations. It persevered through six wars, national financial collapses, recessions and through what has been called the greatest North American environmental catastrophe of the 20th century, the drought of the 1930s. Wildlife resources we have today are a gift from the people of Montana of the 20th century to the people of the 21st century.

***The wildlife resources that we have today are a gift from the people of Montana of the 20th century to the people of the 21st century. This gift comes with a message, DON'T MESS IT UP.***

This gift comes with an implicit message:

DON'T MESS IT UP!

Critical to restoring Montana's wildlife resource were concepts provided by the legal framework of the Pittman-Robertson Act (P-R Act). This unique North American approach is based on the concept of ownership of wildlife by the people, not private landowners or government and mandates the use of science in its management. This North American philosophy of wildlife management

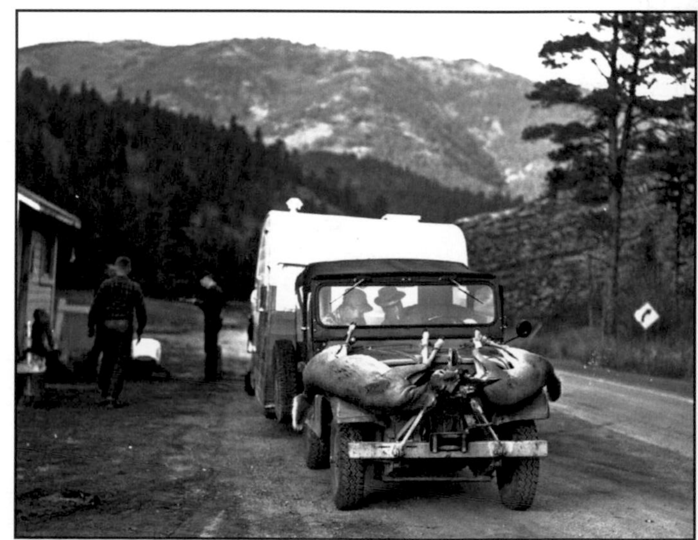

*Bonner Check Station near Missoula, MT - 1959. (Courtesy Robert Cooney Photo Collection)*

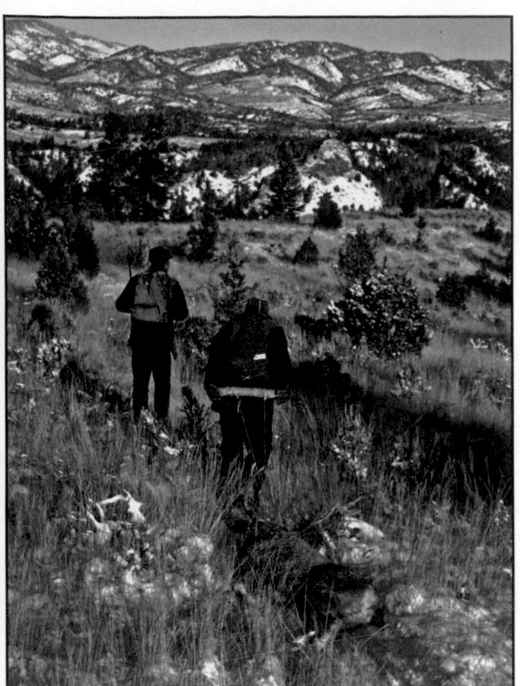

*Montana hunters dragging out a mule deer. 1993.* (Photo courtesy Terry N. Lonner)

demands active participation and cooperation by the people, not just by carrying signs and protesting, but in management processes and continuing the ecological role that humans began playing over 10,000 years ago. It envisions that a great state and a great nation deserve to have a diverse and abundant wildlife resource living in a healthy environment.

The North American philosophy of wildlife conservation has been effective in restoring many species of wildlife. However when humans impact the land, they often leave many species in short supply. These affected species are now often referred to as endangered, threatened or of special concern. The Federal Endangered Species Act enacted by the U.S. Congress in 1973 sought to focus attention and provide areas or refugia for many of these species. In 1974, Montana Fish, Wildlife and Parks appointed Dennis Flath as its first non-game biologist and in 1984 Arnold Dood was assigned as the Endangered Species biologist. Since then, more nongame biologists have been hired, but are now called native species biologists.

Montanans who would like to see nongame included in wildlife management in the state have established a multi-agency Montana Heritage Program to provide a source of information about most wildlife species in the state. A voluntary state income tax check-off was established by the Montana legislature in 1983 to financially support a program for non-game species. The small amount of money generated by this check-off system and some federal funds have allowed Montana wildlife biologists and citizens to work toward including many nongame species in restoring and maintaining a complete ecosystem. Federal legislation patterned after the P-R Act, but directed toward nongame species, has been proposed several times, but never approved.

If the North American philosophy of wildlife management is to be expanded to directly include all wildlife

***If the North American philosophy of wildlife management is to be expanded to directly include all wildlife species, history tells us that broad public and community support experienced in the past has to be re-created.***

*Left - Before 1974 western bluebirds and many other nongame species were politically ignored. However, after Montana's nongame program was initiated in 1974, certain species started to receive special attention. Thanks to a bluebird nest plan and hundreds of concerned citizens, Montana's bluebird populations have made a tremendous recovery.* (Photo courtesy Brent N. Lonner)

species, history tells us that broad public and community support experienced in the past has to be re-created. This will require leaders who believe that Montana should be as ecologically complete as it can possibly be.

*Leroy Ellig, a pioneer Montana Wildlife Biologist, evaluating the condition of browse plants on deer winter range. c. 1965.* (Courtesy Robert Cooney Photo Collection)

*Montana has chosen to invest in knowledge to learn what it takes to enable native species to prosper in the face of human impacts. This approach has come from the core of our society.*

Although Montana has a relatively low human population density, it increased in population at almost the same rate as the overall national population did during the 20th century. However, low human population density is not the only reason for the successful restoration of Montana's wildlife. It took less than 100,000 people in Montana to cause the decimation of its wildlife during the 19th century. Similar events in other states left disrupted wildlife there as well. Various states have followed different pathways toward restoring their wildlife. A few have elected to bring in exotic species from other continents, displacing native species in the process. Some have used agricultural approaches such as artificial feeding and game ranching to produce high concentrations of animals. This has increased incidence of diseases such as tuberculosis, brucellosis and chronic wasting disease.

Montana has chosen to invest in learning what enables native species to prosper in the face of human impacts. This approach has come from the core of our society. Montana has had catastrophic failures caused by bad information. It took over a century for the new wave of humanity to learn to live in Montana without producing ecological disasters and tragedies for individual families. Many years of agricultural and ecological research, education and experience were needed to bring about a relatively stable standard of living. This encourages us to try and develop a thorough understanding of our dry, cold, high altitude but beautiful plains and mountains so that we and our wildlife companions can prosper. The 21st century brings challenges of climate change, disease, persistent organic chemicals, urban attitudes and philosophies disconnected from the land, and impacts of wars and other adventures of mankind. In the face of all this we hope our native wildlife will continue to flourish.

Montana's wildlife management is based upon several pillars established over the years. Law enforcement and the legal system must support management of wildlife populations. This means there has to be effective and scientifically competent management organizations to monitor the needs of wildlife. These needs must then be communicated to the general public and lawmakers, so adjustments of human activities can be made to benefit wildlife. Every advocate, politician and prognosticator puts forth bright, shiny and often hyped views of the future. Research allows us to select the best pathway to the future and to logically throw away those visions that are useless and even down right harmful. Knowledge gained from research effectively applied is the true high tech tool. None of this can function without active public participation in management of Montana's wildlife resource, for it is a resource to be enjoyed by all people. They must have access to the resource and this access should not be denied by those seeking to gain control of it for their own commercial interests.

The future can only be dimly seen. The depression and drought years of the 1930s haunt our thoughts of what the future may bring. Knowledge provided by ecological research applied to routine management efforts will be key to our survival and security. Political leaders have not often liked ecological research because it may bring surprises and challenges to the status quo. Science in the 20th century, mandated by the Montana Fish and Game Commission in 1942, has taught us that dynamic change, not a benign and predictable status quo, is the rule of nature. The encyclopedia contained in this piece of landscape called Montana must be read and allowed to guide the future of its wildlife legacy. If this is done, changes can be managed so Montanans can maintain a livable environment for wildlife and this will in turn provide a healthy environment for human generations to come.

***"As a general policy, we feel that the personnel of the State Fish and Game Department should come to recognize the scientific point of view and as rapidly as possible become acquainted with some of the methods of routine investigation. It is our hope that projects dealing with fish, game birds, game animals and fur-bearers, will be setup as rapidly as possible with the end in view of improving the management program."***

**— Montana Fish and Game Commission 1941-42 biennial report.**

## Policy of the State Fish and Game Commission

**1. State Sovereignity**

To maintain the sovereign rights of the state of Montana in administration and control, propagation and conservation of its wildlife.

**2. Scientific Management of Wildlife**

1. Improvement in the management of our wildlife resources rests not only upon the maintenance of the present number of fish and game population but also upon an increase in the population of the key species. Such a program should rest upon a foundation of investigational work since very little is known concerning the actual life histories and the influence of environment factors upon our wildlife species.

   As a general policy, we feel that the personnel of the State Fish and Game Department should come to recognize the scientific point of view and as rapidly as possible become acquainted with some of the methods of routine investigation. It is our hope that projects dealing with fish, game birds, game animals and fur-bearers will be set up as rapidly as possible with the end in view of improving the management program.

   c. Education of the public.

   d. Cooperation with University and the State College in this educational program.

B. Periodic reports of activities of the Fish and Game Department to be sent to all of its field personnel to promote closer cooperation of the entire department.

**3. Cooperation**

Effective management necessitates cooperation of the fish and game department with federal and other state agencies whose spheres of activity would enable them to contribute to the improvement of wildlife conditions within the state.

**4. Investigation**

To institute an investigation program in order to obtain basic data esential to scientific wildlife management.

**5. Education of the Public**

To keep the public advised of the various game management projects and to explain the necessity of such projects.

*Policy statement from the 1941-42 Montana Fish and Game Commission Biennial Report. (This is only a part of the statement and is truncated at the bottom.)*

# Footnotes

[1] Alt, D. D. and D. W. Hyndman. 1986. Roadside geology of Montana. Mountain Press, Missoula, MT. 427 pp.

[2] Lange, I. M. 2002. Ice age mammals of North America. Mountain Press Publishing Company, Missoula, MT. 225 pp.

[3] Farr, W. E. 2003. Going to buffalo: Indian hunting migrations across the Rocky Mountains Part 1. Montana, the magazine of western history. Winter 2003:53(4):1-21.

[4] Wishart, D. J. 1979. The fur trade of the American West 1807-1840. University of Nebraska Press, Lincoln. 237 pp.

[5] Farr, W. E. 2004. Going to buffalo: Indian hunting migrations across the Rocky Mountains Part 2. Montana, the magazine of western history. Spring 2004:54(1):26-43.

*A successful white-tailed deer hunt in southeastern Montana. c. 2003*
*(Illustration by and courtesy of Jake Dusek)*

# Index

# Index, cont.

# Index, cont.

**– N –**

# Index, cont.

*Let's Build for the Future!*

*From the 1941-42 Montana Fish and Game Commission Biennial Report.*